D0629523

THE
TEACHING
OF
ELEMENTARY
SCHOOL
MATHEMATICS

# THE
# TEACHING
# OF
# ELEMENTARY
# SCHOOL
# MATHEMATICS

## KLAAS
## KRAMER

*COLORADO STATE COLLEGE*

*GREELEY, COLORADO*

ALLYN AND BACON, INC.

*BOSTON, MASS.*

*1966*

To
Joan,
Joanne,
and
Nick

© Copyright, 1966, by ALLYN AND BACON, INC., 150 Tremont Street, Boston. All rights reserved. No part of this book may be reproduced in any form, by mimeograph or any other means, without permission in writing from the publishers.

Printed in the United States of America.

Library of Congress Catalog Card Number: 66-14779

# PREFACE

IT IS THE purpose of this volume to offer a program of instruction in mathematics for the elementary school. The program is based on the author's years of study of, lecturing on, and experience in the teaching of mathematics. The book is intended to be used by elementary-school teachers and by students who are preparing themselves for teaching mathematics in the elementary school.

Important characteristics of the program offered are:

1. Teachers are encouraged to use the inductive approach when introducing a process. This tends to stimulate class discussions and encourages the pupils to form generalizations.

2. The necessity is stressed of supplying practice in using a process after the meaning of that process has been introduced.

3. Promising ideas have been incorporated from exploratory programs in elementary-school mathematics. Important representative topics from these programs are discussed, so that the teacher who has thoroughly studied this book will be acquainted with the contemporary content and vocabulary.

4. The grade placement of topics is considered and suggestions for improvement are presented.

5. A proper sequence of the subject matter is suggested.

6. Number properties and patterns are emphasized.

7. Relationships between operations are stressed.

8. Systematic instruction in mental computation is emphasized and several examples are presented.

9. The need for taking care of individual differences is recognized. In many presentations of new processes various methods of solution are offered. In a separate chapter plans and procedures for taking care of individual differences are presented.

The book consists of three parts. Part I discusses past and present trends in the teaching of elementary-school mathematics. Part II introduces the student to selected topics in modern mathematics programs.

For a more complete presentation of "modern elementary-school mathematics" the student is referred to: K. Kramer, *Mathematics for the Elementary-School Teacher* (Boston: Allyn and Bacon, Inc., 1965). This Worktext is intended for teachers who lack a sufficient background in mathematics, and can be used in workshops or in in-service training courses.

Part III presents content, procedures, and evaluation techniques. In many chapters, review exercises in computation and problem solving are given for the benefit of the teacher who has a limited background in mathematics, and important pieces of research pertaining to the related topics are reported.

Part II of the book may be skipped if the class has recently completed a course in mathematics (at the discretion of the instructor), or it can serve as a review.

The author is indebted to Dr. Paul McKee, formerly of Colorado State College, for stimulating him to write this book and for criticizing its composition, to Dr. Jack N. Sparks, Pennsylvania State University, University Park, Pennsylvania, for reading the manuscript, and to Dr. Herbert F. Spitzer of the State University of Iowa, for stimulating his interest in the teaching of elementary-school mathematics. Special thanks are also due Dr. T. D. Cavanagh of Colorado State College, for reading several of the chapters during production of the book.

K. K.

Greeley, Colorado

# CONTENTS

THE
TEACHING
OF
ELEMENTARY
SCHOOL
MATHEMATICS

# I
PAST
AND
PRESENT
TRENDS

# 1

# BASIC
# TENETS

RECENT ADVANCES IN science have increased the body of mathematical knowledge and have led to a more extensive use of mathematics in technology and in daily life. More scientists are now needed than ever before. The citizen needs to be better founded in mathematics in order to understand his environment and interpret it intelligently. These developments have placed upon the institutions of learning a greater responsibility to improve and accelerate the mathematics curriculum. The elementary school shares in this responsibility, for there the foundation of mathematics has to be laid, its underlying principles have to be taught, and a reasonable degree of skill in computation and problem solving has to be acquired.

A search for improved programs has been undertaken by mathematicians, educators, and psychologists. Several nationally recognized committees have formulated suggested programs involving far-reaching changes in the mathematics curriculum. Experimental materials incorporating these suggestions are being tried out all across the country. Characteristics of representative exploratory programs in elementary-school mathematics will be discussed in Chapter 3 of this volume.

Changes have taken place and are taking place in the methods of teaching mathematics, in the content offered, and in the way of dealing with individual differences. Methods of teaching have been improved during the last few decades as a result of new ideas concerning the learning process. At present, great emphasis is being placed upon the teaching of the structure of mathematics, the development of thought patterns, the discovery of relationships, and the forming of generalizations. Also, a more accurate knowledge of the child has caused educators to put forth efforts to plan programs which fit the varying abilities of children.

A greater emphasis upon the mathematical aim of teaching mathematics has resulted in the inclusion of additional topics such as simple algebra and geometry.

As an introduction to this volume's proposed program, the first chapter presents in order the objectives of the instruction to be carried on, the characteristics of a desirable mathematics program in the elementary school, and recommended procedures for the introduction of a new case in the mathematics curriculum.

## Objectives

The history of arithmetic as a school subject—a survey of which is presented in Chapter 2—reveals that the aims of teaching the subject have been under continuous change. The disciplinary, utilitarian, mathematical, and social aims have each been dominant at various times. At present, the mathematical and social aspects of the subject are emphasized, and programs stressing mathematical understandings and presenting social content are favored.

A statement of general purposes is a basic requirement for the construction of an elementary-school curriculum and for the evaluation of teaching and learning. Several such statements have been prepared and can be found in professional books dealing with the curriculum. A statement of the purposes of education which has been favorably received was prepared in 1938 by the Educational Policies Commission of the National Education Association. Its four sets of broad objectives are presented under the headings: (1) The objectives of self-realization—which include the fundamental processes; (2) The objectives of human relationship; (3) The objectives of economic efficiency; and (4) The objectives of civic responsibility. The Educational Policies Commission[1] emphasized in a recent statement that the general purpose which runs through and strengthens all other purposes is the development of the ability to think. Thus the school must focus on this general purpose in the teaching of the fundamental processes.

Such general purposes should be developed into sets of clear objectives for each of the subject areas. Then, the school faculty should agree on the desired outcomes for each grade level. Each mathematics teacher should be acquainted with the scope and sequence of the mathematics subject matter which his pupils[2] have studied in the preceding grades and which they will

---

[1] Educational Policies Commission, National Education Association, *The Central Purpose of Education* (Washington, D.C.: The Association, 1961).

[2] In this book, references to *pupils* mean elementary-school pupils; references to *students* mean the students of the teaching of elementary-school mathematics—the readers of this book.

study in the following grades. Finally, the teacher should be skillful in the preparation of lesson plans so that he knows what he is to teach, how he can teach it, and how he should evaluate the teaching and learning.

To assist the teacher in the formulation of his objectives for mathematics instruction in the elementary school, the following objectives are suggested for consideration:

The pupil should acquire:

1. An *understanding* of the structure of the real number system, of basic geometric ideas, and of principles underlying the basic mathematical processes.

2. Functional *knowledge* of quantitative terms and symbols; of graphs, scale drawings, charts, and tables; of simple geometric terms and figures; and of common measures.

3. *Skill* in:
   a) thinking critically by following and building patterns of organized thought;
   b) performing with reasonable speed and accuracy common written and mental computations;
   c) appraising the correctness of acquired results;
   d) applying acquired techniques intelligently in verbal problems, in other school subjects, and in daily life.

4. Favorable *attitudes* toward mathematics and an awareness of the place and importance of mathematics in life.

5. *Confidence* in his ability to reason independently.

## Characteristics of a Desirable Program

An elementary-school mathematics program should possess these characteristics:

I. *The pupils are encouraged to discover mathematical principles, patterns, and procedures.*

The best learning takes place when the pupils acquire a concept and find a procedure leading to the correct answer as a result of their being actively engaged in the learning process. The teacher's pertinent guide questions and his interpretations assist the pupils in their building and refining of mathematical concepts, in their developing of thought patterns, and in their discovering of relationships. The pupils are encouraged to think critically, to find, use, and test alternate methods of solution, and to prove their conclusions. New concepts are developed as an outgrowth of previous learnings. The process of learning as well as the product is emphasized. Thus, not only the desire to arrive at the correct answer is fostered, but also a questioning attitude toward and a critical evaluation of procedures is encouraged. This method of teaching should stimulate curiosity and elicit internal motivation. It is called the *discovery method*, but it should be realized that the process is one of directed discovery. The time element and the ability of some pupils may make it almost impossible to adhere to this approach at all times. Yet the teacher should strive to use the allotted time wisely and should guide the children as frequently as possible to the discovery of mathematical patterns, principles, rules, and relationships.

II. *Generalizations are formed inductively and applied deductively.*
When a generalization is to be formed, the teacher presents the problem in a situation and invites the pupils to find the answer. The pupils attempt to do so by using concepts and knowledge they have already acquired. Then, in the class discussion, the processes are explored, patterns are identified, and the pupils are guided to form the generalization. This generalization is applied deductively in several exercises and word problems, and the pupils are encouraged to test the principle in more difficult cases. An outline of a lesson in which this procedure is followed is presented elsewhere in this chapter.

III. *The pupil is guided through necessary stages of development toward the formation of mathematical concepts. During this process, proper visual aids are used.*
The pupils should be provided with experiences which build a meaningful background for mathematical abstraction. In early number experiences, most children are led through the concrete and semiconcrete stages of development to the abstract stage.
Manipulative materials are used for the concrete stage. Physical experiences such as working with the counting frame, the abacus, toy money, rods, and pegs will be helpful for most pupils in the acquisition of mathematical concepts. For the semiconcrete stage, representations such as pictures, diagrams, dots, and marks are employed. During the abstract stage, the pupils work with mathematical symbols. The manipulation of materials by the children, the representation of the situation on paper, and the gradual increase in the difficulty level of the stages offer the opportunity to even the below-average pupil to learn to understand the process and to acquire the mathematical concepts involved. Because of the differences in mathematical maturity among the children, some of them will not need to pursue the first stage of development identified above. On the other hand, there may be children for whom it will be difficult or even impossible to

move to the abstract stage for a long time. It is the teacher's task to determine the degree of the child's maturity and to encourage him to work at a level which stimulates his continued progress.

IV. *Practice exercises are presented after the process to be mastered has been explored meaningfully.*

The abstract rote drill of several decades ago has been replaced by practice which aims at automatic mastery of facts the pupil understands and at anchoring skills he has explored meaningfully. The modern teacher recognizes the significance of such purposeful practice. He strives to make a process meaningful to the pupil and follows or accompanies this activity by supplying a sufficient amount of practice exercises.

When assigning practice, the teacher should consider the following principles:

1. The pupil should understand what he is practicing. Reasons for following this principle are:
    a) Processes that are understood require a minimum amount of practice to be mastered.
    b) Retention of processes is easier when those processes are understood.
    c) Forgotten skills seem to be more easily regained when the processes have been originally understood.
    d) Meaningful work incites motivation for practice, since the pupil is more apt to see the need for the skill.

2. Practice should extend and consolidate understandings established as a result of previous learning.

3. The pupil should be motivated to work the exercises and see a need for the practice.

4. Practice on the basic facts should aim at complete mastery.

5. Practice periods should be relatively short and should be scheduled frequently.

6. Practice should be carefully arranged so that mastered skills are reviewed in practice periods which are spaced by intervals that become gradually longer.

7. Practice on a skill should include different kinds of exercises, so that monotony is avoided.

8. A result of practice should be that the pupil develops confidence in his mathematical skill.

V. *In the selection of content the mathematical and social aims are considered.*
To satisfy the mathematical aim, content is selected which is to build mathematical understandings. Anticipated outcomes include: an

understanding of the structure of the real number system; an understanding of the fundamental operations; the discovery of principles,
patterns, and relationships; the formulation of generalizations; and
the ability to reason logically and think critically.

Content selected with the social aim in mind should serve to increase
the pupils' proficiency in using mathematical knowledge in school and
in daily life. For this purpose skills such as the following are stressed:
written and mental computation; making change; estimation;
measuring; problem solving; the use of quantitative terms; the
reading of graphs, charts, tables, and scale drawings; and the interpretation of quantitative situations presented in newspapers, maga-
zines, and books.

VI. *The program is mathematically correct and presents a sequential plan
for the introduction of topics which is pedagogically sound.*

Good mathematics programs are built on unifying ideas such as structure, operations, and generalizations. In these programs correct
mathematical language is emphasized.

Since the acquisition of mathematical concepts is difficult for children,
a sequential plan is followed in which the pupils are guided to form
new abstractions by using knowledge and concepts which they already
have acquired. However, the logical sequence of the subject matter is
not followed when it appears that for psychological reasons topics
should be delayed.

VII. *The spiral plan is followed in the presentation of the content.*

The spiral plan calls for an organization of content in which learnings
are maintained and extended at successive grade levels. This should
result in a better mastery of skills and in the refinement and extension
of already established concepts.

The spiral type of content organization is illustrated in modern programs in which, for example, fractions are presented at each grade
level. Whereas decades ago fractions were introduced in the intermediate grades, at present some simple concepts of fractional numbers
are developed as early as grade one. In each successive grade the
learnings are then reviewed and extended to include more difficult
concepts.

VIII. *The program provides for individual differences.*

Analyses of test results reveal a wide range in intelligence and in level
of achievement among pupils in the same grade. The range in ability
in quantitative problem solving and in computation is usually quite
wide and increases if good teaching and learning conditions prevail.
This places upon the teacher the responsibility to acquaint himself

thoroughly with the intellectual ability and mathematical achievement of each pupil and to plan his teaching and assigning of work accordingly. A specified amount of practice may be too much for one pupil and not enough for another. ~~The identification of each pupil's background, motivation, and ability is a most difficult and important task of the teacher~~. After a pupil's need has been determined, every effort should be made to meet it. In a good school each pupil is challenged to achieve as much as his ability allows.

Since individual instruction is impossible in the typical class of approximately 30 pupils, the teacher will have to select procedures for dealing with the problem from several available techniques. Such techniques include: ability grouping; assigning different amounts of practice; assigning different kinds of exercises; allowing different amounts of time; assigning contracts as in the Dalton system; departmentalization; enrichment which pursues topics presented to the class in more depth; enrichment which comprises additional topics which are more advanced than those presented to the class; and remedial work for the slow learners.

IX. *Mathematical skills are used in quantitative problem situations which arise in class.*

Number situations emerge frequently from daily school activities and from the various school subjects. Money has to be counted, the cost per pupil for a trip has to be estimated, results of drives have to be reported, tickets have to be sold, records have to be kept, etc. Various experiences which call for the use of mathematical skills are provided in the social studies where, for example, maps have to be read, and in science where such activities as the interpretation of statistics are often required. Such practical situations and applications make the pupils see the importance of mastering mathematical skills and offer opportunities for practice on meaningful materials. At each grade level, the resourceful teacher will identify situations in which quantitative problem solving is required and which can make a real contribution to mathematics. He will use such situations to advantage.

X. *Proper motivational techniques are applied in order to arouse the child's interest in mathematics.*

~~The pupil learns best when he is actively engaged in the learning process~~. Such an involvement of the child is caused by motives, which are conditions that stimulate his activity. These motives incite him to pursue learnings. Thus, it is the task of the teacher to create an intellectual environment in the classroom which will develop proper motives.

~~The use of incentives which stimulate the child to perform in the desired way is called *motivation*.~~ Motivation may be *extrinsic* ~~or intrinsic.~~

~~In extrinsic motivation, external incentives or devices are applied to cause the child to perform the task in order to attain some goal besides the mere completion of the assigned work.~~ The child sees his activities as a means toward an end. By rewarding a pupil for good work or punishing him for poor work, he may be stimulated to meet the teacher's requirements. Rewards may consist of a high score, a prize, praise, prestige, etc. Punishment may also take several forms. ~~In intrinsic motivation, the incentives are embodied in the task itself and the child has as his goal the fulfillment of the task to be performed. Such motives incite in the child the desire to study the subject for its own sake. It should be the teacher's goal to develop intrinsic motivation.~~

Usually, extrinsic motives prevail originally. A child will enter upon a task which has no appeal to him, only because it has been assigned. In a wholesome learning environment, he should gradually begin to see the importance of the work he is doing, so that his motivation becomes intrinsic and he will acquire a strong interest in the subject itself.

Many motivational techniques have been suggested for the teaching of elementary-school mathematics. ~~Such techniques include: arousing the pupil's interest in the content presented and stirring his curiosity; making the pupil see the importance of what he is doing and thereby feel the need for the work; conducting interviews with pupils for guidance purposes; teaching patterns of thought which the child can apply successfully; recognizing good work; reproof; presenting enrichment activities including games, puzzles, and mathematical tricks; allowing pupils to study programed materials that fit their level of achievement; and using teaching aids such as films, film strips, slides, bulletin boards, posters, clippings, pictures, and teaching machines.~~ Several of these techniques will be described in the following chapters.

## Recommended Procedures for Introducing a New Case in Mathematics

When introducing a new case in elementary-school mathematics, the teacher will guide his pupils through several steps. The number of these steps and the extensiveness of their use will depend upon the mathematical maturity of the pupils. Therefore, the following are suggested not as a recipe but only as a frame of reference:

1. The case is introduced in a situation.

2. The situation is discussed by the pupils and the number question is translated into a mathematical sentence.

3. The pupils are encouraged to suggest possible solutions.

4. While these suggestions are discussed, the teacher directs the children through his guide questions and interpretations toward the best procedure.

5. The answer is checked.

6. Similar exercises are presented.

7. The generalization is arrived at by the inductive method.

8. The textbook presentation of the case is studied.

9. The practice exercises are worked by the pupils.

10. The generalization is applied in situations presented by the textbook or the teacher.

The following example illustrates the use of each of the ten steps:

1. *Situation:* When training for track, Tom ran three times around the school grounds. The distance around the grounds was 0.4 mile. How many miles did Tom run?

2. *Mathematical sentence:* $3 \times 0.4 = \square$

3. The pupils are invited to suggest solutions. The following ways of solving the problem may be suggested by the class:

a) Horizontal addition:

Tom ran 0.4 mile + 0.4 mile + 0.4 mile = 1.2 miles.

b) Vertical addition:

$$
\begin{array}{r}
0.4 \\
0.4 \\
0.4 \\
\hline
1.2
\end{array}
$$
Tom ran 1.2 miles.

c) The number line:

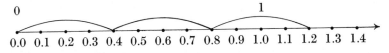

Tom ran 1.2 miles.

d) Some pupils may suggest to multiply as with whole numbers.

4. The teacher commends all the suggestions which lead to a correct answer. He capitalizes on the suggestion to multiply as with whole numbers, and re-emphasizes the fact that multiplication is a fast form of addition. If the suggestion to multiply as with whole numbers has not been made, the teacher leads up to the regular method of multiplication, for example, as follows:

$3 \times 4$ books $= 12$ books     $3 \times 4$ tenths $= 12$ tenths $= 1.2$     $3 \times 0.4 = 1.2$

$$
\begin{array}{r}
4 \text{ tenths} \\
\times\ 3 \\
\hline
12 \text{ tenths} = 1.2
\end{array}
\qquad
\begin{array}{r}
0.4 \\
\times\ \ 3 \\
\hline
1.2
\end{array}
$$

The teacher asks questions such as:
Can 12 be the answer?  Why not?
Would .12 be a sensible answer?  Why not?
Does the answer 1.2 make sense?  How can we check the answer?

5. The answer is checked by using the fraction method:

$$3 \times 0.4 = 3 \times \frac{4}{10} = \frac{3 \times 4}{10} = \frac{12}{10} = 1.2$$

6. Several similar exercises such as $2 \times 0.8 = \square$;  $3 \times 0.16 = \square$;  and $5 \times 0.11 = \square$ are worked.

7. The teacher encourages the pupils to explain what has been done in all the examples and he directs them toward the formulation of the rule:

> Multiply decimal numbers just as you do whole numbers and then place the decimal point.  Point off as many places in the product as there are in the multiplicand.  Begin pointing off from the right.

8. The textbook presentation of the case is studied.

9. The pupils work the practice exercises provided in the textbook.  The teacher gives individual help and supplies additional practice to pupils who need it.

10. The pupils' ability in applying their newly acquired skill in situations is tested by presenting word problems involving the principle learned, and the children are stimulated to carry this principle over into further situations in order to consolidate and extend the acquired concepts.

# EXERCISES

1. Find examples to prove that a more extensive use is being made of mathematics at present than ever before.

2. Explain the statement: The best learning takes place when the child takes an active part in the learning process.

3. Illustrate the use of the inductive and the deductive approach in elementary-school mathematics.

4. On the basis of the characteristics of a desirable program as outlined in this chapter, describe some differences between contemporary elementary-school mathematics programs and those in use at the time you were an elementary-school pupil.

5. Explain the statement: The best motivation is intrinsic motivation.

# SELECTED REFERENCES

Banks, J. H., *Learning and Teaching Arithmetic*, 2nd Ed. Boston: Allyn and Bacon, Inc., 1964, Ch. I.

Dutton, W. H., *Evaluating Pupils' Understanding of Arithmetic*. Englewood Cliffs, N.J.: Prentice-Hall, Inc., 1964, Ch. II.

Dutton, W. H. and L. J. Adams, *Arithmetic for Teachers*. Englewood Cliffs, N.J.: Prentice-Hall, Inc., 1961, Ch. I.

Grossnickle, F. E. and L. J. Brueckner, *Discovering Meanings in Elementary School Mathematics*. New York: Holt, Rinehart & Winston, Inc., 1963, Ch. II.

Marks, J. L., C. R. Purdy, and L. B. Kinney, *Teaching Arithmetic for Understanding*. New York: McGraw-Hill, Inc., 1958, Ch. I.

Morton, R. L., *Teaching Children Arithmetic*. Morristown, N.J.: Silver Burdett Company, 1953, Chs. I and II.

National Council of Teachers of Mathematics, *Evaluation in Mathematics, Twenty-sixth Yearbook*. Washington, D.C.: The Council, 1961, Ch. III.

Shipp, D. E. and S. Adams, *Developing Arithmetic Concepts and Skills*. Englewood Cliffs, N.J.: Prentice-Hall, Inc., 1964, Ch. I.

# 2

# HISTORICAL ANTECEDENTS OF CURRENT MATHEMATICS TEACHING

THE PLACE WHICH mathematics presently occupies in the curriculum of the elementary school, the content which is taught, and the methods of presentation are a result of a gradual development of the subject, the differing and increased needs of society, and the findings of educators and psychologists concerning the way in which children learn. An examination of literature available on the history of mathematics as a school subject reveals a gradual expansion of the content, changes in purposes of teaching the subject, and a continuous improvement in method of presentation.[1]

There are indications that as early as four or five thousand years ago a book on mathematics was written in Egypt, where the subject was studied by the priests and its main principles taught to children. The Babylonians made great advances in mathematics. Recordings and materials which were

---

[1] For much of the information contained in this chapter the author is indebted to Bulletin No. 10, "Development of Arithmetic as a School Subject," Commissioner of Education (Washington D.C.: U.S. Government Printing Office, 1917).

discovered, such as tablets with mathematical data, bank accounts, and specimens of pupils' arithmetic work point to a high level of mathematical achievement. The Greeks included mathematics in the requirements for a liberal education. They distinguished two branches of mathematics: *arithmetica*, which dealt with the theory of numbers, and *logistica*, which was the art of calculation. Greek philosophers such as Pythagoras and Plato were interested in studying the abstract arithmetica as a basic discipline for the study of philosophy, science, music, and art, whereas the Sophists— itinerant teachers who taught for a fee—were attracted to logistica, which was the practical phase of mathematics. The Romans, who were practical people, stressed the art of calculation in their schools in order to prepare the pupils to meet the mathematical problems of daily life; those, for example, which could arise when surveying land, building roads, levying taxes, and carrying on trade.

During the Middle Ages, arithmetic was included in the *Seven Liberal Arts* and it was taught in the church schools for religious purposes such as to perpetuate the ability to compute the dates of religious holidays. The creation of the *Hanseatic League*, an organization founded in the thirteenth century to protect trade routes, was the cause for the establishment of "Rechen Schulen," which were special schools in which commercial arithmetic was taught.

During the Renaissance, several factors caused the expansion of mathematics. The invention of the art of printing aided the process of standardizing mathematical terms and symbols and caused the knowledge of mathematics to spread gradually. The increase in trade necessitated the teaching of the subject to more people. The replacement of the Roman system by the Hindu-Arabic system, which was finally accomplished in the sixteenth century, simplified calculation. Through all these influences, arithmetic became gradually established as one of the common-school subjects. However, since the use of the Hindu-Arabic symbols made calculation simpler, the abacus was discarded, and throughout the following few centuries the teaching of arithmetic consisted primarily of having pupils copy examples, memorize rules, and juggle figures. It was not until the eighteenth century that improvements were made. Methods were suggested by which objects and pictures were used to make the fundamental processes more meaningful to children and to introduce arithmetic problems in a concrete way. The greatest influence on the method of teaching arithmetic was exerted by the Swiss educator Johann Heinrich Pestalozzi (1746–1827), who utilized objects in his teaching, insisted upon clearness of understanding of arithmetical concepts before drill, introduced the subject as early as grade one, and emphasized the importance of mental arithmetic. Pestalozzi's influence even reached the United States.

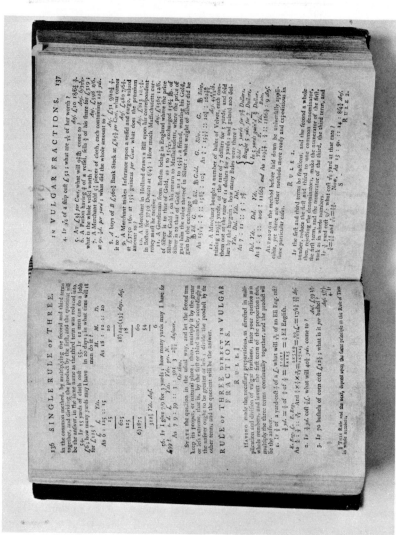

Two-page spread from A New and Complete System of Arithmetic, by Nicolas Pike, published in 1788 by John Mycall of Newburyport, Mass. Supplied through the courtesy of Esther Unkel, Assistant Professor of Education, College of Education, University of Connecticut, Storrs, Conn.

# Arithmetic as a School Subject in the United States

## I. From the Beginnings in the Colonies to 1821

From the time that the colonies were founded, arithmetic was probably taught in many public schools to satisfy the need of the settlers for some knowledge of the subject in order to carry on their many activities in trade and commerce. During the middle of the eighteenth century, Benjamin Franklin encouraged the teaching of arithmetic because of its utility. When, in 1789, the teaching of arithmetic was made obligatory in the states of Massachusetts and New Hampshire, and when colleges began to require the subject for entrance, arithmetic became an essential part of the grammar-school curriculum.

During this time, arithmetic textbooks were very scarce. Before the close of the period, it was an exception for a pupil to possess a book and many teachers had only their own written copy. The child was provided with a blankbook or ciphering book, in which he daily wrote "sums," rules, and solutions. The master set the pupil a "sum," told him the rule for its solution without giving any explanation, and the child had to try to work the "sum" on scrap paper or on a slate. When it had been solved to the master's satisfaction, the pupil had to copy the solution in his ciphering book. If the pupil's answer did not agree with that in the master's book, the child had to try again.

The earliest arithmetic books used in the colonies were of English authorship. Dilworth's *Schoolmaster's Assistant* was very popular. The first American arithmetic textbook was written by Isaac Greenwood in 1729, but it did not receive much recognition. Nicolas Pike's *A New and Complete System of Arithmetic*, published in 1788, was the first book to receive a wide circulation. It was used primarily in colleges and academies, and was followed by several other American arithmetic books. The most popular textbook was probably Nathan Daboll's *Schoolmaster's Assistant*, published in 1799, although several other texts were also widely used.

The arithmetic books of this period presented a large number of rules. The "sum" had to be solved by written computation, and exercises in mental arithmetic were not included. The order of instruction was from the abstract to the concrete. The children were instructed to begin by committing the rule to memory. Very little time was devoted to practice. The presentations were topical. Usually the topics "notation" and "numeration" were followed by the fundamental operations of addition, subtraction, multiplication, and division and were presented and completed in that order. Fractions were dealt with extensively in some books; in others they received only minor attention. Decimals were stressed after 1786, when federal money was established. Other topics included denominate numbers, the rule of three, barter, partnership, exchange, applications of percentage, progressions, permutations, longitude and time, mensuration, duodecimals, and puzzles.

## II. From 1821 to 1892

Warren Colburn published his *First Lessons in Arithmetic on the Plan of Pestalozzi* in 1821. He is said to have exerted a greater influence upon the development of arithmetic as a school subject in the United States than any other person.

Pestalozzi held that the faculties or capacities of the child are developed naturally, but that man has to assist the development by using the materials and art of instruction employed by nature. To him sense impressions were the foundation of all knowledge, and arithmetic was the most important means of giving mental training which would result in the power to form clear ideas. Thus, the elements of arithmetic had to be identified, and in the method of instruction a series of steps had to be formulated. When the elements of the subject were then taught in the proper sequence, clear ideas would be formed. A clear idea of the number seven, for example, had to be acquired by counting seven objects. Children used their fingers, pebbles, or other objects to obtain the proper sense perceptions.

Several "tables" were devised by Pestalozzi to serve as aids. The units table consisted of ten rows of ten rectangles. Each rectangle in the first row had one vertical mark, each rectangle in the second row had two vertical marks, etc. Eight sets of exercises were to follow the presentations. One consisted of counting exercises; another of expressing a number of units as twos, threes, fours, etc.

Pestalozzi had attempted to analyze psychologically the process of the human mind and had aimed at training the child's mental powers by using arithmetic exercises in which the subject had been reduced to its elements. During the first part of the training, no arithmetic symbols were presented, since clear number ideas and their relations were stressed. These were to be acquired by counting, expressing numbers in different ways, putting units together, and separating them. Such activities were meant to lead the child to the consciousness of "the real relations of things which lie at the bottom of all calculations." Consequently, beginning arithmetic instruction was oral.

Colburn's indebtedness to Pestalozzi can be inferred from the original title of his arithmetic textbook. He was probably introduced to Pestalozzi's ideas during his college days and had the intelligence and courage to break with the method of instruction by which he had learned arithmetic. His

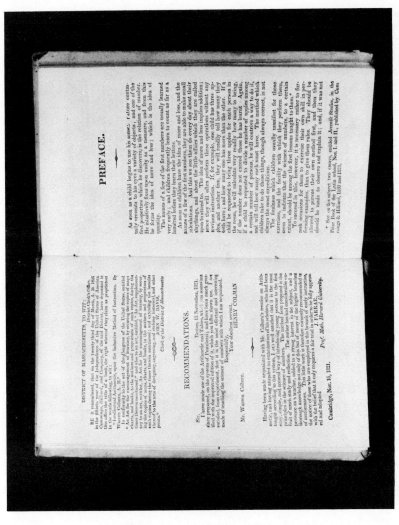

*Two-page spread from Colburn's First Lessons. Intellectual Arithmetic upon the Inductive Method of Instruction, by Warren Colburn, published in 1844 by William J. Reynolds of Boston. Supplied through the courtesy of Esther Unkel, Assistant Professor of Education, College of Education, University of Connecticut, Storrs, Conn.*

43. Fifteen and five are how many?
44. Sixteen and two are how many?
45. Sixteen and three are how many?
46. Sixteen and four are how many?
47. Seventeen and two are how many?
48. Seventeen and three are how many?
49. Eighteen and two are how many?

E. 1. A man bought a sheep for nine dollars, and to pay for it he gave five bushels of corn worth four dollars, and the rest in money; how much money did he pay?

2. If a barrel of flour is worth eight dollars, and a hundred weight of sugar is worth twelve dollars, how much more is the sugar worth than the flour?

3. If a man had eleven dollars, and should buy three bushels of corn for five dollars, how much money would he have left?

4. A man bought a firkin of butter for fifteen dollars, but, it being damaged, he was willing to sell it again for eight dollars less than he gave for it; what did he sell it for?

5. A man bought three barrels of flour for eighteen dollars, and sold it again for eleven dollars; what did he lose by the bargain?

6. A man bought a keg of tobacco for thirteen dollars, and sold it again for eighteen; what did he gain by the bargain?

7. Five *less* two are how many?
8. Seven less three are how many?
9. Three less three are how many?
10. Nine less three are how many?
11. Six less two are how many?
12. Seven less four are how many?
13. Eight less three are how many?
14. Five less four are how many?

15. Seven less five are how many?
16. Nine less five are how many?
17 Eight less six are how many?
18. Eleven less two are how many?
19. Twelve less four are how many?
20. Ten less seven are how many?
21. Thirteen less five are how many?
22. Fourteen less eight are how many
23. Twelve less five are how many?
24. Seventeen less seven are how many?
25. Seventeen less five are how many?
26. Thirteen less seven are how many?
27. Sixteen less seven are how many?
28. Fifteen less seven are how many?
29. Nineteen less six are how many?
30. Eighteen less five are how many?
31. Eighteen less eight are how many?
32. Fourteen less nine are how many?
33. Sixteen less five are how many?
34. Fifteen less eight are how many?
35. Fourteen less nine are how many?
36. Sixteen less ten are how many?
37. Seventeen less nine are how many?
38. Eighteen less seven are how many?

F. 1. How many are nine and two? Nineteen and two? Twenty-nine and two? Thirty-nine and two? Forty-nine and two? Fifty-nine and two? Sixty-nine and two? Seventy-nine and two? Eighty-nine and two? Ninety-nine and two?

2. How many are nine and three? Nineteen and three? Twenty-nine and three? Thirty-nine and three? Forty-nine and three? Fifty-nine and three? Sixty-nine and three? Seventy-nine and three? Eighty-nine and three? Ninety-nine and three?

3. How many are nine and four? Nineteen and

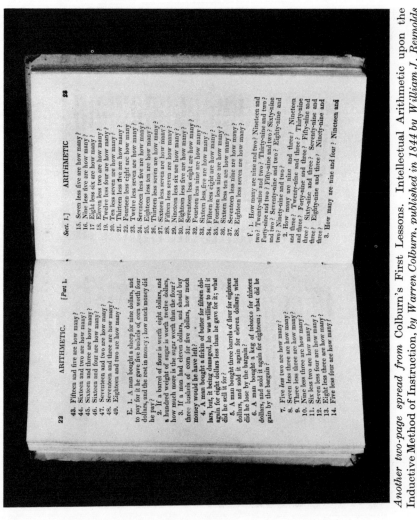

*Another two-page spread from Colburn's First Lessons. Intellectual Arithmetic upon the Inductive Method of Instruction, by Warren Colburn, published in 1844 by William J. Reynolds of Boston. Supplied through the courtesy of Esther Unkel, Assistant Professor of Education, College of Education, University of Connecticut, Storrs, Conn.*

first book was intended for children of 5 or 6 to 8 or 9 years old. ~~This book was published later under the title *Colburn's First Lessons. Intellectual Arithmetic upon the Inductive Method of Instruction.*~~ As this title indicates, Colburn departed from the deductive method. ~~He had his pupils develop their own rules. His aim was twofold: to provide practical problems, and to train the mind.~~ **2** .

In the first part of his first book Colburn did not use arithmetic symbols. The numbers used were small enough so that the answers to the problems could be computed without the use of paper and pencil. Consequently, the master had to be actively engaged in the teaching process and, instead of "setting a sum" for each individual pupil, he had to teach the class. Colburn used objects extensively; for example, he originally used the Pestalozzian tables. He omitted from his books several difficult topics which formed a part of the ciphering books, and included exercises for drill.

Colburn's second book, *The Sequel*, was intended for pupils who had completed his *First Lessons*.

Several arithmetic textbooks, patterned after Colburn's books, were published during the period from 1821 to 1857. Joseph Ray's series, dating from 1834, appears to have been very popular.

~~The period of Colburn's influence was followed by a static period. After 1857, arithmetic textbooks became deductive again.~~ Rules were presented instead of developed, drill was stressed, and motivation was mostly the result of artificial incentives.

~~In 1870 the *German Grube method* was introduced in the United States. A new principle in this method was the introduction of the four fundamental operations simultaneously for each number before proceeding to the next number.~~ The plan was called a *concentric circle plan*, in which, during the first year of school, the operations were presented for the numbers 1 to 10 and, for the next three years, for the numbers 10 to 100. The method, aiming at a complete mastery of the fundamentals and employing objects for concrete presentation, was thorough. However, since it carried illustrations to an extreme and dealt with the four fundamental operations simultaneously, it resulted in mechanical instruction and did not elicit much motivation. ~~The method was criticized by John Dewey.~~

## III. From 1892 to 1935

During the last decade of the nineteenth century, American educators became actively interested in the educational principles of the German philosopher and psychologist ~~Johann Friedrich Herbart~~ (1776–1841). Herbart developed the principle of *apperception*, according to which new experiences are interpreted and given meaning by means of old, existing ideas which are the result of past experiences. This principle is expressed by the phrase "teach the new in terms of the old."

~~The apperception theory opposed the disciplinary concept of education which had been dominant for a long time~~. It emphasized the content of a subject. The greater the number of clear concepts which were formed in the child's mind, the better prepared he would be to cope with new situations. Thus, the mind was considered to be a storehouse in which ideas were accumulated for future help in meeting new situations.

Herbart's immediate end of education was to develop in the child a "many-sided interest," by introducing him to many aspects of the external world. Consequently, the Herbartians emphasized history and literature as elementary-school subjects and were therefore responsible for a reduction in the time allotted to arithmetic.

The Herbartian movement led to the inductive approach in the teaching of arithmetic. Every arithmetic topic was to be developed or rationalized and the "why" of a process was to be explained. The general processes were derived by presenting the topics according to the Herbartian "steps:" (1) preparation; (2) presentation; (3) comparison or abstraction; and (4) generalization. Followers of Herbart distinguished five steps: (1) preparation—a review of related materials; (2) presentation—the presentation of the new materials; (3) comparison—an organization of the facts; (4) conclusion—a generalization from the old to the new facts; and (5) application—an application of the principles learned.

The influence of Herbart's theory was most pronounced in the United States in the 1890's. At the same time William James published his *Principles of Psychology*, in which he contradicted the existence of general transfer of training and denied that a general capacity—for example, the power to remember—can be trained by specific exercises. Consequently, the way in which arithmetic was taught in the public schools, especially the great emphasis on memorization and the generous amount of time allotted to the subject, were severely criticized.

~~In 1893 the *Committee of Ten* recommended that obsolete topics be eliminated from the arithmetic curriculum~~. In line with Herbart's theory, the chairman of the committee stated that "the main end of mathematical teaching · · · is to store the mind with clear conceptions of things and their relations." ~~The *Committee of Fifteen* recommended, in 1895, that arithmetic instruction begin in the second school year and that it end with the close of the sixth year~~. The committee also suggested that the practice of teaching two arithmetic lessons daily—a "mental" and a "written" lesson—be discontinued.

Another critic of educational theory and practice was John Dewey, who emphasized that the environment of the child provides many problems which are solved by number and number relations. Thus, according to Dewey, authors of arithmetic textbooks and teachers of the subject must present situations which call for measurement and the relating of quantities. Soon after these views had been published, some arithmetic textbooks appeared which, according to the authors, were based upon the ideas of Dewey. Since problems arising from practical situations were emphasized, the social value of arithmetic received more recognition.

At the turn of the century, the recommendations of the Committees of Ten and Fifteen attracted favorable attention and elementary-school arithmetic topics were screened. In doing this, the *theory of social utility* was applied. This theory stressed the social phase of arithmetic instruction and aimed at including only those topics in the curriculum which were useful and served a real need in life. This movement reached its peak in 1920. Studies were conducted to determine what arithmetic topics were used by adults in their vocational activities and in daily life. Topics which were considered to be not functional and which were therefore eliminated from the curriculum included square root, cube root, factors, fractions with large denominators, repeating decimals, proportions, and commercial-arithmetic topics. Though the application of the social utility theory served some useful purposes, the theory was rightly criticized by educators who pointed out that the teaching of more arithmetic and the use of improved methods would result in an increased use of arithmetic in daily life.

In the meantime the method of teaching arithmetic had been reconsidered. Results of experiments had indicated that there is no general transfer of learning. One of the psychologists who conducted experiments which showed that there was no automatic transfer of learning was Edward L. Thorndike, who developed his *stimulus-response bond (S—R Bond)* or *connectionist theory*. This association theory held that for every stimulus or situation there is a particular response and that these two are associated by a bond. For example, the stimulus $3 \times 2$ should elicit the response 6. The elements of complex learnings had to be isolated, taught, and mastered separately. Thus, the arithmetic skills were presented in sequential order, and the steps were analyzed. Thorndike's *law of exercise*, stating that repetition strengthens a bond, was applied and skills were mastered by drill. Indeed, drill was used excessively to fix in the minds of the pupils the numerous arithmetic facts. Critics disliked the theory because it broke up arithmetic into unrelated facts; they called it an atomistic theory. It was also called a mechanistic theory, since mechanical drill was emphasized and teaching for understanding was de-emphasized.

During the 1920's the *Child Study Movement*, which was started by G. Stanley Hall in 1880, was quite popular. The proponents of this movement investigated the growth and development of children and claimed that the curriculum and instructional procedures should be the result of an understanding of the interests and needs of the children. This movement was a part of and gave impetus to the *Progressive Education Movement*, which encouraged unit teaching, incidental learning, the teaching of arithmetic in activity programs, and arithmetic instruction as an integrated part of other school subjects. The proponents of the incidental method claimed that the various topics of arithmetic should be taught when the child shows an interest in them, since internal motivation is more important than the logical sequence of the subject. Therefore, in such programs no specific time was set aside for the teaching of arithmetic, but topics were taught as the need arose.

The incidental theory met with valid criticisms. Though the best teaching is done when the pupils are internally motivated, the method did not produce the desired results. Serious gaps were discovered in the knowledge of the pupils, since not all topics which must be studied arose from problem situations. Moreover, the sequential nature of arithmetic did not lend itself to such an approach.

## IV. From 1935 to the Present

Since 1935 the *Gestalt theory of learning* has exercised a great influence upon the teaching of arithmetic in the United States. The theory was first presented in Germany by Max Wertheimer.

According to the Gestalt theory, the learning process is not built up of elements, nor is it a process of association, but it is a result of seeing the over-all pattern or unity which gives meaning to all of the parts. The result is a configuration or a Gestalt. When by means of insight the learner recognizes the interrelationship of elements and the over-all relationship that exists between the parts and the whole, he has acquired a basic understanding. Learning is not exclusively an inductive process and does not proceed basically by trial and error, but it is a function of insight and maturation. The pupil must see the goals and must be motivated to learn, and the teacher has the responsibility to guide the child toward seeing the goals and to incite him to learn.

The belief that memorization would result in automatic transfer of learning was not accepted. The Gestaltists considered transfer of learning possible only when the learning to be transferred could be associated with the area to which transfer was desired. The need for functional subject matter was stressed, since greater transfer seemed to occur when the teacher made use of content which was meaningful to the child. From this it can be inferred that the Gestaltist is more interested in arriving at general understandings or general principles which will enable him to grasp the meanings of individual experiences or concrete facts.

In the Tenth Yearbook of the National Council of Teachers of Mathematics, published in 1935, the *meaning theory* was presented. During the following years it gradually became widely accepted. ~~Based on Gestalt psychology, it maintains that children must understand the structure of the number system and be able to perform number operations meaningfully.~~ When the meaning theory is properly applied, children are guided to develop procedures by applying what they have learned, they are encouraged to find rules inductively and to apply them deductively, they are urged to take part in class discussions when number relations and number principles are explored, and they are stimulated to apply their mathematical knowledge creatively and imaginatively in other school subjects and in daily life.

When the meaning theory was introduced, great emphasis was placed upon the development of meaning in arithmetic and there was no general agreement concerning the necessity for drill. At the present time, the need for practice after a meaningful introduction of a topic is recognized.

During the last decade several attempts have been made to construct improved programs in elementary-school mathematics. In these programs the structure of mathematics is emphasized, the principle of discovery is stressed, new content is included, misnomers are removed from the mathematical vocabulary, and mathematical reasoning is developed. It is anticipated that these experimental programs will lead to improved teaching and learning in elementary-school mathematics. The characteristics of exploratory programs are presented in Chapter 3.

## EXERCISES

1. Enumerate and explain different aims of arithmetic instruction which have been dominant in the past.

2. Distinguish between the words *arithmetica* and *logistica*.

3. State the difference between the inductive and the deductive approach in the teaching of a mathematical process.

4. Describe the method by which arithmetic was taught and learned during the ciphering-book period.

5. What was, in your opinion, the importance of Colburn's first arithmetic book?

6. Explain and illustrate the utilitarian aim of arithmetic instruction.

7. Find, in an old arithmetic book, some examples of arithmetic problems which were presented to train the mind.

8. Present the various sides of the social utility theory as an aid in selecting content for the arithmetic curriculum.

9. How could the Herbartian movement in the United States cause the reduction in time allotment in arithmetic?

10. Why was mental computation an important part in Colburn's method of arithmetic instruction?

11. Explain the S—R Bond theory with respect to the teaching of arithmetic.

12. Explain the Gestalt theory of learning with respect to the teaching of arithmetic.

13. Present the various sides of the following theories with respect to arithmetic instruction:
    a) Drill theory
    b) Incidental theory
    c) Meaning theory.

14. What is, in your opinion, the role of drill in the teaching of elementary-school mathematics?

15. What is your opinion about the necessity of a sequential elementary-school mathematics program in grade I?


## SELECTED REFERENCES

Brownell, W. A., *Arithmetic in Grades I and II*. Durham, N. C.: Duke University Press, 1941.
———, "The Place of Meaning in the Teaching of Arithmetic." *The Elementary School Journal*, January, 1947, pp. 256–65.
Buswell, G. T., "The Psychology of Learning in Relation to the Teaching of Arithmetic," *The Teaching of Arithmetic*. Fiftieth Yearbook of the National Society for the Study of Education. Chicago: University of Chicago Press, 1951, Part II, Ch. VIII.
Dewey, J., *How We Think*. Boston: D. C. Heath & Company, 1933.
Dutton, W. H., *Evaluating Pupils' Understanding of Arithmetic*. Englewood Cliffs, N.J.: Prentice-Hall, Inc., 1964, Chs. I and II.
Fehr, H. F., "Theories of Learning Related to the Field of Mathematics," *The Learning of Mathematics, Its Theory and Practice*. Twenty-first Yearbook of the National Council of Teachers of Mathematics. Washington, D.C.: The Council, 1953, Ch. I.
Harris, C. W. (ed.), *Encyclopedia of Educational Research*. New York: The Macmillan Co., 1960, pp. 63–67.
Jones, Sister M. E., *A Course in Methods of Arithmetic*. Boston: D. C. Heath & Company, 1926, Chs. I and II.

Monroe, W. S., *Development of Arithmetic as a School Subject*. Bulletin No. 10. Washington, D.C.: U.S. Government Printing Office, 1917.

Smith, D. E., *The Teaching of Elementary Mathematics*. New York: The Macmillan Co., 1900, Chs. I–V.

Wilson, G. M., "The Social Utility Theory as Applied to Arithmetic, Its Research Basis, and Some of Its Applications." *Journal of Educational Research*, January, 1948, pp. 321–37.

# 3

# THE
# SEARCH
# FOR
# IMPROVED
# PROGRAMS

WHEN THE RESULTS of the teaching of elementary-school mathematics are considered, often two criticisms are made:

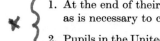

1. At the end of their elementary-school years the pupils do not perform as well as is necessary to continue their studies in mathematics efficiently;

2. Pupils in the United States cannot compete favorably with European children of the same age.

Not many people quarrel with the first criticism. One has only to watch the average man in the street who has to perform the computation $4 \div \frac{1}{2}$, the average high-school student who has to find the answer to a multiplication question such as $7 \times 16 = \square$ without the use of paper and pencil, or the average college student who is faced with the problem of finding the interest on $850 at 6 % for 3 months, to decide that the teaching of arithmetic should be improved. Research pertaining to the level of achievement in arithmetic at secondary and college level has shown that students lack much skill and do not understand many important mathematical ideas. Brueckner[1]

[1] L. J. Brueckner, "Testing the Validity of Criticisms of the Schools," *Journal of Educational Research*, February, 1943, pp. 465–67.

administered a 30-item test in the four fundamental operations and percentage to seniors in more than 20 states in all parts of the country and found the median score to be 17.1 or 57 % correct. In reporting on the results of a selective examination given to 4200 entering freshman at 27 universities and colleges, Admiral Nimmitz[2] stated that more than 50% of the students taking the examination were unable to pass the arithmetic reasoning test. Orleans and Sperling[3] concluded that common computations by graduate students enrolled in a course in statistics indicated a lack of competence in division and an inadequacy in handling fractions.

The criticism that children in the United States are no match in arithmetic computation and problem solving for their European counterparts has also been substantiated by studies. Buswell[4] tested 3191 English and 3179 California randomly selected ten- and eleven-year-old pupils on a 100-item test constructed by the National Foundation for Research in Education in England and Wales. The mean score for the English pupils was 29.1, and for the California pupils 12.1, the difference being statistically significant. Tracy[5] administered the same test to a representative sample of urban classes in North Carolina and compared their scores with the scores made by the urban population of Buswell's study. He found significant differences in the scores in favor of the English children. In fact, the scores of the English children were approximately equal to the scores of those pupils in the North Carolina sample who had had two additional years of arithmetic instruction.

The author[6] administered two tests to 1511 Dutch fifth- and sixth-graders and to 1530 Iowa pupils of grades V, VI, VII, and VIII. One test dealt with arithmetic problem solving and the other with arithmetic concepts and processes. The test was a modification of a part of the *Iowa Tests of Basic Skills* and had been approved by Dutch educators. The sample was considered by several experts to be representative. The mean score on the problem-solving test (35 items) was 27.3 for the Dutch sixth-graders, and 19.2 for the Iowa sixth-graders. The mean scores on the test on concepts and processes (59 items) were 38.7 and 26.4 respectively. The differences on both tests were statistically significant. The average performance for the sixth-grade classes in the Netherlands was somewhat higher than the Iowa average for eighth-graders. Of course, all the studies just reported had limitations, but the

---

[2] Admiral C. W. Nimmitz, in "The Importance of Mathematics in the War Effort," *The Mathematics Teacher*, February, 1942, pp. 88–89.

[3] J. S. Orleans and J. L. Sperling, "The Arithmetic Knowledge of Graduate Students," *Journal of Educational Research*, November, 1954, pp. 177–86.

[4] G. T. Buswell, "A Comparison of Achievement in Arithmetic in England and Central California," *The Arithmetic Teacher*, February, 1958, pp. 1–9.

[5] N. H. Tracy, "A Comparison of Test Results—North Carolina, California, and England," *The Arithmetic Teacher*, October, 1959, pp. 199–202.

[6] K. Kramer, "Arithmetic Achievement in Iowa and the Netherlands," *The Elementary School Journal*, February, 1959, pp. 258–63.

consistency of the sizable differences makes it apparent that arithmetic instruction in England and Holland results in better performance than in the United States.


## New Mathematics Programs in the Elementary School

During the last few decades groups of people who wanted to improve and accelerate the mathematics curriculum have been doing considerable work on new, experimental programs in mathematics. Exploratory mathematics programs for the elementary school which have been in the limelight for some time include the following:

1. The University of Illinois Arithmetic Project
2. The School Mathematics Study Group (SMSG)
3. The Greater Cleveland Mathematics Program
4. The Syracuse University-Webster College Madison Project
5. The Projects of Suppes and Hawley at Stanford University
6. The Minnesota Elementary Curriculum Project

The characteristics of the new programs as described by authorities include the following:

1. The programs have been produced by or with the assistance of mathematicians.
2. Precise language and terminology is emphasized.
3. A main objective is to teach the child to think critically by developing skill in following and building patterns of organized thought.
4. New content has been added. Examples of topics included in all or many of the new programs are: prime numbers, composite numbers, factors, exponents, different numeration systems, properties of number, additional terms and symbols, algebraic equations, inequalities, mathematical sentences and frames, number patterns, the number line, logic, simple probability, sets, graphing, and geometry. It should be noted, however, that a number of these topics have already been included in good "traditional" programs for several years.

*Know*

The new mathematics programs have met with objections. Criticisms which have been directed at some or all of the new materials are:

1. New programs have a tendency to be unbalanced. Topics such as sets have been overemphasized in some programs.
2. Authors who know about teaching elementary-school children should have had a greater part in the preparation of the materials.

3. The typical classroom teacher is not able to teach a new program before he has thoroughly studied the new content and vocabulary. Examples of topics with which the typical teacher has to become acquainted are: different systems of numeration and notation, sets, mathematical sentences, and geometry.

Some claims have been made by advocates of exploratory programs which do not do justice to several textbook series which antedated these programs:

1. It has been suggested that the new mathematics stresses concepts rather than rote memorization of the proper steps to perform, as in the old system. A careful study of good "traditional" programs will reveal that they also are emphasizing the understanding of processes and are paying a great deal of attention to the proper formation of concepts.

2. The implication has been made that the "discovery" method is a unique characteristic of experimental programs. However, the "discovery" method has long been used and is being employed in many recent "traditional" mathematics curricula.

It should be acknowledged that the experimental programs in the elementary school have been serving a very useful purpose. Professional people, representing various disciplines, have struggled with the problem of how to improve the mathematics curriculum and have made a number of valuable contributions. New enthusiasm for mathematics in many schools, better attitudes among teachers, the addition of content, the presentation of several topics at lower grade levels, the refinement of terminology and vocabulary, the stimulation of the child's imagination, a desire among authors and publishers to produce superior materials, the creation of workshops for teachers of mathematics, and many more things have been a result of the promotion of exploratory programs. These efforts should result in better teaching and learning through the use of improved, properly-balanced programs. In order to accomplish this goal, promising new materials should be tried out in the classroom under carefully controlled conditions, before they are promoted for countrywide use or rejected as inferior.

## Needed Revisions

A study of the research conducted in the field of mathematics reveals several shortcomings in the mathematics curriculum of the public school. The remediation of these diagnosed weaknesses should result in a distinct improvement in the program. In the following paragraphs some issues related to the teaching of mathematics in the elementary school will be presented and research on the topics will be reported.

## 1. Meaning theory

~~The superiority of insight over rote memorization, of understanding the reasons why a process is performed over mechanical manipulation, and of encouraging children to form their own generalizations over dictating the rules has been demonstrated repeatedly.~~ Thiele[7] conducted an experiment with two groups of beginning second-graders, totaling 512 pupils. The 100 basic addition facts were taught to one group by the "generalization (meaning) method" and to the other group by a drill method. The "generalization method" resulted in significantly better performance and in better transfer of training than the drill method.

Swenson[8] taught the 100 basic addition facts to three groups of second-graders, totaling 332 pupils. Three different methods were used: (1) the generalization (meaning) method; (2) the drill method; and (3) the drill-plus method. The drill-plus method was a drill method with certain concessions made to the ideas of concrete meaning and organization. The following findings stand out: (1) The generalization group was significantly superior to both of the other groups on the net total achievement; (2) The order of performance on the tests which were to determine the amounts of transfer of training was, from highest to lowest, generalization, drill, and drill-plus.

Brownell, Moser, and others[9] investigated the effectiveness of four methods of teaching borrowing in subtraction: (1) the equal additions method, taught rationally; (2) the equal additions method, taught mechanically; (3) the decomposition method, taught rationally; and (4) the decomposition method, taught mechanically. Of the several findings, the following are important for the purpose of this chapter: (1) The meaningfully taught sections quite consistently excelled the mechanically taught sections; (2) There was some evidence that rational instruction produced greater uniformity in accuracy of computation than did mechanical instruction.

Though the importance of meaningful teaching has been shown in such studies as these and has been emphasized by an increasing number of educators, there still is a question as to the extent to which arithmetic teaching is done meaningfully in practice. ~~There are indications that much more~~

---

[7] C. L. Thiele, "The Contribution of Generalization to the Learning of the Addition Facts," Contributions to Education, No. 763 (New York: Bureau of Publications, Teachers College, Columbia University, 1938).

[8] E. J. Swenson, "Organization and Generalization as Factors in Learning, Transfer, and Retroactive Inhibition," *Learning Theory in School Situations*, University of Minnesota Studies in Education, No. 2 (Minneapolis: University of Minnesota Press, 1949), pp. 9–39.

[9] W. A. Brownell, H. E. Moser, and others, *Meaningful versus Mechanical Learning: A Study in Grade III Subtraction*, Duke University Research Studies in Education, No. 8 (Durham, N.C.: Duke University Press, 1949).

~~lip-service is being paid to the meaning theory and that in practical situations~~
~~many teachers still use the drill method~~. In 1949 Glennon[10] concluded a
study in which he sought to determine the degree to which persons above the
level of grade VI have possession of the meanings and understandings basic
to the several computational skills commonly taught in grades I through
VI, as follows:

The data . . . are limited evidence of the meager degree with which teachers are
succeeding in bringing about growth in meanings and understandings. The
evidence does not lend much support to the argument often heard that 'we are
already teaching meanings.'

More recent research has corroborated the findings of Glennon.

## 2. Readiness program

At present practically all educators insist upon systematic instruction in
mathematics in the first grade of the elementary school. When this systematic instruction is planned, it is of great importance to determine the mathematical background of the pupils, so that no time will be lost by presenting
topics which children already have mastered. Much of the content in the
typical first-grade textbook is too easy to challenge the average first-grade
pupil. ~~Research has demonstrated that entering first-graders know more~~
~~about arithmetic than is expected~~.

Brownell[11] made an extensive study of arithmetic known by school
beginners. He also summarized several investigations already made in this
area. Some of the findings of these studies are presented below. Since the
data were taken from several studies (as reported by Brownell), the per cents
and the ratios are approximations.

1. Nine out of every ten preschool children tested could count by rote to 10,
   and one out of every ten to 100.

2. Ninety per cent of all the preschool children tested could count rationally
   to 10, and more than fifty percent to 20.

3. Eighty per cent of the school entrants tested were able to identify a group of 5
   and seventy per cent could identify a group of 10.

4. Sixty per cent of the preschool children tested could reproduce a group of 10.

---

[10] V. J. Glennon, "Testing Meanings in Arithmetic," *Arithmetic 1949*, Supplementary
Educational Monographs, No. 70 (Chicago: University of Chicago Press, 1949), pp. 64–74.

[11] W. A. Brownell *et al.*, *Arithmetic in Grades I and II: A Critical Summary of New
and Previously Reported Research*, Duke University Research Studies in Education, No. 6
(Durham, N.C.: Duke University Press, 1941).

5. Nine out of every ten school entrants tested knew the meaning of the words *longest* and *shortest*.

6. More than fifty per cent of a group of preschool children tested could solve verbal problems in which the combinations $2 + 2$ and $3 - 2$ were individually presented.

7. The numerals from 1 to 9 could be identified by two out of every three preschool children tested.

8. Twenty per cent of a group of school entrants tested could write the numerals 4, 7, 2, 5, 9, and 6.

9. Three out of every four children of a group of school entrants tested knew the terms *square* and *circle*.

10. Half of a group of school entrants tested could tell time to the hour.

11. Nine out of every ten of a group of beginning first-graders tested could identify a penny, a nickel, a dime, a quarter, and a half dollar.

More recently, Priore[12] conducted a study to determine how much arithmetic children know when they enter the first grade. The children tested (70) were only those enrolled in one school and, by request, these children had not been instructed in arithmetic in kindergarten. The following findings were revealing:

1. The average number to which children could count by rote was 30.

2. The average number to which they could count rationally was 30.

3. Over seventy-five per cent of the children tested could reproduce numbers to 10 by selecting the correct number of blocks.

4. Sixty per cent of the children could identify all the numbers up to 10. This was determined by showing the child a specific number of beads and asking him to tell how many there were.

5. Fifty per cent knew the value of the fractions $\frac{1}{2}$, $\frac{1}{4}$, and $\frac{1}{3}$.

6. Forty-three per cent of the children recognized the numerals through 10.

7. Forty-four per cent of the children could estimate which of four boxes contained a pound of candy.

8. Over seventy-five per cent of the children knew which is more—3 pennies or a nickel.

Miller,[13] after reviewing the results of some studies on the background of entering first-graders, wrote:

---

[12] A. Priore, "Achievement, Entering Grade I," *The Arithmetic Teacher*, March, 1957, pp. 55–60.

[13] G. H. Miller, "Shall We Change Our Arithmetic Program?" *The Arithmetic Teacher*, April, 1962, pp. 193–97.

Thus a comparison of the arithmetical ability of entering first-grade children and the requirements of the general proposed curriculum in arithmetic shows that well over 50 percent of the students can already do the work which is required for the first grade. ~~It appears that the majority of first graders simply review, for one year, material which they have already mastered~~.

Schutter and Spreckelmeyer[14] concluded, after comparing European and American textbooks for the primary grades:

By requiring additional time per week on arithmetic in the primary years, and by simultaneous development of concepts of numbers and operations with them, European texts permit the child to develop a broad background in a briefer span of time than do accepted American texts. The European children are more strongly challenged.

### 3. Grade placement

~~In the 1930's the grade placement of arithmetic topics was changed partly as a result of the influence of the Committee of Seven~~.[15] This committee sought to determine the mental-age level at which specific topics could be taught to completion. The findings of the committee seemed to indicate that many topics were introduced too early. Though critics offered valid objections to the findings and exposed some serious limitations of the study, the report had a tremendous influence. The teaching of several topics was postponed until higher grades. As a result, a heavy burden was placed on pupils, by requiring them to study more material at a faster rate in the upper grades.

~~More recently, a trend to move topics down in the grades has been evident~~. The new emphasis on science and mathematics, the experiences of teachers indicating that many children can do more in mathematics than is required of them, and comparisons of mathematics programs of the United States and foreign countries have been influential in establishing this new trend. Schutter and Spreckelmeyer[16] prepared a table presenting a summary of the grade levels at which selected basic topics are principally studied in seven European countries and in the United States. Where the grade levels for the topics are the same, the European students have had a longer acquaintance with concepts and skills which serve as foundations for the development

---

[14] C. H. Schutter and R. L. Spreckelmeyer, *Teaching the Third R* (Washington, D.C.: Council for Basic Education, 1959), p. 23.

[15] C. C. Washburne, "The Grade Placement of Arithmetic Topics: A 'Committee of Seven' Investigation." *Report of the Society's Committee on Arithmetic.* Twenty-ninth Yearbook, Part II, National Society for the Study of Education (Bloomington, Ill.: Public School Publishing Co., 1930), Ch. XIII.

[16] Schutter and Spreckelmeyer, *op. cit.*, pp. 17–18.

of these topics. Buswell[17] found that many arithmetic topics had been studied by English children for a longer period of time than by the California children. The author,[18] after a study of comparative curricula, concluded that Dutch schools were about a year ahead of Iowa schools in the grade placement of concepts and processes in arithmetic.

## 4. Time allotment

The meaning method consumes a great deal of time because of added pupil activities and class discussions. The necessity of practice after a new process has been understood by the pupils is also realized. Some time ago Buckingham[19] stated: "Our position is not that drill should be avoided but rather that it should be made more intelligent in the fields to which it is now applied and that it should be applied still more widely." In the opinion of the author of this volume, the meaning method tends to consume more time than the drill method. In practice, however, the third R does not seem to have received its due share of time. Even before the meaning method had become evident in children's textbooks, the time allotted to arithmetic had been gradually reduced. Sueltz[20] noted:

During most of the nineteenth century, arithmetic occupied at least 25 per cent of the total school time. In 1928, this had been reduced to 11.6 per cent as shown in a study of how schools use their time by Carlton H. Mann.

Miller[21] studied the time allotments for arithmetic in 34 large school systems and 44 small school systems in the United States, and reported the following findings:

(1) The amount of time spent in arithmetic ranged from a median score of 23 minutes per day to 45 minutes per day in the large city schools and 30 minutes per day to 47 minutes per day in the small school systems. (2) There is a marked difference in the amount of time spent in the lower grades (1st, 2nd, and 3rd). The lower the grade, the less time devoted to arithmetic.

The same investigator[22] compared the time allotments in arithmetic of 32 foreign countries and the United States. The data for the American schools

---

[17] Buswell, *op. cit.*, p. 7.

[18] Kramer, *op. cit.*, p. 260.

[19] B. R. Buckingham, "What Becomes of Drill?" *Arithmetic in General Education.* Sixteenth Yearbook, National Council of Teachers of Mathematics (New York: Bureau of Publications, Teachers College, Columbia University, 1941), p. 200.

[20] B. A. Sueltz, "Arithmetic in Historical Perspective," *The National Elementary Principal*, October, 1959, p. 14.

[21] G. H. Miller, "How Much Time for Arithmetic?" *The Arithmetic Teacher*, November, 1958, pp. 256–59.

[22] G. H. Miller, "Shall We Change Our Arithmetic Program?" *The Arithmetic Teacher*, April, 1962, pp. 193–97.

were taken from the study quoted above. He concluded that other countries devote a greater amount of time to arithmetic during the first six years of school than does the United States. Schutter and Spreckelmeyer[23] stated that it is evident that European schools spend more time on the study of arithmetic than do American schools. They felt that this extra time has an effect both upon the pace at which the subject is developed and upon the challenging achievement levels to which the basic topics are carried. One of their recommendations was that more time be allotted to arithmetic in the elementary school.

The author[24] found that in The Netherlands the average pupil spends 1064 hours of class time on arithmetic in six years of elementary school, whereas the Iowa pupil spends, during these six years, 537 hours on arithmetic. Jarvis[25] conducted a study in which the achievement of 329 sixth-grade pupils who had spent 55 to 60 minutes daily in studying arithmetic through grades IV, V, and VI was compared with the achievement of 384 sixth-graders who had studied 35 to 45 minutes daily over the same period of time. The difference in intelligence between the groups was not statistically significant. However, it was found that, without exception, achievement of the pupils who had studied under the longer daily class periods of 55 to 60 minutes excelled that of the children of the group with the shorter 35- to 45-minute periods. The difference was statistically significant. ~~It was concluded that, for the average, the dull, and the bright pupils, the longer periods in arithmetic resulted in substantially more significant arithmetic achievement~~.

## 5. Mental computation

Studies conducted to determine the ability of pupils to compute mentally and surveys for the purpose of determining the amount of mental computation in current textbooks have resulted in findings which expose the weakness of this phase of arithmetic in the curriculum. Flournoy[26] stated that perhaps 75% or more of the non-occupational uses of arithmetic are mental. The same investigator[27] concluded that a sample of intermediate-grade pupils who had finished a program in mental computation showed significant gains in mental arithmetic and in problem solving. Hall[28] studied the scores of a

---

[23] Schutter and Spreckelmeyer, *op. cit.*, pp. 32–33.

[24] Kramer, *op. cit.*, pp. 261–62.

[25] O. T. Jarvis, "Time Allotment Relationships to Pupil Achievement in Arithmetic," *The Arithmetic Teacher*, May, 1963, pp. 248–50.

[26] M. Flournoy, "Providing Mental Arithmetic Experiences," *The Arithmetic Teacher*, April, 1959, pp. 133–39.

[27] M. F. Flournoy, "The Effectiveness of Instruction in Mental Arithmetic," *The Elementary School Journal*, November, 1954, pp. 148–53.

[28] J. V. Hall, "Solving Verbal Arithmetic Problems without Pencil and Paper," *The Elementary School Journal*, December, 1947, pp. 212–17.

sample of intermediate-grade pupils on mental arithmetic exercises and found a positive correlation between general intelligence and the ability to solve verbal arithmetic problems without the use of paper and pencil. Brown,[29] after studying the work of pupils of grades VI–XII, concluded that they needed more skill in mental computation. After reviewing research on mental computation, Gane[30] stated:

A regular and carefully planned program of mental arithmetic provides a realistic preparation for the everyday use of arithmetic which the child encounters out of school. Improvement in mental arithmetic tends to improve ability in all phases of arithmetic.

Thorpe,[31] interpreting findings of Flournoy, wrote:

· · · progressive proficiency in mental arithmetic will not be attained by elementary pupils by occasional incidental experiences, but rather by systematic, well-planned, direct teaching experiences for which teachers at every grade level have some responsibility.

## 6. Training of elementary-school mathematics teachers

The results of several studies indicate that the typical elementary-school teacher does not possess an adequate background in mathematics. Time and again it has been demonstrated that teachers need to know more mathematics and understand mathematical processes better than they do. After reviewing several studies on the mathematical background of elementary-school teachers, Sparks[32] noted:

The most general conclusion that can be drawn from these studies is that teachers are considered by all of these authors to be:
1. Particularly deficient in understanding of underlying principles;
2. Deficient in computational skills, particularly with decimals and per cents;
3. Deficient in problem-solving ability.

Sparks sees the need for a long-term investigation with sound theoretical bases and sound experimental design, to determine what content material and types of presentation provide teachers with the knowledge found most valuable for elementary-school teachers.

[29] B. I. Brown, "A Study in Mental Arithmetic: Proficiency and Thought Processes of Pupils Solving Subtraction Examples," unpublished doctoral dissertation (Pittsburgh: The University of Pittsburgh, 1957).
[30] J. T. Gane, "Research Should Guide Us," *The Arithmetic Teacher*, December, 1962, pp. 441–45.
[31] C. B. Thorpe, *Teaching Elementary Arithmetic* (New York: Harper & Row, Publishers, 1962), p. 301.
[32] J. N. Sparks, "Arithmetic Understandings Needed by Elementary-school Teachers," *The Arithmetic Teacher*, December, 1961, pp. 395–403.

In a chapter dealing with background mathematics for elementary teachers, Ruddell, Dutton, and Reckzeh[33] present the results of a survey of research and literature on the problem, identify current practices in teacher training, and report the results of a questionnaire. The questionnaire was submitted to the elementary-teacher training department of all members of the American Association of Colleges of Teacher Education. The purpose of the questionnaire was to establish a solid base of professional opinion for recommending a background course in mathematics for all elementary-school teachers who are to be certified to teach in grades I through VIII. Among the recommendations of the investigators were the following:

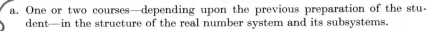

1. Each student admitted to the elementary teacher training program should be required to take a minimum of six semester hours of background mathematics.

2. Teachers of arithmetic in grades seven and eight should complete a minor in college mathematics.

3. All elementary school teachers should have a course in the teaching of arithmetic which should follow the background sequence in mathematics.

Important work with hopefully far-reaching consequences is being done by the Committee on the Undergraduate Program in Mathematics (CUPM), which is a committee of the Mathematical Association of America and which is supported in part by the National Science Foundation. This committee aims to develop a broad program of improvement in the undergraduate mathematics curriculum of the nation's colleges and universities.[34] For college training of teachers of elementary-school mathematics, the following courses are recommended by the committee:

a. One or two courses—depending upon the previous preparation of the student—in the structure of the real number system and its subsystems.

b. A course devoted to the basic concepts of algebra.

c. A course in informal geometry.

## Recommendations

The results of the research studies reported in this chapter and the recent emphasis on mathematics seem to warrant the following recommendations

[33] A. K. Ruddell, W. Dutton, and J. Reckzeh, "Background Mathematics for Elementary Teachers," *Instruction in Arithmetic*, Twenty-fifth Yearbook of the National Council of Teachers of Mathematics (Washington, D.C.: The Council, 1960), Ch. XIII.

[34] "Recommendations of the Mathematical Association of America for the Training of Mathematics Teachers." *American Mathematical Monthly*, December, 1960, pp. 982–91.

for the improvement of the elementary-school mathematics curriculum:

1. Teachers should introduce mathematical processes meaningfully, stimulate children to see relationships, encourage them to form generalizations, and guide them to an understanding of the structure of the real number system.

2. A sufficient amount of practice should be provided, in order to anchor needed skills.

3. The arithmetic readiness program should be reconsidered. Apparently, most first-graders do not need many of the arithmetic readiness exercises which the typical program presents.

4. Several arithmetic topics should be introduced or mastered sooner. This should result in more challenge to the lower-grade pupils, in a less heavy load for the upper-grade pupils, and in a greater depth to which topics can be carried.

5. More time should be allotted to elementary-school mathematics, or allotted time should be used more wisely. This will allow the teacher to use the meaning method to better advantage and to set aside a sufficient amount of time for practice exercises.

6. Mental computation should be taught systematically in all grades.

7. Proper methods for dealing with individual differences should be identified and used.

8. Prospective teachers should be required to take a sufficient number of semester hours of mathematics, followed by a course in the teaching of elementary-school mathematics.

9. Teachers in the field should prepare themselves better by taking college courses or workshops in the content and the teaching of elementary-school mathematics. Such preparation should include the study of modern mathematics topics.

10. The findings of exploratory programs in elementary-school mathematics should be used to advantage. Modern topics presented in these programs should be included in the curriculum when their efficiency has been proven.

## EXERCISES

1. Try to determine why so many pupils at the end of the elementary school show deficiencies in arithmetic.

2. React to this statement: "Children do not have to learn to compute, since there are machines which can perform the computations for them."

3. Describe what is meant by "modern mathematics."

4. List some of the important exploratory programs in elementary-school mathematics.

5. Investigate which elementary-school mathematics textbook is in use in an elementary school selected by you.

6. Quote research which supports the meaning theory.

7. Report some research findings which suggest that elementary-school entrants can already do much of the work which is required for the first grade.

8. Do you approve of the trend to move mathematics topics down in the grades? Give reasons for your answer.

9. In your opinion, how much classroom time should be allotted to mathematics? Suggest an amount of time for each elementary grade.

10. Discuss the role of mental computation in the elementary-school mathematics curriculum.

## SELECTED REFERENCES

Corle, G. C., "The New Mathematics." *The Arithmetic Teacher*, April, 1964, pp. 242–47.

Deans, E., *Elementary School Mathematics*, U.S. Department of Health, Education, and Welfare. Bulletin 1963, No. 13. Washington, D.C.: U.S. Government Printing Office, 1963.

Delon, F. G., "The Aftermath of a Revolution." *The Arithmetic Teacher*, December, 1963, pp. 481–83.

Dutton, W. H., *Evaluating Pupils' Understanding of Arithmetic*. Englewood Cliffs, N.J.: Prentice-Hall, Inc., 1964, Ch. I.

Educational Services Incorporated, *Goals for School Mathematics*, Report of the Cambridge Conference on School Mathematics. Boston: Houghton Mifflin Company, 1963.

Fehr, H. F., "Modern Mathematics and Good Pedagogy." *The Arithmetic Teacher*, November, 1963, pp. 402–11.

National Council of Teachers of Mathematics, *The Revolution in School Mathematics*. Washington, D.C.: The Council, 1961.

Spitzer, H. F., "Modern Mathematics in the Elementary School," *Epsilon Bulletin*, Phi Delta Kappa. Iowa City: College of Education, State University of Iowa, 1963, pp. 18–30.

Swenson, E. J., *Teaching Arithmetic to Children*. New York: The Macmillan Co., 1964, Ch. XX.

Thorpe, C. B., *Teaching Elementary Arithmetic*. New York: Harper & Row, Publishers, 1962, Ch. III.

Thurlow, V., "Mathematical Understanding of Seventh- and Eighth-grade Pupils, 1948 and 1963." *The Arithmetic Teacher*, January, 1965, pp. 43–44.

Van Engen, H., "Twentieth Century Mathematics for the Elementary School." *The Arithmetic Teacher*, March, 1959, pp. 71–76.

# II

## INTRODUCTION TO MODERN ELEMENTARY-SCHOOL MATHEMATICS

# 4

# NUMBERS, NUMERALS, AND NOTATION SYSTEMS

THE NUMBER SYSTEM which we use today is the result of a continuous development. From simple record keeping, man moved first toward the use of numbers in counting objects. Then the number system was gradually extended to include other number systems. In this chapter the development of number ideas is briefly traced, frequently used terms are explained, important properties of the whole numbers are identified, and notation systems (systems of writing numbers) are presented.

## The Development of Number Ideas[1]

Early man had little use for number. He took care of his own needs and was quite independent of the services of others. His challenge was to adjust to his environment. Consequently, he had to become aware of the relationships

---

[1] The student is referred to E. M. Churchill, *Counting and Measuring* (Toronto: University of Toronto Press, 1961).

in space and the sequences in time. While observing the natural phenomena, he gradually learned to ascribe patterns to them. His periods of rest and work were determined by the rising and setting of the sun. The times of harvest appeared to have certain characteristics. There seemed to be a correlation between the phases of the moon and the height of the tides. The position of the sun in the sky had something to do with the temperature. The movements and phases of the moon were regular, and so were the apparent movements of the sun.

Man began to record the days as they passed, the phases of the moon as it waxed and waned, and the position of the sun as it seemed to change. He found patterns of relationship and definite sequences of time.

The first recording of the passing of time may have been done by putting at an isolated place a rock or a pebble for each day that passed. A record of the total time passed was therefore available.

There were other needs for recording in the life of early man. He may have kept a record of the number of sheep he owned by putting as many pebbles in a bag as he had sheep, one pebble for each sheep. As a result, the pebbles were in a *one-to-one relationship* with the number of sheep he possessed. When, at night, he wanted to determine whether all his sheep were in, he would match the pebbles and the sheep. There was supposed to be a *one-to-one correspondence* between the pebbles and the sheep, which means that there was one and only one pebble for each sheep and one and only one sheep for each pebble. Thus it could be determined by the matching process whether all the sheep were in.

As time passed, man began to assign specific names to small groups. Originally, descriptive names were used for such small collections. There was not just one universal word to denote any set[2] of two, but different names were used to represent different objects. Number was considered a quality of specific things. In our language we have retained residues such as couple, twin, brace, team, yoke, etc. Large collections did not have to be called by specific names, since words meaning heap, lot, and flock were sufficient for communication.

Another technique was to match model groups against groups under consideration. A pair of wings or a pair of ears could represent a group of two; for three a clover leaf could be used, for four the legs of a deer, for five the fingers of one hand, and for ten the fingers of both hands. However, as culture advanced, this technique was again insufficient, since larger numbers had to be represented more efficiently. Man began to employ the tallying

---

[2] A *set* may be described as a collection of concrete or abstract entities. (Sets are introduced in Chapter 6.)

technique more extensively, probably by using the fingers of both hands and the toes of both feet, by making marks on a tree or on another object, or by putting aside pebbles, grains, etc. In doing this, he gradually created words and *numerals* to express numbers. Certainly, the realization that two pebbles, two men, two hills, and two birds have an attribute or property in common—the *number* of each of these sets—represents a high level of abstraction. When counting his fingers (one, two, three, etc.), man used number names which expressed how many objects there were and these numbers came to be known as *cardinal numbers*. He also discovered that order was involved (first, second, third, etc.), and such numbers (stating which object was considered) were called *ordinal numbers*.

The use of tallies or other figures to represent larger numbers soon became unwieldy, and man began to see a need for grouping to express and record larger numbers conveniently. In the Hindu-Arabic system which we use, the numbers are grouped by tens. It is assumed that ten was selected as the *base* or the first collection in the system because we have ten fingers. In early history other bases have been used at different times in different parts of the world: Base 2 was probably developed from the technique of comparing quantities with model groups of two. Base 5 was selected because we have five fingers on one hand. Base 12 had its origin in the fact that there are twelve moons in a year. Base 20 was used by the Mayas and, as we assume, was adopted because man has a total of twenty fingers and toes. Base 60 was used by the Babylonians, probably because a hand of twelve moons equals sixty moons.

## Terms

A *number*[3] is an abstract idea. It is a property or an attribute common to all members of a collection of paired groups. For example, a group of two triangles, a group of two circles, and a group of two squares have the number property "two" in common. These groups can be *matched* and their members can be placed in one-to-one correspondence:

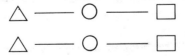

---

[3] In the interest of easy communication with the reader, in this volume the term "number" will be used frequently according to popular usage. For example, the term "2-digit number" will be used, rather than "number expressed by a 2-digit numeral."

A *numeral* is a symbol for a number. Various symbols may represent the same number. For example, the number of the fingers on one hand may be named by the symbols: 5, V, $3 + 2$, $5 \times 1$, five.

A *cardinal number* indicates how many objects are being considered. *Example:* There are *five* books.

An *ordinal number* identifies an object; it tells which place the object occupies in a series. *Example:* The *fourth* book in the pile is mine.

Cardinal numbers are often used in an ordinal sense. *Example:* Open your book to page 4.

The numbers which man used originally and which the child learns first are often called the *natural numbers*. The set of natural numbers is expressed as $\{1, 2, 3, \cdots\}$.[4] Since the numbers are used in the counting series, they are also called *counting numbers*.

The set of numbers expressed as $\{0, 1, 2, 3, \cdots\}$ we shall call the set of *whole numbers*:

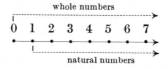

Numbers which are greater than zero are called *positive numbers*. When man had a need for expressing numbers which are less than zero he invented the *negative numbers*. The numerals for these numbers are preceded by a negative sign, as in $^-5$. Pairs of numbers such as $^+1$ and $^-1$, $^+3$ and $^-3$, $^+5$ and $^-5$, are additive inverses since their sums equal 0.

The whole numbers and their additive inverses are called the *integers*. The set of integers is expressed as $\{\cdots, ^-3, ^-2, ^-1, 0, ^+1, ^+2, ^+3, \cdots\}$.

The need to describe parts of a unit or of a group required the extension of the number system, and so fractional numbers were identified. The resulting new number system was called the system of *rational numbers*. Examples of rational numbers are: $\frac{1}{2}$, $\frac{3}{4}$, and $\frac{5}{2}$. Integers are included in the set of rational numbers ($5 = \frac{5}{1}$, $3 = \frac{-3}{1}$).

A number that cannot be expressed as the quotient of an integer and another non-zero integer is called an *irrational number*. In the elementary school the irrational number represented by the symbol $\pi$ (pi) is introduced in connection with circles.

The *real numbers* consist of both the rational and the irrational numbers.

---

[4] This expression is read "the set whose members are 1, 2, 3, and so on infinitely." The names of the elements of a set are listed between braces. The three dots denote that there is an endless number of elements.

## The Hindu-Arabic System of Notation

The elements of our system of notation—the Hindu-Arabic system—were probably invented in India by the Hindus and transmitted to Europe by the Arabs. The earliest examples of the system date from a few centuries before Christ. At that time neither positional value nor zero was used. Several centuries later positional value was employed and the zero was invented. The Arabic people used the system and probably introduced it to Europeans. By the sixteenth century the Hindu-Arabic system of notation was well established in Europe.

### Characteristics of Our Notation System

1. *It has the base of ten.* The base is the basic counting group or the first collection in the number series. Collections less than ten are represented by the digits through 9. When a collection of ten is to be represented by a numeral, a 1 is put in the tens place and a 0 in the ones place. Thus 10 is the first collection in the series. When ten groups of ten are to be represented by a numeral, a 1 is put in the hundreds place, a 0 in the tens place, and a 0 in the ones place. Because of the grouping by tens and powers of ten, our system is called a *decimal system*. The word *decimal* is derived from the Latin *decem* which means ten.

The role of 10 and the powers of ten in the system is clearly illustrated by expressing a number in exponential notation. For example, $10,000 = 10^4$ (ten to the fourth power), $1000 = 10^3$ (ten to the third power, or ten cubed), and $100 = 10^2$ (ten to the second power, or ten squared). In $10^3$, the *exponent* (the superscript) indicates the number of times the *base* (10) is used as a factor: $10^3 = 10 \times 10 \times 10 = 1000$. It should be noted that any non-zero number raised to the zero power is equal to 1. Thus $10^0 = 1$.

2. *Ten symbols are used: 1, 2, 3, 4, 5, 6, 7, 8, 9, and 0.* A natural number can be expressed as a numeral by using one or more of these ten symbols. A zero in a numeral indicates that there is no quantity for the power of ten for which it holds the place.

3. *It has place value or positional value.* The positional value of a digit in a numeral depends upon the place it occupies in the numeral. In 32, the 3 has a face value of 3 and a positional value of 30, since it represents three tens. In 321, the 3 has a face value of 3 and a positional value of 300, since it represents three hundreds. In 3210, the 3 has a face value of 3 and a positional value of 3000, since it represents three thousands. Thus, in the decimal

system, the positional value of a digit increases tenfold each successive place to the left. The following diagram illustrates the principle of place value:

| hundred thousand | ten thousand | thousand | hundred | ten | one |
|---|---|---|---|---|---|
| 100,000 | 10,000 | 1,000 | 100 | 10 | 1 |
| $10^5$ | $10^4$ | $10^3$ | $10^2$ | $10^1$ | $10^0$ |
| 2 | 2 | 2 | 2 | 2 | 2 |

$$2 \times 10^5 = 200,000$$
$$2 \times 10^4 = \phantom{0}20,000$$
$$2 \times 10^3 = \phantom{00}2,000$$
$$2 \times 10^2 = \phantom{000}200$$
$$2 \times 10^1 = \phantom{0000}20$$
$$2 \times 10^0 = \phantom{00000}2$$
$$\overline{\phantom{0000}222,222}$$

~~*4. It has the additive property.*~~ In the diagram above, it is shown that $222,222 = 200,000 + 20,000 + 2,000 + 200 + 20 + 2$.

## Some Important Properties of Whole Numbers

1. *Commutative property of addition:* In adding two whole numbers, the order of the addends can be changed without affecting the sum.
Thus, if $a$ and $b$ are whole numbers, then $a + b = b + a$.

*Example:* $2 + 3 = 3 + 2$.

2. *Commutative property of multiplication:* In multiplying two whole numbers, the order of the factors can be changed without affecting the product.
Thus, if $a$ and $b$ are whole numbers, then $a \times b = b \times a$.

*Example:* $2 \times 3 = 3 \times 2$.

3. *Associative property of addition:* In adding more than two whole numbers, the way in which the addends are grouped does not affect the sum.

Thus, if $a$, $b$, and $c$ are whole numbers, then $(a + b) + c = a + (b + c)$.

*Example:* $(5 + 7) + 3 = 5 + (7 + 3)$.

4. *Associative property of multiplication:* In multiplying more than two whole numbers, the way in which the factors are grouped does not affect the product.

Thus, if $a$, $b$, and $c$ are whole numbers, then $(a \times b) \times c = a \times (b \times c)$.

*Example:* $(3 \times 4) \times 5 = 3 \times (4 \times 5)$.

5. *Distributive property of multiplication with respect to addition:* When the sum of two whole numbers is to be multiplied by a given number, it is proper to multiply each addend by the given number and to add the products.

Thus, if $a$, $b$, and $c$ are whole numbers, then $a \times (b + c) = (a \times b) + (a \times c)$.

*Example:* $3 \times (4 + 5) = (3 \times 4) + (3 \times 5) = 12 + 15 = 27$.

An application of this property follows.

*Number question:* $6 \times 17 = \square$.

*Solution:* $17 = 10 + 7$. renamed

$$6 \times 17 = 6 \times (10 + 7)$$
$$= (6 \times 10) + (6 \times 7)$$
$$= 60 + 42$$
$$= 102.$$

5a. *Distributive property of division with respect to addition:* When the sum of two whole numbers is to be divided by a given number, it is proper to divide each addend by the given number and to add the quotients.

Thus, if $a$, $b$, and $c$ are whole numbers with $c \neq 0$, then $(a + b) \div c = (a \div c) + (b \div c)$.

*Example:* $(12 + 6) \div 3 = (12 \div 3) + (6 \div 3) = 4 + 2 = 6$.

An application of this property follows.

*Number question:* $91 \div 7 = \square$.

*Solution:* renamed
$$91 \div 7 = (70 + 21) \div 7$$
$$= (70 \div 7) + (21 \div 7)$$
$$= 10 + 3$$
$$= 13.$$

6. *Closure property of addition:* The result of the addition of any two whole numbers is a whole number. We say that the set of whole numbers is closed

with respect to addition.  Thus, if $a$ and $b$ are whole numbers, then $a + b$ is always a whole number.

*Example:* $7 + 9 = 16$.

7. *Closure property of multiplication:* The result of the multiplication of any two whole numbers is a whole number.  We say that the set of whole numbers is closed with respect to multiplication.

Thus, if $a$ and $b$ are whole numbers, then $a \times b$ is always a whole number.

*Example:* $7 \times 9 = 63$.

8. *Identity element for addition:* If zero is added to any whole number, the result is the same number.  Zero is the identity element for addition.

Thus, if $a$ is a whole number, then $a + 0 = a$.

*Example:* $6 + 0 = 6$.

9. *Identity element for multiplication:* If any whole number is multiplied by 1, the result is the same number.  One is the identity element for multiplication.

Thus, if $a$ is a whole number, then $1 \times a = a$.

*Example:* $1 \times 6 = 6$.

10. *Property of order:* For any whole numbers, $a$ and $b$, one and only one of the following three relationships exists: $a = b$; $a > b$; $a < b$.  (The symbol $>$ means "is greater than"; the symbol $<$ means "is less than.")

*Examples:* If $a = 5$ and $b = 5$, then $a = b$.

If $a = 5$ and $b = 6$, then $a < b$.

If $a = 5$ and $b = 4$, then $a > b$.

## Numeration

Numeration is the art of expressing numbers by words and of reading numerals.

The number names through ten are independent of one another.  Since—in the Hindu-Arabic system—numbers are grouped by powers of ten, man conveniently expressed larger numbers with the help of number names expressing smaller numbers.

Eleven and twelve come from words meaning "one left" and "two left" (after ten).  Thirteen means "three and ten."  It is not difficult to decide the origin of the number names fourteen, fifteen, etc.  Similarly, twenty, thirty, forty, etc., mean two tens, three tens, four tens, etc.

The characteristic of positional value of our notation system simplifies the reading of numerals.  Each digit in a numeral has both face value and positional value.  The positional value of a digit increases tenfold each successive

~~place to the left. The face value is constant~~. This is shown in the following example, in which 6666 is written in expanded notation:

$$6666 = (6 \times 10^3) + (6 \times 10^2) + (6 \times 10^1) + (6 \times 10^0)$$
$$= (6 \times 1000) + (6 \times 100) + (6 \times 10) + (6 \times 1)$$
$$= 6000 + 600 + 60 + 6.$$

~~The numeral 6666 is read "six thousand six hundred sixty-six."~~
~~The word "and" should be reserved for the decimal point when reading a~~ numeral. *Note!*

*Examples:* 406—four hundred six.
46.6—forty-six and six tenths.

~~The set of natural numbers is endless.~~ Sometimes very large numerals must be read. Since the reading of large numerals such as 20594781 would require some time for determining what the digits stand for, the digits are grouped into periods of three digits each. In the United States, these periods are set off by commas. The numeral above is therefore written as 20,594,781. It should be noted that the grouping into periods starts at the right and that, therefore, the period at the extreme left in the numeral above has only two digits.

~~Each period has a name: ones period, thousands period, millions period,~~ etc. The periods are subdivided, as shown in the following diagram.

Many more successive periods have been named, and of course, more names can be devised when needed. Some period names with the required number of zeros follow.

| Name | Number of Zeros |
|---|---|
| thousand | 3 |
| million | 6 |
| billion | 9 |
| trillion | 12 |
| quadrillion | 15 |

Recently two more number names have been given. ~~The number expressed by 1 followed by 100 zeros is called~~ *googol*. ~~The number expressed by 1 followed by googol zeros is called~~ *googolplex*. The magnitude of googolplex can hardly be described! It may be an amusing exercise for an interested student to figure out how long it would take to write googol zeros.

The American and French systems differ from the English and German systems in the writing of large numbers. In the English-German system, a billion is a million millions, a trillion is a billion billions, a quadrillion is a trillion trillions, etc. ~~The English-German system is the original~~. The French changed it and other countries, including the United States, adopted the change.

## The Roman System

~~Roman numerals are still being used for special purpos~~es. They are often used on clock faces, tombstones, and cornerstones, and may be employed to express chapter numbers, volume numbers, and dates.

*Note*

~~The Hindu-Arabic and the Roman system have the same number base, but~~ differ in notation.

The Roman system employs seven capital letters as symbols to express numbers: $I = 1$; $V = 5$; $X = 10$; $L = 50$; $C = 100$; $D = 500$; $M = 1000$. It should be noted that these symbols stand for 1, 10, 100, 1000, and for the numbers which are, in each case, one half the next power of ten. In addition to these letters, a bar is used to multiply a number by 1000.

*Example:* $\bar{L} = 50,000$.

Four principles are evident in the system:

1. ~~The principle of repetit~~ion. For example, in XXX the X has been repeated three times and the meaning of XXX is 30. Only the symbols I, X, C, and M are repeated.

2. ~~The principle of addition~~. XI means $10 + 1$. The symbols are written in order of increased numerical value.

3. ~~The principle of subtraction~~. This principle results in the use of fewer symbols. Instead of IIII, IV is written, with the understanding that, when a symbol of smaller value precedes a symbol of larger value, the smaller value must be subtracted from the larger. Only the symbols I, X, and C may precede a symbol expressing a larger numeral for this purpose, and not more than one symbol at a time is used.

4. ~~The principle of multiplication~~. Placing a bar over a symbol multiplies its value by 1000.

*Example:* $\overline{CLX} = 160,000$.

~~The principles of subtraction and multiplication were not adopted by the Romans, but were added much later~~.

The Roman system of notation shows many shortcomings when it is compared to our system. Especially, the ease with which we can perform the fundamental operations should make us appreciate our system.

## The Egyptian System

About 5000 years ago the Egyptians employed a system in which representations of common objects were used to stand for powers of ten, as follows:

| Object Represented | Numeral | Hindu-Arabic Equivalent |
|---|---|---|
| Staff or vertical stroke | | 1 |
| Heel bone or arch | | 10 |
| Scroll or coiled rope | | 100 |
| Lotus plant | | 1000 |
| Bent finger | | 10,000 |
| Burbot (fish) | | 100,000 |
| Man in astonishment | | 1,000,000 |

In the Egyptian system, the principles of addition and repetition were used. Thus, any symbol could be used nine times, and for the tenth one another symbol was employed.

*Examples:*

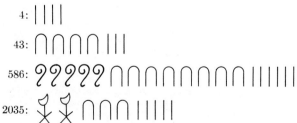

## Bases Other Than Ten

The decimal scale we use requires ten symbols. Grouping is done by tens and by powers of ten. When expressing a number as a numeral, we record the ones, tens, hundreds, thousands, etc., each in their assigned places by the use of the principle of place value. Each digit represents a power of ten.

*Example:* $1325 = (1 \times 10^3) + (3 \times 10^2) + (2 \times 10^1) + (5 \times 10^0)$
$$= (1 \times 1000) + (3 \times 100) + (2 \times 10) + (5 \times 1).$$

When 3 is to be added to 9, we have to regroup. First 1 is added to form one ten and then we add 2 more: $9 + 3 = 9 + (1 + 2) = (9 + 1) + 2 = 10 + 2 = 12$. The result is one group of ten and two ones.

### Base five

In base five, grouping is done by fives and powers of five. Therefore, each digit in a numeral written to base five is a power of five.

Only five symbols are needed in base five: 0, 1, 2, 3, and 4. The numeral 10 means one group of five and no ones.

The following number line is accompanied by two scales of notation: one in base five, and one in base ten.

base five →

| 0 | 1 | 2 | 3 | 4 | 10 | 11 | 12 | 13 | 14 | 20 | 21 | 22 | 23 | 24 | 30 | 31 | 32 | 33 | 34 | 40 | 41 | 42 | 43 | 44 | 100 |
|---|---|---|---|---|----|----|----|----|----|----|----|----|----|----|----|----|----|----|----|----|----|----|----|----|-----|
| 0 | 1 | 2 | 3 | 4 | 5 | 6 | 7 | 8 | 9 | 10 | 11 | 12 | 13 | 14 | 15 | 16 | 17 | 18 | 19 | 20 | 21 | 22 | 23 | 24 | 25 |

base ten →

EXAMPLES[5]:
1. The numeral $12_{\text{five}}$ (read as "one, two, base five") means 1 group of five and 2 ones.
Therefore, $12_{\text{five}} = 7_{\text{ten}}$.

2. $43_{\text{five}} = (4 \times 5^1) + (3 \times 5^0)$
$$= (4 \times 5) + (3 \times 1)$$
$$= 20 + 3$$
$$= 23_{\text{ten}}.$$

---

[5] The base is indicated by the subscript. Since there is no 5 in the number base under consideration, an expression such as $4 \times 5^1$—as used in the second example—would be better written as $4 \times 10^1{}_{\text{five}}$. However, in the interest of easy communication with the reader, the presented notation is used.

3. $122_\text{five} = (1 \times 5^2) + (2 \times 5^1) + (2 \times 5^0)$
$= (1 \times 25) + (2 \times 5) + (2 \times 1)$
$= 25 + 10 + 2$
$= 37_\text{ten}.$

4. $4312_\text{five} = (4 \times 5^3) + (3 \times 5^2) + (1 \times 5^1) + (2 \times 5^0)$
$= (4 \times 125) + (3 \times 25) + (1 \times 5) + (2 \times 1)$
$= 500 + 75 + 5 + 2$
$= 582_\text{ten}.$

This problem can also be worked as follows:

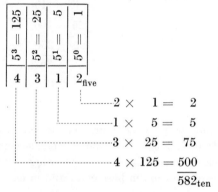

When a numeral in base ten is changed to a numeral in base five, we regroup by fives and by powers of five. It can be read from the number line above that $9_\text{ten} = 14_\text{five}$. By drawing arrows on the number line it can be demonstrated that 9 ones equal 1 five and 4 ones.

*Problem:* Change $362_\text{ten}$ to base five.
*Solution:* In base five, the positional value of the successive digits starting from the right is a multiple of: one; five; five $\times$ five; five $\times$ five $\times$ five; etc. In base ten: $5^0 = \text{one} = 1$; $5^1 = \text{five} = 5$; $5^2 = \text{twenty-five} = 25$; $5^3 = \text{one hundred twenty-five} = 125$; etc.

It can be determined by division how many 125's, 25's, 5's, and 1's, there are in $362_\text{ten}$. An easy way to perform this division is shown below.

$$362 \div 125 = 2$$
$$\underline{250}$$
$$112 \div 25 = 4$$
$$\underline{100}$$
$$12 \div 5 = 2$$
$$\underline{10}$$
$$2$$

Thus, in $362_{\text{ten}}$ there are two $5^3$'s, four $5^2$'s, two $5^1$'s, and two $5^0$'s. Therefore, $362_{\text{ten}} = 2422_{\text{five}}$. The answer can be checked by changing it again to base ten:

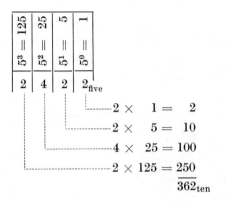

## Base eight

In base eight, grouping is done by eights and powers of eight. Only eight symbols are needed: 0, 1, 2, 3, 4, 5, 6, and 7. In base eight, the numeral 10 means 1 group of eight and no ones. The following number line is accompanied by the scales of notation in base eight and in base ten.

base eight →
0   1   2   3   4   5   6   7   10 11 12 13 14 15 16 17 20 21 22 23 24 25 26 27 30 31
•   •   •   •   •   •   •   •   •  •  •  •  •  •  •  •  •  •  •  •  •  •  •  •  •  •
0   1   2   3   4   5   6   7   8  9  10 11 12 13 14 15 16 17 18 19 20 21 22 23 24 25
base ten →

EXAMPLES:

*Problem:* $25_{\text{eight}} = $ _____$_{\text{ten}}$.

*Solution:* In $25_{\text{eight}}$ there are 2 eights and 5 ones, as shown in the diagram below. $2 \times 8 + 5 = 21$.

$$
\begin{array}{c|c}
8^1 = 8 & 8^0 = 1 \\
\hline
2 & 5_{\text{eight}}
\end{array}
$$

$$\cdots\cdots 5 \times 1 = \phantom{0}5$$
$$\cdots\cdots 2 \times 8 = \overline{16}$$
$$\phantom{\cdots\cdots 2 \times 8 = }\;21_{\text{ten}}$$

$$25_{\text{eight}} = 21_{\text{ten}}.$$

*Problem:* $354_{\text{eight}} = $ _____$_{\text{ten}}$.

*Solution:* $354_{\text{eight}} = (3 \times 8^2) + (5 \times 8^1) + (4 \times 8^0)$

$$= (3 \times 64) + (5 \times 8) + (4 \times 1)$$

$$= 192 + 40 + 4 = 236_{\text{ten}}.$$

*Problem:* $4652_{\text{ten}} = $ _____$_{\text{eight}}$.

*Solution:* In base eight, the positional value of the successive digits starting from the right is a multiple of: one; eight; eight $\times$ eight; eight $\times$ eight $\times$ eight; eight $\times$ eight $\times$ eight $\times$ eight; etc. In base ten: $8^0 = 1$; $8^1 = 8$; $8^2 = 8 \times 8 = 64$; $8^3 = 8 \times 8 \times 8 = 512$; $8^4 = 8 \times 8 \times 8 \times 8 = 4096$; etc.

By division it can be determined how many 4096's, 512's, 64's, 8's, and 1's there are in $4652_{\text{ten}}$:

$$4652 \div 4096 = 1$$
$$\underline{4096}$$
$$556 \div 512 = 1$$
$$\underline{512}$$
$$44 \div 64 = 0$$
$$\underline{0}$$
$$44 \div 8 = 5$$
$$\underline{40}$$
$$4$$

In $4652_{\text{ten}}$ there are one $8^4$, one $8^3$, zero $8^2$, five $8^1$, and four $8^0$. Therefore, $4652_{\text{ten}} = 11054_{\text{eight}}$. The answer can be checked by changing it again to base ten.

## Base two

In base two (the binary base) grouping is done by twos and powers of two. Only two symbols are needed: 0 and 1. In base two, the numeral 10 means 1 group of two and no ones. The following number line compares the scales of notation in base two and in base ten.

base two →

| 0 | 1 | 10 | 11 | 100 | 101 | 110 | 111 | 1000 | 1001 | 1010 | 1011 | 1100 |
|---|---|----|----|-----|-----|-----|-----|------|------|------|------|------|
| 0 | 1 | 2 | 3 | 4 | 5 | 6 | 7 | 8 | 9 | 10 | 11 | 12 |

base ten →

EXAMPLES:

*Problem:* $10101_{two}$ = ———————$_{ten}$.

*Solution:* $10101_{two} = (1 \times 2^4) + (0 \times 2^3) + (1 \times 2^2) + (0 \times 2^1) + (1 \times 2^0)$

$$= (1 \times 16) + (0 \times 8) + (1 \times 4) + (0 \times 2) + (1 \times 1)$$

$$= 16 + 0 + 4 + 0 + 1$$

$$= 21_{ten}.$$

*Problem:* $27_{ten}$ = ———————$_{two}$.

*Solution:* In base two, the positional value of the successive digits starting at the right is a multiple of: one; two; two × two; two × two × two; two × two × two × two; etc. In base ten: $2^0 = 1$; $2^1 = 2$; $2^2 = 2 \times 2 = 4$; $2^3 = 2 \times 2 \times 2 = 8$; $2^4 = 2 \times 2 \times 2 \times 2 = 16$; etc.

The number of each of these powers of two which are in $27_{ten}$ is again determined by division.

$$27 \div 16 = 1$$
$$\underline{16}$$
$$11 \div 8 = 1$$
$$\underline{8}$$
$$3 \div 4 = 0$$
$$\underline{0}$$
$$3 \div 2 = 1$$
$$\underline{2}$$
$$1$$

In $27_{ten}$ there are one $2^4$; one $2^3$; zero $2^2$; one $2^1$; and one $2^0$. Therefore, $27_{ten} = 11011_{two}$. The answer can be checked by changing it again to base ten.

**Base twelve**

In base twelve (the duo-decimal base) grouping is done by twelves and powers of twelve. Twelve symbols are needed. If the two extra symbols are called *a* and *b*, there would be these symbols: 0, 1, 2, 3, 4, 5, 6, 7, 8, 9, *a*, and *b*. In base twelve, the numeral 10 means 1 group of twelve and no ones.

EXAMPLES:

*Problem:* $39_{twelve}$ = ———————$_{ten}$.

*Solution:* $39_{twelve} = (3 \times 12^1) + (9 \times 12^0)$

$$= (3 \times 12) + (9 \times 1)$$

$$= 36 + 9$$

$$= 45_{ten}.$$

*Problem:* $37_{\text{ten}} =$ _____$_{\text{twelve}}$.

*Solution:* $37 \div 12 = 3$

$$\frac{36}{1}$$

In $37_{\text{ten}}$ there are 3 twelves and 1 one. Therefore, $37_{\text{ten}} = 31_{\text{twelve}}$. The answer should be checked by changing it again to base ten.

## Some Simple Operations in Bases Other Than Ten

1. *Problem:* $4 + 3 =$ _____$_{\text{five}}$.

   *Solution:*

   0   1   2   3   4   10   11   12   13   14   20

   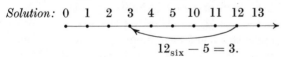

   $$4 + 3 = 12_{\text{five}}.$$

2. *Problem:* $13_{\text{four}} + 12_{\text{four}} =$ _____$_{\text{four}}$.

   *Solution:*

   0   1   2   3   10   11   12   13   20   21   22   23   30   31

   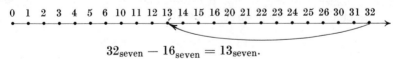

   $$13_{\text{four}} + 12_{\text{four}} = 31_{\text{four}}.$$

3. *Problem:* $12_{\text{six}} - 5 =$ _____$_{\text{six}}$.

   *Solution:*

   0   1   2   3   4   5   10   11   12   13

   $$12_{\text{six}} - 5 = 3.$$

4. *Problem:* $32_{\text{seven}} - 16_{\text{seven}} =$ _____$_{\text{seven}}$.

   *Solution:*

   0  1  2  3  4  5  6  10  11  12  13  14  15  16  20  21  22  23  24  25  26  30  31  32

   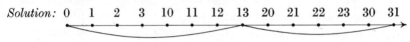

   $$32_{\text{seven}} - 16_{\text{seven}} = 13_{\text{seven}}.$$

5. *Problem:* $3 \times 4 =$ _____$_{\text{five}}$.

   *Number question:* Three 4's are how many in base five?

   *Solution:*

   0   1   2   3   4   10   11   12   13   14   20   21   22   23

   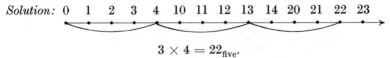

   $$3 \times 4 = 22_{\text{five}}.$$

6. *Problem:* $33_{\text{four}} \div 3 = $ ———$_{\text{four}}$.

   *Number question:* How many 3's are there in $33_{\text{four}}$?

   *Solution:*  0   1   2   3   10   11   12   13   20   21   22   23   30   31   32   33

   There are $11_{\text{four}}$ threes in $33_{\text{four}}$.

   $$33_{\text{four}} \div 3 = 11_{\text{four}}.$$

7. *Problem:* $21_{\text{four}} \div 3 = $ ———$_{\text{four}}$.

   *Solution:* See number line under problem 6.

   There are 3 threes in $21_{\text{four}}$.

   $$21_{\text{four}} \div 3 = 3.$$


## SELECTED ACTIVITIES FOR PUPILS

In order to give the student some idea how the content presented in Chapters 4–8 can be used in the mathematics program of the elementary school, ten samples of possible activities have been selected for each topic and are listed at the end of these chapters. The student should also acquaint himself with some of the modern programs in elementary-school mathematics, and, with the help of these materials, determine a proper grade placement for the activities presented. An excellent source of information is *Implementing Mathematics Programs in California,* listed among the selected references at the end of this chapter. In this book a comprehensive analysis of mathematics programs in California in Grades K-VIII is presented. Of special interest are: (1) illustrations of suggested topics organized by grade levels (pp. 41–100), (2) a listing of appropriate mathematics content for each grade level organized by topics (pp. 101–130), and (3) a description of several suggested activities for pupils (pp. 131–139):

1. Developing the concept of one-to-one correspondence

   *Example:* Is there a flag for each boy? From each boy draw a line to a different flag.

2. Assigning a cardinal number to a set

   *Example:* Draw a line around the numeral that tells how many trees there are.

   4   5   6   7

3. Determining the ordinal number of a specific object in a series

   *Example:* Mark the third boy in the row.

4. Developing the idea that a number has many names

   *Example:* The same number is expressed by 6, ⊞⊞ /, 5 + 1, _____,

   _____, _____.

5. Assigning positional value to a digit

   *Example:* In 21, the 2 represents _____.

6. Expressing a number in expanded notation

   *Examples:* 26 = 20 + _____; 325 = _____ + _____ + _____.

7. Using number properties

   *Example:* 5 + 7 = 7 + □. Complete this sentence and illustrate it on the number line. Supply more examples and formulate the rule.

8. Working preparatory exercises for learning to use bases other than ten

   *Example:* If you have 37 pennies, you can exchange them into _____ quarters, _____ nickels, and _____ pennies.

9. Performing fundamental operations involving negative integers

   *Examples:* 6 + ⁻2 = _____; 9 − ⁻3 = _____.

10. Interpreting mathematical terms

    *Example:* True or false: A numeral is a symbol for a number.

## EXERCISES

1. Explain the difference between a number and a numeral.

2. Give examples of cardinal numbers.

3. Give examples of ordinal numbers.

4. List the characteristics of the Hindu-Arabic system of notation.

5. What is the difference between face value and positional value?

6. What positional value does each digit in the numeral 12,345 represent?

7. List the properties of whole numbers presented in this chapter and give an example of each.

8. Explain the difference between numeration and notation.

9. List and give examples of the principles of the Roman system of notation.

10. a) Complete the following grids:

| $10^3$ | $10^2$ | $10^1$ | $10^0$ |
|---|---|---|---|
| 1000 | | | 1 |

| $8^3$ | $8^2$ | $8^1$ | $8^0$ |
|---|---|---|---|
| | 64 | | 1 |

| $2^3$ | $2^2$ | $2^1$ | $2^0$ |
|---|---|---|---|
| | | | |

    b) What generalization can you make about raising any number to the zero power? *Note:* The student may want to consult J. W. Heddens, *Today's Mathematics.* Chicago: Science Research Associates, Inc., 1964, Unit VII.

11. Work the following problems:

$32_{five} = $ _____$_{ten}$      $28_{ten} = $ _____$_{five}$      $7 + 4 = $ _____$_{eight}$

$131_{four} = $ _____$_{ten}$      $129_{ten} = $ _____$_{four}$      $13_{five} - 4 = $ _____$_{five}$

$723_{eight} = $ _____$_{ten}$      $904_{ten} = $ _____$_{eight}$      $3 \times 3 = $ _____$_{four}$

$1011_{two} = $ _____$_{ten}$      $37_{ten} = $ _____$_{two}$      $20_{five} \div 2 = $ _____$_{five}$

## SELECTED REFERENCES

Banks, J. H., *Learning and Teaching Arithmetic*, 2nd Ed. Boston: Allyn and Bacon, Inc., 1964, Chs. II and III.

Bell, C., C. D. Hammond, and R. B. Herrera, *Fundamentals of Arithmetic for Teachers.* New York: John Wiley & Sons, Inc., 1962, Ch. II.

Briggs, J., F. Mettler, and R. Denholm, *Implementing Mathematics Programs in California.* Menlo Park, Calif.: Pacific Coast Publishers, n.d.

Brumfield, C. F. *et al.*, *Principles of Arithmetic*. Reading, Mass.: Addison-Wesley Publishing Company, Inc., 1963, Chs. III and IV.

Churchill, E. M., *Counting and Measuring*. Toronto: University of Toronto Press, 1961, Chs. II and III.

Educational Research Council of Greater Cleveland, *Key Topics in Mathematics for the Primary Teacher*. Chicago: Science Research Associates, Inc., 1962.

Heddens, J. W., *Today's Mathematics*. Chicago: Science Research Associates, Inc., 1964, Units V–IX.

Howard, C. F. and E. Dumas, *Basic Procedures in Teaching Arithmetic*. Boston: D. C. Heath & Company, 1963, Ch. XV.

Johnson, D. A. and W. H. Glenn, *Understanding Numeration Systems*. St. Louis: Webster Publishing Company, 1960.

Larsen, H. D. and H. G. Ludlow, *Arithmetic for Colleges*. New York: The Macmillan Co., 1963, Ch. I.

Marston, H., *Worktext in Modern Mathematics*. New York: Harper & Row, Publishers, 1962, Ch. VII.

Mueller, F. J., *Arithmetic—Its Structure and Concepts*, 2nd Ed. Englewood Cliffs, N.J.: Prentice-Hall, Inc., 1964, Units I–IV.

National Council of Teachers of Mathematics, *Topics in Mathematics*. Washington, D.C.: the Council, 1964, Bklts. 2 and 3.

School Mathematics Study Group, *Studies in Mathematics: Vol. IX, A Brief Course in Mathematics for Elementary School Teachers*. Stanford: Leland Stanford Junior University, 1963, Chs. III and IV.

Smith, T., *Number*. Oxford: Basil Blackwell, 1960, Ch. VI.

Taylor, E. H. and C. N. Mills, *Arithmetic for Teacher-training Classes*. New York: Holt, Rinehart & Winston, Inc., 1955, Chs. I and II.

Thorpe, C. B., *Teaching Elementary Arithmetic*. New York: Harper & Row, Publishers, 1962, Chs. VIII and IX.

Van Engen, H. *et al.*, *Seeing Through Mathematics*. Chicago: Scott, Foresman and Company, 1962, Book I, Ch. V.

Williams, S. M., H. G. Read, and F. L. Williams, *Modern Mathematics in the Elementary and Junior High Schools*. Syracuse: The L. W. Singer Company, Inc., 1961, Units I–IV.

# 5

# FACTORS
# AND
# MULTIPLES

ONE OF THE main objectives in the teaching of mathematics is the development of an understanding of the structure of numbers. To become effective in computational procedures, the child must acquire skill in expressing given numbers as products of factors and prime factors and in finding multiples of given numbers.

In this chapter the natural numbers will be examined and various groups or sets of natural numbers will be classified according to distinctive properties they possess. Moreover, relationships between given numbers and their integral factors or parts will be illustrated, and factorization of natural numbers will be introduced.

## Factors

The numbers that are multiplied to form a product are *factors* or *divisors of that product*. Thus, in $3 \times 4 = 12$, 3 and 4 are factors of the product 12. Since 12 has several factors, it may be expressed in various ways:

$$12 = 1 \times 12 = 2 \times 6 = 3 \times 4 = 4 \times 3 = 6 \times 2 = 12 \times 1.$$

## Multiples

A *multiple* of a number is any number of which the given number is a factor. Thus a multiple of a number can be divided by the given number without leaving a remainder. For example, in $3 \times 4 = 12$, 12 is a multiple of 4, since 4 is a factor of 12. Four, of course, has an infinite number of multiples: 4, 8, 12, 16, 20, $\cdots$

## Even and Odd Numbers

A natural number is either an even or an odd number.

*Even numbers* are numbers which are evenly divisible by 2. The set of even natural numbers is expressed as $\{2, 4, 6, \cdots\}$. Since any even number has 2 as a factor, it may be represented by $2 \times n$, in which $n$ is a natural number. *Examples:* $2 = 2 \times 1$; $24 = 2 \times 12$; $36 = 2 \times 18$.

*Odd numbers* are numbers which, when divided by 2, leave a remainder of 1. They do not have the factor 2. The set of odd numbers is expressed as $\{1, 3, 5, \cdots\}$. Any odd number may be represented by $(2 \times n) - 1$, in which $n$ is a natural number. *Examples:* $3 = (2 \times 2) - 1$; $21 = (2 \times 11) - 1$. Thus, any odd number is equal to an even number minus one.

## Primes and Composites

There are three classes of natural numbers:

1. The number 1.
2. The numbers greater than 1 that have exactly two factors: the number itself and 1. *Examples:* The factors of 2 are 2 and 1; the factors of 5 are 5 and 1. These numbers are called *prime numbers* or *primes*.
3. The numbers that have factors other than the number itself and 1. *Examples:* The factors of 4 are 1, 2, and 4; the factors of 10 are 1, 2, 5, and 10. These numbers are called *composite numbers* or *composites*.

The number 1 is neither prime nor composite, but is a unique or special number. It is a factor of every natural number.

Prime numbers are isolated in a simple way by using a method called the *Sieve of Eratosthenes*. In order to determine the prime numbers less than 25, the numbers from 2 to 25 are listed:

(2) (3) 4 (5) 6 (7) 8 9 10 (11) 12 (13)
14 15 16 (17) 18 (19) 20 21 22 (23) 24 25

Next this procedure is followed:

1. The first prime number (2) is encircled.
2. All the multiples of 2 are crossed out.

3. The prime number 3 is encircled.

4. All the multiples of 3 are crossed out.

5. The prime number 5 is encircled.

6. All the multiples of 5 are crossed out.

In order to find the primes between 2 and 25, we have to carry the process only to 5 and its multiples. The student should ascertain that the identification of multiples of primes greater than 5 results in a duplication of the process.

~~The Greek Eratosthenes~~, who lived a few centuries before Christ, used this method. He probably cut holes in a parchment scroll instead of crossing out the figures. His paper finally looked like a sieve.

## Tests for Divisibility

The teacher of modern elementary-school mathematics will have to apply important tests for divisibility frequently—for example, when numbers must be factored. Some of the rules and their explanations are presented below.

*1. A number is divisible by 2 if and only if the number represented by the right-hand digit is divisible by 2.*

*Examples:* 18; 150; 2478; are divisible by 2.
*Explanation:* $2478 = 2470 + 8$ or $247 \times 10 + 8$. Since 2 is a factor of 10, any multiple of 10 is divisible by 2. Hence, when determining whether a number is divisible by 2, we need only be concerned with whether the units digit is divisible by 2.

*2. A number is divisible by 3 if and only if the sum of its digits is divisible by 3.*

*Examples:* 12 is divisible by 3, since the sum of the digits ($1 + 2 = 3$) is divisible by 3.
2403 is divisible by 3, since the sum of the digits ($2 + 4 + 0 + 3 = 9$) is divisible by 3.
*Explanation:* Any power of 10, when divided by 3, yields 1 as remainder, as shown below.

$111 = 100 + 10 + 1$

$\qquad = (99 + 1) + (9 + 1) + 1$

$\qquad = 99 + 9 + 1 + 1 + 1$. Since $99 + 9$ is a multiple of 3, it follows that 111 equals a multiple of 3 plus the sum of the digits.

In 7641, the 7 represents 7000 or $(7 \times 999) + (7 \times 1)$,

*Expanded* the 6 represents 600 or $(6 \times 99) + (6 \times 1)$,

*Notation* the 4 represents 40 or $(4 \times 9) + (4 \times 1)$,

the 1 represents 1

Hence, $7641 = (7 \times 999) + (7 \times 1) + (6 \times 99) + (6 \times 1) +$

$$(4 \times 9) + (4 \times 1) + 1$$

$$= (7 \times 999) + (6 \times 99) + (4 \times 9) + (7 \times 1) +$$

$$(6 \times 1) + (4 \times 1) + 1$$

$$= (7 \times 999) + (6 \times 99) + (4 \times 9) + 7 + 6 + 4 + 1$$

*any power of*
*$10 \div 3 = 1$ R.*

Since $7 + 6 + 4 + 1 = 18$ is divisible by 3, the number 7641 is also divisible by 3.

*Note:* If 999 is evenly divisible by 3, then $7 \times 999$ is also evenly divisible by 3, since a factor of a number is also a factor of any of its multiples.

3. *A number is divisible by 4 if and only if the number represented by the two right-hand digits is divisible by 4.*

*Examples:* 124; 3428; 159,080; are divisible by 4.
*Explanation:* $3428 = 3400 + 28$. Since 4 is a factor of 100, any multiple of 100 is divisible by 4. Hence, when determining whether a number is divisible by 4, we need only be concerned with whether the number represented by the two right-hand digits is divisible by 4.

4. *A number is divisible by 5 if and only if it ends in 5 or 0.*

*Examples:* 75; 130; 2435; 7940; are divisible by 5.
*Explanation:* $2435 = 2430 + 5$. Since 5 is a factor of 10, any multiple of 10 is divisible by 5. Hence, when determining whether a number is divisible by 5, we need only be concerned with whether the units digit is divisible by 5.

5. *A number is divisible by 6 if and only if it is divisible by 2 and by 3.*

*Examples:* 48; 144; 2316; 17,994; are divisible by 6.
*Explanation:* $6 = 2 \times 3$, and 2 and 3 are primes and have only 1 as a common factor.

6. *A number is divisible by 8 if and only if the number represented by the three right-hand digits is divisible by 8.*

*Examples:* 1800; 4408; 73,960; are divisible by 8.
*Explanation:* $73,960 = 73,000 + 960$. Since 8 is a factor of 1000, any multiple of 1000 is divisible by 8. Hence, when determining whether a number is divisible by 8, we need only be concerned with whether the number represented by the three right-hand digits is divisible by 8.

7. *A number is divisible by 9 if and only if the sum of its digits is divisible by 9.*

*Examples:* 18,279; 4563; 19,467; are divisible by 9.
*Explanation:* Any power of ten when divided by 9 gives 1 as remainder. The explanation is similar to that for the rule of divisibility for 3.

8. *A number is divisible by 10 if and only if it ends in 0.*

*Examples:* 60; 150; 2560; 94,300; are divisible by 10.
The student should try to explain the rule of divisibility for 10.

9. *A number is divisible by 12 if and only if it is divisible by 3 and by 4.*

*Examples:* 1788; 4044; 35,220; are divisible by 12.
*Explanation:* $12 = 3 \times 4$, and 3 and 4 have only 1 as a common factor.

Students who understand the rules of divisibility for 2, 4, and 8, will be able to formulate the rule of divisibility for 16. Similarly, if the rules of divisibility for 6 and for 12 are understood, it will not be difficult to formulate and explain the rule of divisibility for 15.

## Factorization

If a composite number is expressed as a product of prime numbers, these numbers are called the *prime factors* of the number. In such a case exponential notation may be used to advantage, as illustrated in the following examples.

*Examples:*   $9 = 3 \times 3 = 3^2$.
$8 = 2 \times 2 \times 2 = 2^3$.
$625 = 5 \times 5 \times 5 \times 5 = 5^4$.

The *Fundamental Theorem of Arithmetic* tells us that a composite number can be expressed as a product of primes in a unique way. Such prime factorization is unique in the sense that—apart from the order of the factors—one and only one set of primes can be used.

*Examples:* 6 can be expressed in prime factors only as $2 \times 3$; 40 can be expressed in prime factors only as $2 \times 2 \times 2 \times 5$.
When the prime factors of a number must be determined, it is advisable to follow a specific procedure. A method is illustrated below.

EXAMPLE:
*Problem:* Resolve 1260 into prime factors.
*Solution:* The number is divided by prime numbers, in order of size, starting

with the smallest prime number, as follows:

1260 is divisible by 2:
630 is divisible by 2:
315 is divisible by 3:
105 is divisible by 3:
35 is divisible by 5:
7 is a prime number.

$$2 \overline{)1260}$$
$$2 \overline{)630}$$
$$3 \overline{)315}$$
$$3 \overline{)105}$$
$$5 \overline{)35}$$
$$7$$

Thus: $1260 = 2 \times 2 \times 3 \times 3 \times 5 \times 7 = 2^2 \times 3^2 \times 5 \times 7$.

## Greatest Common Divisor

The *greatest common divisor* (G.C.D.) of two or more numbers is the largest of all the common divisors of the numbers. The greatest common divisor is also called the *highest common factor* (H.C.F.).

EXAMPLE 1:
*Problem:* Find the greatest common divisor of 72 and 90.
*Solution:* First 72 and 90 are resolved into prime factors:

$$2 \overline{)72} \qquad 2 \overline{)90}$$
$$2 \overline{)36} \qquad 3 \overline{)45}$$
$$2 \overline{)18} \qquad 3 \overline{)15}$$
$$3 \overline{)9} \qquad 5$$
$$3$$

Thus: $72 = 2^3 \times 3^2$, and
$90 = 2 \times 3^2 \times 5$.

To find the greatest common divisor of 72 and 90, the common factors, each with the smallest exponent, are selected. These are 2 and $3^2$. The greatest common divisor of 72 and 90 is, therefore, the product of these factors: $2 \times 3^2 = 18$. Eighteen is the largest number which evenly divides 72 and 90.

EXAMPLE 2:
*Problem:* Find the greatest common divisor of 36, 48, and 108.
*Solution:*

$$2 \overline{)36} \qquad 2 \overline{)48} \qquad 2 \overline{)108}$$
$$2 \overline{)18} \qquad 2 \overline{)24} \qquad 2 \overline{)54}$$
$$3 \overline{)9} \qquad 2 \overline{)12} \qquad 3 \overline{)27}$$
$$3 \qquad 2 \overline{)6} \qquad 3 \overline{)9}$$
$$3 \qquad 3$$

$$\text{Thus:} \quad 36 = 2^2 \times 3^2,$$
$$48 = 2^4 \times 3, \text{ and}$$
$$108 = 2^2 \times 3^3.$$

The G.C.D. of 36, 48, and 108 is $2^2 \times 3 = 12$. Twelve is the largest number which evenly divides 36, 48, and 108.

A fraction can be reduced to its lowest terms by dividing both terms of the fraction by the greatest common divisor of the numerator and the denominator of the fraction.

EXAMPLE:

*Problem:* Reduce the fraction $\frac{525}{630}$ to its lowest terms.

*Solution:* The greatest common divisor of two numbers is the largest of all the common divisors of the numbers. Hence, it has to be determined what the greatest common divisor is of 525 and 630.

$$
\begin{array}{r}
3\overline{)525} \\
5\overline{)175} \\
5\overline{)35} \\
7
\end{array}
\qquad
\begin{array}{r}
2\overline{)630} \\
3\overline{)315} \\
3\overline{)105} \\
5\overline{)35} \\
7
\end{array}
$$

$$\text{Thus:} \quad 525 = 3 \times 5^2 \times 7, \text{ and}$$
$$630 = 2 \times 3^2 \times 5 \times 7.$$
$$\text{G.C.D. is } 3 \times 5 \times 7 = 105.$$

Now it has been determined that the largest of all the common divisors of 525 and 630 is 105. Therefore, both the numerator and the denominator of the fraction $\frac{525}{630}$ are divided by 105:

$$\frac{525}{630} = \frac{525 \div 105}{630 \div 105} = \frac{5}{6}$$

## Least Common Multiple

The least (lowest) common multiple (L.C.M.) of two or more numbers is the smallest number that is evenly divisible by each of these numbers.

*Example:* Find the least common multiple of the numbers 72, 150, and 200.

*Solution:* The numbers are first resolved into prime factors:

$$
\begin{array}{r}
2\overline{)72} \\
2\overline{)36} \\
2\overline{)18} \\
3\overline{)9} \\
3
\end{array}
\qquad
\begin{array}{r}
2\overline{)150} \\
3\overline{)75} \\
5\overline{)25} \\
5
\end{array}
\qquad
\begin{array}{r}
2\overline{)200} \\
2\overline{)100} \\
2\overline{)50} \\
5\overline{)25} \\
5
\end{array}
$$

Thus:  $72 = 2^3 \times 3^2$,
$150 = 2 \times 3 \times 5^2$, and
$200 = 2^3 \times 5^2$.

To find the least common multiple of 72, 150, and 200, all the different factors, each with the highest exponent, are selected. These are $2^3$, $3^2$, and $5^2$. The least common multiple of 72, 150, and 200 is the product of these factors:

$$2^3 \times 3^2 \times 5^2 = 1800.$$

Why are all the different factors, each with the highest exponent, a necessary and sufficient set of factors to make up the least common multiple? The L.C.M. must contain 72, which equals $2^3 \times 3^2$; also 150, which equals $2 \times 3 \times 5^2$; and 200, which equals $2^3 \times 5^2$. Hence, the L.C.M. will contain all the different factors, each with the highest exponent. The different factors are 2, 3, and 5. These factors are represented in the three numbers more than once. If the factor $2^3$ is included, then also the factor 2 is included. Consequently, it is sufficient to select the factors with the highest exponent.

The L.C.M. is used in the addition and subtraction of unlike fractions. The smallest common denominator of two or more fractions is the L.C.M. of the denominators of the fractions.

EXAMPLE:
*Problem:* Add $\frac{2}{15}$, $\frac{1}{12}$, and $\frac{3}{50}$.
*Solution:* The first step is to resolve 15, 12, and 50 into prime factors:

$$
\begin{array}{r}
3\overline{)15} \\
5
\end{array}
\qquad
\begin{array}{r}
2\overline{)12} \\
2\overline{)6} \\
3
\end{array}
\qquad
\begin{array}{r}
2\overline{)50} \\
5\overline{)25} \\
5
\end{array}
$$

Thus:  $15 = 3 \times 5$,
$12 = 2^2 \times 3$, and
$50 = 2 \times 5^2$.

Then the L.C.M. of 15, 12, and 50 can be found. The L.C.M. of these numbers is $2^2 \times 3 \times 5^2 = 300$. Hence, the smallest common denominator of $\frac{2}{15}$, $\frac{1}{12}$, and $\frac{3}{50}$ is 300. Finally, $\frac{2}{15}$, $\frac{1}{12}$, and $\frac{3}{50}$ are renamed as fractions with a denominator of 300, and the addition is performed:

$$\frac{2}{15} + \frac{1}{12} + \frac{3}{50} = \frac{40}{300} + \frac{25}{300} + \frac{18}{300} = \frac{83}{300}$$

## SELECTED ACTIVITIES FOR PUPILS

1. Identifying odd numbers and even numbers

   *Example:* Encircle the odd numbers: 3; 5; 12; 22; 31; 59.

2. Identifying prime numbers and composite numbers

   *Example:* Underline the prime numbers: 7; 11; 5; 9; 15; 26.

3. Expressing a composite number as a product of primes

   *Example:* 15 = _____ × _____ .

4. Finding the factors of a number

   *Example:* Find the factors of 12:  12 = 1 × _____
   
                                        12 = 2 × _____
   
                                        12 = 3 × _____
   
                                        12 = 4 × _____
   
                                        12 = 6 × _____
   
                                        12 = 12 × _____

5. Finding multiples of a number

   *Example:* List four multiples of 3.

6. Using exponential notation

   *Examples:* $5 \times 10^2$ = _____;  $250 = 2 \times 5^{\square}$.

7. Developing simple rules of divisibility and applying tests for divisibility

   *Example:* Test each of these numbers for divisibility by 2, 5, and 10:
   25; 78; 110; 111.

8. Finding patterns

   *Example:* Multiply five even numbers by any number and decide
   whether the product is an even number or an odd number.
   Do you see a pattern?

9. Finding common factors

   *Example:* Find the common factors of 9 and 12.

10. Finding the greatest common divisor

    *Example:* Find the greatest common divisor of 12 and 18.

# EXERCISES

1. Supply the integral factors of:

    24; 40; 75; 65; 100.

2. Express each number as a product of two factors in every possible way:

    20; 24; 65; 50; 60.

3. How many even numbers are greater than 20 and less than 45?

4. Supply five multiples of 7.

5. For each of the numbers expressed below, decide whether it is a prime number or a composite number.

    16; 11; 23; 41; 74; 99; 3; 13; 37; 52.

6. Test each of the numbers expressed below for divisibility by 2, 3, 4, 5, 6, 8, and 10.

    312; 927; 14,928; 64,500; 134,880.

7. Resolve into prime factors:

    252; 540; 375; 3150; 2112.

8. Determine the smallest common denominator of these fractions:

    $\frac{1}{3}$, $\frac{2}{5}$, $\frac{7}{15}$, and $\frac{9}{10}$.

9. Find the L.C.M. of 12, 21, and 50.

10. Find the G.C.D. of 14, 21, and 49.

11. Find both the G.C.D. and the L.C.M. of 30 and 54.

12. Write this expression in a shorter form by using exponents:

    $2 \times 2 \times 3 \times 3 \times 5 \times 5 \times 5$.

# SELECTED REFERENCES

Banks, J. H., *Learning and Teaching Arithmetic*, 2nd Ed. Boston: Allyn and Bacon, Inc., 1964, Ch. VI.

Bell, C., C. D. Hammond, and R. B. Herrera, *Fundamentals of Arithmetic for Teachers*. New York: John Wiley & Sons, Inc., 1962, Ch. VII.

Briggs, J., F. Mettler, and R. Denholm, *Implementing Mathematics Programs in California*. Menlo Park, Calif.: Pacific Coast Publishers, n.d.

Educational Research Council of Greater Cleveland, *Key Topics in Mathematics for the Primary Teacher*. Chicago: Science Research Associates, Inc., 1962.

Heddens, J. W., *Today's Mathematics*. Chicago: Science Research Associates, Inc., 1964, Unit XII.

Mueller, F. J., *Arithmetic—Its Structure and Concepts*, 2nd Ed. Englewood Cliffs, N.J.: Prentice-Hall, Inc., 1964, Unit XVI.

National Council of Teachers of Mathematics, *Topics in Mathematics*. Washington, D.C.: the Council, 1964, Bklt. 5.

School Mathematics Study Group, *Studies in Mathematics: Vol. IX, A Brief Course in Mathematics for Elementary School Teachers*. Stanford: Leland Stanford Junior University, 1963, Ch. XVII.

Taylor, E. H. and C. N. Mills, *Arithmetic for Teacher-training Classes*. New York: Holt, Rinehart & Winston, Inc., 1955, Ch. VIII.

Thorpe, C. B., *Teaching Elementary Arithmetic*. New York: Harper & Row, Publishers, 1962, Ch. XV.

# 6

# SETS

THE CONCEPT OF set is not new. In any primary grade the children work with sets or collections, groups are joined, and elements are removed from a given collection. Each person is acquainted with such expressions as a pair of shoes, a team of horses, a set of dishes, and a herd of cattle.

Many mathematicians want to introduce set concepts and terminology in the elementary school in order to assist the child better in his formation of proper number concepts and to guide him toward more precise mathematical language. It is anticipated that, at a later level, the child can build advanced mathematical concepts more easily if he has acquired simple concepts of sets in the elementary grades. Consequently, in many programs for the elementary school, basic ideas of and simple operations on sets are introduced and important terminology is presented. Ideally the rapid learner is then introduced to more difficult operations and to more complicated terms and symbols.

In this chapter simple set concepts, terms, and symbols are presented in order to acquaint the student with much of the content which is introduced in contemporary programs for the elementary school. The presentation of this content does not mean that the author recommends that all of this subject matter should be introduced to all elementary-school pupils. Similarly, the selected activities for pupils which appear at the end of the chapter are intended to be only illustrations of activities which are presented in various contemporary programs. More study and research are needed in order to determine which set concepts, terms, and symbols can be efficiently taught in the elementary school and to decide upon the grade level at which these concepts should be presented.

Since, for obvious reasons, the teacher cannot afford to be ignorant of present trends in mathematics and of the subject matter included in contemporary programs, he needs to be acquainted with the content to be presented in this chapter.

## Sets

A set may be described as a collection of concrete or abstract entities. It may consist of a collection of objects, persons, animals, letters, etc. The items which make up a set are called *members* or *elements* of the set.

Examples of sets are: a family; a class; a team of basketball players; the numbers greater than 10 and less than 20.

A capital letter is usually used to designate a set. A set is tabulated as follows: $A = \{1, 3, 5, 7, 9\}$. This sentence is read "$A$ is the set whose members are $1, 3, 5, 7, 9$," or "$A$ is the set of odd numbers from 1 through 9." Note that the names of the elements of the set are listed between braces. Elementary-school pupils often draw a ring around the pictured elements of a set instead of using braces. A set whose elements are a house and a tree can be pictured as follows:

The cardinal number of a set tells us how many elements are contained in the set. If $A = \{\Box, \triangle, \bigcirc\}$, we say that its cardinal number is three. This may be expressed as $n(A) = 3$, which is read "The number of set $A$ is three." If $B = \{a, b, c, d, e\}$, we say that its cardinal number is five, and we write $n(B) = 5$.

## The Empty Set

The empty set has no members at all. For example, there are no members in the set made up of the states of our country the names of which begin with the letter Z. The *empty set* is also called the *null set*. The symbol for the empty set is $\varnothing$. The empty set may be represented as follows:

$$A = \{\,\} \quad \text{or} \quad A = \varnothing \quad \text{or}$$

The cardinal number of set $A$ is zero. Thus $n(A) = 0$.

## Finite Sets

If the number of elements in a set is limited, the set is called a *finite set*. Some finite sets have so many elements, however, that to tabulate their names would be impractical. Generally, such sets have some pattern to their elements and, once this pattern has been indicated, three dots are used to denote continuation of the pattern, with the last element named to identify the end of the pattern. Thus $N = \{2, 4, 6, \cdots, 40\}$ expresses the set of even integers from 2 through 40.

## Infinite Sets

If a set is not finite it is an *infinite set*. The number of members in an infinite set is endless. Examples of infinite sets are: the set of natural numbers; the set of even numbers; the set of points on a line.

The set of natural numbers is tabulated as follows: $N = \{1, 2, 3, \cdots\}$. This sentence may be read "the set of natural numbers 1, 2, 3, and so on infinitely."

## Equal or Identical Sets

If $A$ and $B$ are sets which have precisely the same members, then $A$ and $B$ are said to be *equal* or *identical sets*. Thus, if $A$ and $B$ are equal sets, then every element of $A$ is an element of $B$, and vice versa. We write $A = B$. In designating the elements of a set, each object should be named once and only once. The order in which the elements are listed is immaterial.

*Example 1:* Let $A$ represent all the books in John's library, and let $B$ represent all the arithmetic books John has. John has only arithmetic books.

$$A = \{\text{the books in John's library}\}.$$

$$B = \{\text{John's arithmetic books}\}.$$

$$A = B$$

*Example 2:* Let $A$ represent all the odd numbers between 2 and 8, and let $B$ represent all the prime numbers between 2 and 8.

$$A = \{3, 5, 7\}.$$
$$B = \{3, 5, 7\}.$$
$$A = B$$

If two sets $C$ and $D$ are not equal, we write: $C \neq D$.

## Equivalent Sets

If the elements in one set can be placed in a one-to-one correspondence with another set (that is, if for each member of one set there is one and only one member of the other set, and vice versa), the sets are said to be *equivalent sets.*

*Example:*  $A = \{\text{boy, girl}\}.$
       $B = \{\text{flag, balloon}\}.$

$A$ is equivalent to $B$, since the two sets can be *matched.* This means that the members of the sets can be placed in a one-to-one correspondence as follows:

$A = \{\text{boy, girl}\}$         Set A                    Set B

or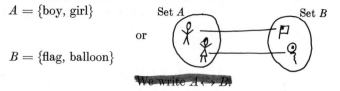

$B = \{\text{flag, balloon}\}$

We write $A \leftrightarrow B$.

Two equal sets are always equivalent, since they can be matched. If $A = \{3, 5, 7\}$, and $B = \{5, 3, 7\}$, then $A$ and $B$ are equal and equivalent.

However, two equivalent sets are not necessarily equal. If $C = \{\text{Dick, Tom, Harry}\}$, and $D = \{\text{train, car, bus}\}$, then $C$ and $D$ are equivalent, since there is a one-to-one correspondence between elements of the sets. But $C$ and $D$ are not equal, since all members are not common to both sets.

If two sets $E$ and $F$ are not equivalent, we write: $E \not\leftrightarrow F$.

## The Universal Set and Subsets

Consider the following example:

$$U = \{\text{all people in New York City}\}.$$
$$A = \{\text{all men in New York City}\}.$$

This universal set and the subset can be represented in a diagram:

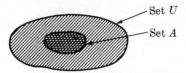

Set A is contained in set $U$ and is called a *subset* of the universal set $U$. We write $A \subset U$. This sentence is read "$A$ is a subset of $U$." The specified set from which subsets are derived is called the *universe* or the *universal set.* Examples of other subsets which can be drawn from the universe expressed above are the set of all women in New York City, the set of all men above 20 years of age in New York City, etc. Hence, a subset of a set, $U$, is any set whose members are members of $U$. Observe that the empty set is also a subset of the universal set. Note, furthermore, that a set is a subset of itself.

*Example:* Set $C = \{1, 2, 3\}$.

Subsets of $C$ are:

$$\{1\} \quad \{1, 2\} \quad \{1, 2, 3\} \quad \{\,\}$$
$$\{2\} \quad \{2, 3\}$$
$$\{3\} \quad \{1, 3\}$$

Set $C$ has 8 subsets.

A set with 3 elements has $2^3 = 8$ subsets.
A set with 4 elements has $2^4 = 16$ subsets.
A set with $n$ elements has $2^n$ subsets.

## Operations on Sets

The two operations commonly performed on sets are union and intersection.

### Union

The *union* of two sets is the set whose members belong to one set or the other set or to both sets.

*Example:* $A = \{1, 3, 4, 6\}$.

$B = \{3, 6, 8, 9\}$.

The set consisting of the members which are in either $A$ or $B$ or in both is

$\{1, 3, 4, 6, 8, 9\}$. We write $A \cup B = \{1, 3, 4, 6, 8, 9\}$, and we say: "*A* union *B* is the set whose members are 1, 3, 4, 6, 8, 9."

The union of two sets is not the same operation as addition of two numbers in arithmetic. In the example above, the union of *A* and *B* does not result in 8 elements but in 6, since *A* and *B* have two elements in common, whose names are not to be included twice in the tabulation. However, if *A* and *B* do not have any elements in common, the sets are *disjoint* sets, and the number of elements in the union of *A* and *B* is the sum of the number of elements in *A* and *B*. Thus if $A = \{1, 2, 3\}$ and $B = \{4, 5\}$, then $A \cup B = \{1, 2, 3, 4, 5\}$. The cardinal number of *A* is 3, and the cardinal number of *B* is 2. The cardinal number of the union of the sets is 5, and we write $n(A \cup B) = 5$.

### Intersection

The intersection of two sets is the set that contains the members which are common to both sets. Hence, the new set consists only of the elements common to the original sets.

*Example:* $A = \{1, 3, 5, 7, 9\}$.
$\qquad\quad B = \{5, 7, 9, 11, 13\}$.

The set consisting of the members which are in both set *A* and set *B* is $\{5, 7, 9\}$.

We write $A \cap B = \{5, 7, 9\}$, and we say: "*A* intersection *B* is the set whose members are 5, 7, 9." As stated before, if the intersection of two sets consists of no members and is therefore the empty set, the two sets are *disjoint* sets.

### Venn Diagrams

Relations between sets and operations on sets can be shown graphically by the use of Venn diagrams. In a *Venn diagram*, usually a picture of a rectangle represents the universal set, and pictures of circles represent subsets. However, other shapes may also be used.

*Examples:* In the following examples, $U =$ the set of all pupils of Lincoln School.

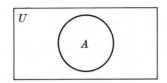

*size not important*

$A$ = the set of all boys in grade VI of Lincoln School.
Set $A$ is a subset of the universe $U$.

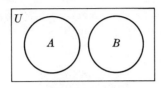

*Concrete*

$A$ = the set of all boys in grade VI of Lincoln School.
$B$ = the set of all girls in grade VI of Lincoln School.
Set $A$ and set $B$ are both subsets of the universe $U$.
The intersection of set $A$ and set $B$ is the empty set.
Set $A$ is disjoint from set $B$.

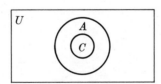

$A$ = the set of all boys in grade VI of Lincoln School.
$C$ = the set of all boys in grade VI of Lincoln School who are members
of the choir.
Set $A$ is a subset of the universe $U$.
Set $C$ is a subset of set $A$.

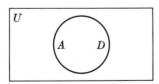

$A$ = the set of all boys in grade VI of Lincoln School.
$D$ = the set of all boys in grade VI who take physical education.
Set $A$ is equal to set $D$ or coincides with set $D$, because all the boys in
grade VI take physical education.

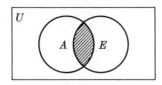

$A$ = the set of all boys in grade VI of Lincoln School.

$E$ = the set of all boys in Lincoln School who are members of the choir.

The intersection of $A$ and $E$ is not empty. The shaded part of the circles represents the intersection, and its members are the boys who are pupils of grade VI and who are also members of the choir.

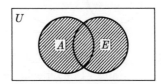

$A$ = the set of all boys in grade VI of Lincoln School.

$E$ = the set of all boys in Lincoln School who are members of the choir.

The union of set $A$ and set $E$ is shown in the diagram. The sum of the number of members in $A$ and the number of members in $E$ is larger than the number of members in $A \cup E$.

*More Examples:*

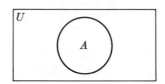

$U = \{1, 2, 3, \cdots\}$ ($U$ is the set of natural numbers).

$A = \{2, 4, 6, \cdots\}$ ($A$ is the set of even numbers).

$A$ is a subset of $U$.

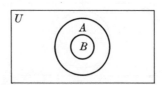

$U = \{1, 2, 3, \cdots\}$ ($U$ is the set of natural numbers).

$A = \{2, 3, 4, 5, 6\}$ ($A$ is the set whose members are 2, 3, 4, 5, 6).

$B = \{3, 4\}$ ($B$ is the set whose members are 3, 4).

$B$ is a subset of $A$.

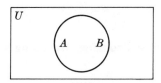

$U = \{2, 3, 4, 5, 6, 7, 8\}$ ($U$ is the set whose members are 2, 3, 4, 5, 6, 7, 8).

$A = \{3, 5, 7\}$ ($A$ is the set whose members are the odd numbers between 2 and 8).

$B = \{3, 5, 7\}$ ($B$ is the set whose members are the prime numbers between 2 and 8).

$A$ coincides with $B$, or $A$ equals $B$.

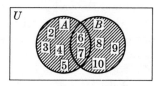

$U = \{1, 2, 3, \cdots\}$ ($U$ is the set of natural numbers).

$A = \{2, 3, 4, 5, 6, 7\}$ ($A$ is the set whose members are 2, 3, 4, 5, 6, 7).

$B = \{6, 7, 8, 9, 10\}$ ($B$ is the set whose members are 6, 7, 8, 9, 10).

$A \cup B = \{2, 3, 4, 5, 6, 7, 8, 9, 10\}$ ($A$ union $B$ is the set whose members are 2, 3, 4, 5, 6, 7, 8, 9, 10).

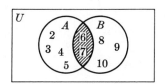

$U = \{1, 2, 3, \cdots\}$ ($U$ is the set of natural numbers).

$A = \{2, 3, 4, 5, 6, 7\}$ ($A$ is the set whose members are 2, 3, 4, 5, 6, 7).

$B = \{6, 7, 8, 9, 10\}$ ($B$ is the set whose members are 6, 7, 8, 9, 10).

$A \cap B = \{6, 7\}$ ($A$ intersection $B$ is the set whose members are 6, 7).

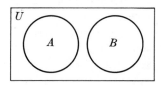

$U = \{1, 2, 3, \cdots\}$ ($U$ is the set of natural numbers).

$A = \{2, 3, 4, 5\}$ ($A$ is the set whose members are 2, 3, 4, 5).

$B = \{8, 9, 10\}$ ($B$ is the set whose members are 8, 9, 10).

$A$ and $B$ are disjoint sets.

## Solving Problems by Using Sets

Of the junior class of Grant High School,
    7 girls are in the choir;
    9 girls are in the band;
    10 girls are in the orchestra;
Of these girls:
    1 girl is only in the choir and the band;
    1 girl is only in the choir and the orchestra;
    2 girls are only in the band and the orchestra;
    2 girls are in the band, the choir, and the orchestra.

How many girls take one or more of these three music activities? *Note:* In the following Venn diagram the numerals used represent cardinal numbers and not elements. Thus, for example, "3" in part of $A$ refers to three girls.

Three intersecting circles are drawn, each circular region representing one music activity. (Thus sets $A$, $B$, and $C$ are each represented by a circular region.)

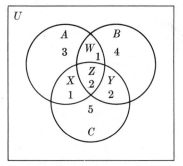

$U$ = the set of girls in the junior class of Grant High School.

$A$ = choir; $B$ = band; $C$ = orchestra; $W$ = choir and band; $X$ = choir and orchestra; $Y$ = band and orchestra; $Z$ = choir, band, and orchestra.

2 girls take choir, band, and orchestra. Write 2 in region $Z$.

1 girl takes choir and band. Write 1 in region $W$.

1 girl takes choir and orchestra. Write 1 in region $X$.

2 girls take band and orchestra. Write 2 in region $Y$.

Since 7 girls take choir and 4 of them are in one or more other activities, 3 girls take only choir. Write 3 in circle $A$.

9 girls take band and 5 of them are in one or more other activities. Write 4 in circle $B$.

10 girls take orchestra and 5 of them are in one or more other activities. Write 5 in circle *C*.

Now it can be determined how many girls take one or more of the music activities:

3 girls take only choir;
4 girls take only band;
5 girls take only orchestra;
1 girl takes choir and band;
1 girl takes choir and orchestra;
2 girls take band and orchestra;
2 girls take choir, band, and orchestra;

18 girls take one or more music activities.
Thus $n(A \cup B \cup C) = 18$.

## SELECTED ACTIVITIES FOR PUPILS

1. Assigning a cardinal number to a set

   *Example:* How many trees are there in the set?

2. Developing the concept of equivalent sets

   *Example:* How many boys are there in set *A*? In set *B* there should be as many boats as there are boys in set *A*. Draw the boats.

   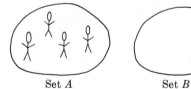

   Set *A*          Set *B*

3. Listing the members of a set

   *Example:* List the members of the set of whole numbers greater than 5 and less than 10.

4. Developing the concept of the empty set

   *Example:* Express the set whose members are the pupils of your class who are three years old.

5. Describing sets

   *Example:* Describe set $A$ in words.

   $$A = \{10, 11, 12, 13, 14\}.$$

6. Identifying equal sets

   *Example:* Which of these sets are equal sets?

   $$A = \{1, 2, 3\} \quad B = \{2, 3, 4\} \quad C = \{4, 5, 6\} \quad D = \{1, 3, 2\}$$

7. Listing subsets

   *Example:* Find all possible subsets of set $A$.

   $$A = \{\text{John, Bill, Tom}\}.$$

   *[handwritten:]* ② John  ⑥ John · Bill  Empty set ⑧  John Tom ⑦ John · Tom  Bill Tom  ④ Bill ① Tom  Bill

8. Forming the union of two sets

   *Example:* If $A = \{\square, \triangle\}$, and $B = \{\bigcirc, \square, \square\}$, then $A \cup B = $ ___.  *[handwritten:]* □ △ ○ □

9. Forming the intersection of two sets

   *Example:* If $A = \{\female, \male\}$, and $B = \{\female, \male\}$, then $A \cap B = $ ___. *[handwritten drawing]*

10. Describing disjoint sets

    *Example:* If $A \cup B = \{1, 2, 3, 4\}$, describe a pair of disjoint sets which could have formed this union.

    *[handwritten:]* $A = \{2, 4\}$  $B = \{1, 3\}$

## EXERCISES

1. Tabulate the set of even numbers greater than 15 and less than 24.

2. Tabulate the set of natural numbers less than 70 that are evenly divisible by 5.

3. Tabulate the set of factors of 21.

4. Read this sentence: $N = \{1, 2, 3, \cdots, 50\}$.

5. Tabulate the set of even numbers.

6. Determine the number of elements in this set:
   $A = \{\text{all the students in your class}\}$.

7. $A = \{1, 3, 5, 7\} \qquad B = \{5, 7, 9, 11\}$
   Is $A$ equal to $B$?    Is $A$ equivalent to $B$?

8. $D = \{e, f, g\} \qquad E = \{h, i, j\}$
   True or false:  $D = E \qquad D \neq E \qquad D \leftrightarrow E \qquad D \not\leftrightarrow E$

9. How many subsets can be derived from a set containing five elements?

10. $A = \{1, 3, 5\} \qquad B = \{5, 7, 9\}$
    $A \cup B = \qquad A \cap B =$

11. $C = \{a, b\}$     $D = \{b, c, d\}$     $E = \{d\}$
    $C \cup D =$     $D \cup E =$     $C \cup E =$
    $C \cap D =$     $C \cap E =$     $D \cap E =$

12. $A = \{7, 8, 9, 10\}$     $B = \{9, 10, 11, 12\}$
    $A \cup B =$     $A \cap B =$
Draw Venn diagrams which illustrate these relations.

13. Decide whether these sets are finite or infinite:
a) The set of natural numbers.
b) The set of fractional numbers.
c) The set of books in your library.

14. In the sixth grade of Jefferson School there are three clubs: the coin collectors club, the stamp collectors club, and the rock collectors club.
18 pupils are members of the coin collectors club.
16 pupils are members of the stamp collectors club.
15 pupils are members of the rock collectors club.
Of these pupils:
5 pupils are only members of the coin collectors club and of the stamp collectors club.
3 pupils are only members of the coin collectors club and of the rock collectors club.
4 pupils are only members of the stamp collectors club and of the rock collectors club.
6 pupils are members of the coin collectors club, of the stamp collectors club, and of the rock collectors club.
How many pupils are members of one or more of these three clubs?

15. $A$ is the set whose members are the prime numbers greater than 5 and less than 23. $n(A) =$

16. Read these sentences:
$A \cup B = \{7, 9, 10\}$
$C \cap D = \{4, 5\}$
$A \leftrightarrow B$
$A \not\leftrightarrow C$
$C \neq D$
$n(E) = 6$

## SELECTED REFERENCES

Aiken, D. J. and C. A. Beseman, *Modern Mathematics: Topics and Problems*. New York: McGraw-Hill, Inc., 1959, Topics I, II, VII, VIII, and IX.
Banks, J. H., *Learning and Teaching Arithmetic*, 2nd Ed. Boston: Allyn and Bacon, Inc., 1964, Ch. IV.

Briggs, J., F. Mettler, and R. Denholm, *Implementing Mathematics Programs in California*. Menlo Park, Calif.: Pacific Coast Publishers, n.d.

Educational Research Council of Greater Cleveland, *Key Topics in Mathematics for the Primary Teacher*. Chicago: Science Research Associates, Inc., 1962.

Heddens, J. W., *Today's Mathematics*. Chicago: Science Research Associates, Inc., 1964, Units II–V.

Howard, C. F. and E. Dumas, *Basic Procedures in Teaching Arithmetic*. Boston: D. C. Heath & Company, 1963, Ch. XV.

Johnson, D. A. and W. H. Glenn, *Sets, Sentences, and Operations*. St. Louis: Webster Publishing Company, 1960.

Marston, H., *Worktext in Modern Mathematics*. New York: Harper & Row, Publishers, 1962, Chs. I, VI, and VIII.

Mueller, F. J., *Arithmetic—Its Structure and Concepts*, 2nd Ed. Englewood Cliffs, N.J.: Prentice-Hall, Inc., 1964, Unit V.

Mueller, F. J. and A. M. Hach, *Mathematics Enrichment*. New York: Harcourt, Brace & World, Inc., 1963, Book E, Unit IV.

National Council of Teachers of Mathematics, *Topics in Mathematics*. Washington, D.C.: the Council, 1964, Bklt. 1.

School Mathematics Study Group, *Studies in Mathematics: Vol. IX, A Brief Course in Mathematics for Elementary School Teachers*. Stanford: Leland Stanford Junior University, 1963, Chs. I and II.

Stein, E. I., *Supplementary Units in Contemporary Arithmetic and Elementary Algebra*. Princeton, N.J.: D. Van Nostrand Co., Inc., 1960, Unit II.

Van Engen, H. *et al.*, *Seeing Through Mathematics*. Chicago: Scott, Foresman and Company, 1962, Book I, Units I and II.

Ward, M. and C. E. Hardgrove, *Modern Elementary Mathematics*. Reading, Mass.: Addison-Wesley Publishing Company, Inc., 1964, Ch. II.

Williams, S. M., H. G. Read, and F. L. Williams, *Modern Mathematics in the Elementary and Junior High Schools*. Syracuse: The L.W. Singer Company, Inc., 1961, Unit VIII.

Zehna, P. W. and R. L. Johnson, *Elements of Set Theory*. Boston: Allyn and Bacon, Inc., 1962.

# 7

# MATHEMATICAL SENTENCES

A SENTENCE IS a group of words that tells or asks something by itself. The words, spoken or written, are symbols which stand for ideas. In a mathematical sentence mathematical symbols express concisely mathematical ideas. For example, instead of expressing the distributive property of multiplication with respect to addition in printed words, the mathematical sentence $a \times (b + c) = (a \times b) + (a \times c)$ (presented in Chapter 4) is used to advantage, since it expresses the idea concisely in comparatively few symbols.

In the mathematical sentence $3 + 2 = 5$, $3 + 2$ acts as the subject, $=$ as the verb, and $5$ as the object of the verb. By itself, $3 + 2$ is not a sentence, since it alone does not tell or ask anything—instead, it is called a *mathematical phrase* or *expression*.

If a mathematical sentence tells something, as in $3 + 2 = 5$ or in $3 + 2 = 4$, it is a *statement* which is true or which is false, and is called a *closed sentence*. If it asks something, as in $3 + \boxed{?} = 5$, it contains an unknown, and is called an *open sentence*.

## Symbols

A mathematical sentence may contain several kinds of symbols: symbols to express the objects under consideration, symbols of operation, symbols of relation or comparison, and punctuation symbols.

1. The symbols which express the *objects* on which the operation is performed may represent numbers or sets.

*Examples:* $4 + 3 = 7$; $\{3, 4\} \cup \{5, 6\} = \{3, 4, 5, 6\}$.

2. The most frequently used symbols indicating operations which must be performed are:

**Note**

| Symbol: | Operation: | Example: |
|---------|------------|----------|
| $+$ | addition | $3 + 2 = 5$ |
| $-$ | subtraction | $5 - 2 = 3$ |
| $\times$ | multiplication | $3 \times 2 = 6$ |
| $\div$ | division | $6 \div 2 = 3$ |
| $\cup$ | union | $\{1\} \cup \{3, 6\} = \{1, 3, 6\}$ |
| $\cap$ | intersection | $\{2, 5\} \cap \{5, 7\} = \{5\}$ |

When more than one number operation is indicated, it is essential to know the order in which they must be performed. When there is any danger of misrepresentation, parentheses, brackets, and braces (shown below) are used to designate the required order of operations—which may be as follows: first those operations indicated within parentheses, then those indicated within brackets, and finally those indicated within braces. If such symbols are not used, the conventional order agreed upon is as follows: (1) *involution*—raising a number to an assigned power—and *evolution*—extracting a root; (2) multiplication and division; and (3) addition and subtraction. An example in which various operations are performed in the order indicated by the punctuation symbols follows.

$$125 - \{80 \div [2 \times (15 - 5)]\} = 125 - \{80 \div [2 \times 10]\}$$

$$= 125 - \{80 \div 20\}$$

$$= 125 - 4$$

$$= 121$$

3. Important relation symbols are:

| Symbol: | Meaning: | Example: |
|---------|----------|----------|
| $=$ | is equal to | $3 + 2 = 5$ |
| $\neq$ | is not equal to | $3 + 2 \neq 6$ |
| $>$ | is greater than | $3 > 2$ |
| $<$ | is less than | $3 < 4$ |
| $\subset$ | is a subset of | If $A = \{1, 2, 3\}$ and $B = \{1, 2\}$, then $B \subset A$. |
| $\leftrightarrow$ | is equivalent to | If $C = \{1, 2, 3\}$ and $D = \{4, 5, 6\}$, then $C \leftrightarrow D$. |
| $\nleftrightarrow$ | is not equivalent to | If $E = \{8\}$ and $F = \{9, 10\}$, then $E \nleftrightarrow F$. |

4. (*Punctuation*) symbols are:

| Symbol: | Name: | Example: |
|---------|-------|----------|
| ( ) | parentheses | $4 \times (2 + 3) = 20$ |
| [ ] | brackets | $60 \div [4 \times (2 + 3)] = 3$ |
| { } | braces | $100 - \{40 \div [4 \times (2 + 3)]\} = 98$ |
| . | decimal point | $4.5$ |
| , | comma | $35,984$ |

## Statements

An *equation* is a sentence that asserts an equality between two expressions. The symbol $=$ is used to express an equality. *Example:* $5 + 2 = 7$. The expression to the left and the one to the right of the equal sign are the *members* of the equation.

An *inequality* states that two expressions are unequal. An inequality may be expressed by the symbol $\neq$, $>$, or $<$.

*Examples:* $5 + 2 \neq 8$;   $5 + 2 \neq 6$;
$\qquad\qquad 5 + 2 < 8$;   $5 + 2 > 6$.

A *closed sentence* is a statement which is true or which is false.

*Examples:* $5 + 2 = 7$ is a true statement.
$\qquad\qquad 5 + 2 = 6$ is a false statement.
$\qquad\qquad 5 + 2 \neq 6$ is a true statement.
$\qquad\qquad 5 + 2 \neq 7$ is a false statement.
$\qquad\qquad 5 + 2 > 6$ is a true statement.
$\qquad\qquad 5 + 2 < 7$ is a false statement.

## Open Sentences

Note

An open sentence contains a symbol for an unknown and cannot be said to be either true or false. For example, the equation $3 + n = 5$ is an open sentence, in which $n$ holds the place for a numeral. Instead of a letter, a question mark, an empty space, or a frame such as $\square$, $\triangle$, or $\bigcirc$ is often used in the elementary school. Though, strictly speaking, $5 + 3 =$ is not a sentence, it is understood that the empty space serves the same purpose as the symbols just presented.

If, in $4 + n = 7$ or in $4 + \square = 7$, the letter or the frame is replaced by 3, the sentence is closed and *the condition is satisfied*, because the statement $4 + 3 = 7$ is a true statement. If, in $4 + n = 7$, the unknown $n$ is replaced by 5, the sentence is closed but the condition is not satisfied, because $4 + 5 = 7$ is a false statement.

The *solution* of each of the sentences $2n = 8$, $1 + n = 5$, and $5 - n = 1$ is 4. Equations which have the same solution are called *equivalent equations*.

When solving an equation these principles may be used:

*Note* {

1. An equivalent equation is obtained if both members of a given equation are increased or decreased by the same number.

2. An equivalent equation is obtained if both members of a given equation are multiplied or divided by the same non-zero number.

EXAMPLE 1:

*Exercise:* Solve $n + 2 = 7$.

*Solution:* Subtract 2 from both members of the equation:

$$\overset{place\ holder}{n} + 2 - 2 = 7 - 2$$
$$n = 5$$

The sentence can be pictured on the number line:

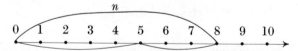

$$n$$

EXAMPLE 2:

*Exercise:* Solve $n - 3 = 5$.

*Solution:* Add 3 to both members of the equation:

$$n - 3 + 3 = 5 + 3$$
$$n = 8$$

Illustration of the sentence on the number line:

$$n$$

EXAMPLE 3:

*Exercise:* Solve $3n = 12$.

*Solution:* Divide both members of the equation by 3:

$$3n \div 3 = 12 \div 3$$
$$n = 4$$

Illustration of the sentence on the number line:

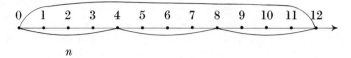

$n$

EXAMPLE 4:
*Exercise:* Solve $n \div 5 = 2$.
*Solution:* Multiply both members of the equation by 5:

$$5 \times (n \div 5) = 5 \times 2$$
$$n = 10$$

Illustration on the number line:

$n$

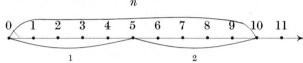

EXAMPLE 5:
*Exercise:* Solve $2n + 5 = 13$.
*Solution:*

    *Step 1.* Subtract 5 from both members of the equation:

$$2n + 5 - 5 = 13 - 5$$
$$2n = 8$$

    *Step 2.* Divide both members of the equation by 2:

$$2n \div 2 = 8 \div 2$$
$$n = 4$$

Illustration on the number line:

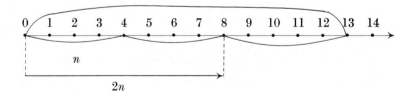

## Mathematical Phrases

In the introduction to this chapter it was stated that $3 + 2$ is not a sentence, because it does not tell or ask something by itself. It was called a *mathematical phrase* or *expression.*

Certain word phrases can be translated into mathematical phrases, such as these:

| Word phrase: | Mathematical phrase: |
|---|---|
| Seven plus two | $7 + 2$ |
| Four times three | $4 \times 3$ |
| A certain number increased by 7 | $n + 7$ |
| A certain number decreased by 5 | $n - 5$ |
| Six subtracted from a certain number | $n - 6$ |
| Seven times a certain number | $7n$ |
| A certain number divided by 2 | $\dfrac{n}{2}$ or $n \div 2$ |
| Three times the difference between eight and six | $3 \times (8 - 6)$ |

## Solving Problems

When solving a verbal problem, the problem must be read carefully, in order to decide what is given and what is asked. Then the situation is expressed in an open mathematical sentence or equation, in which the unknown is represented by a letter or a frame. Finally the equation is solved.

EXAMPLE 1:

*Problem:* Five more than three times a certain number is 17. What is the number?

*Mathematical sentence:* $3n + 5 = 17$.

*Solution:*

*Step 1.* Subtract 5 from both members of the equation:

$$3n + 5 - 5 = 17 - 5$$
$$3n = 12$$

*Step 2.* Divide both members of the equation by 3:

$$3n \div 3 = 12 \div 3$$
$$n = 4$$

The number is 4.

*Check:* $3 \times 4 + 5 = 12 + 5 = 17$.

EXAMPLE 2:

*Problem:* Tom and Ray each have a coin collection. Ray has six more than three times as many coins as Tom. If Ray has 126 coins, how many coins does Tom have?

$3n + 6 = 126$

*Mathematical sentence:* $3n + 6 = 126$.
*Solution:*

    *Step 1.* Subtract 6 from both members of the equation:

$$3n + 6 - 6 = 126 - 6$$
$$3n = 120$$

    *Step 2.* Divide both members of the equation by 3:

$$3n \div 3 = 120 \div 3$$
$$n = 40$$

Tom has 40 coins.
*Check:* $3 \times 40 + 6 = 120 + 6 = 126$.

## Replacement Sets and Solution Sets

In the open sentences $3 + n < 9$ and $3 + \square < 9$ (where $n$ and $\square$ are *place-holders* for any member of the set of natural numbers) the symbols $n$ and $\square$ can be replaced by any natural number. Other letters and frames may also be used as placeholders.

The specified set from which the substitution can be made, which is in this case the set of natural numbers, is called the *replacement set* or the *domain* or the *universe (U)*. The replacement of $n$ in $3 + n < 9$ by a member of the set of natural numbers does not always result in a true statement. For example, $3 + 6 < 9$ is a false statement. In the example under consideration we can only arrive at a true statement by replacing $n$ by 1, 2, 3, 4, or 5. The set containing the members which, when substituted for $n$, satisfies the condition and makes the statement true is called the *solution set* or the *truth set* of the sentence. Thus, in the above example, the solution set is $\{1, 2, 3, 4, 5\}$.

EXAMPLE 1:
$U = \{1, 2, 3, \cdots\}$. Find the solution set of: $3 + n = 4$.

    The only member from the replacement set or universe that, by replacing $n$, causes the statement to be true and therefore satisfies the condition for $n$ in $3 + n = 4$ is 1, since $3 + 1 = 4$. The solution set is $\{1\}$.

EXAMPLE 2:

$$U = \{3, 4, 5, 6, 7, 8, 9, 10\}.$$

| | *Condition:* | *Solution set:* |
|---|---|---|
| a) | $\square + 5 = 8$ | $\{3\}$ |
| b) | $\square - 3 > 4$ | $\{8, 9, 10\}$ |
| c) | $4 + \square < 10$ | $\{3, 4, 5\}$ |

EXAMPLE 3:

$$U = \{1, 2, 3, \cdots\}.$$

*Condition:* $n < 7$

*Solution set:* $\{1, 2, 3, 4, 5, 6\}$

The replacement of $n$ by any member of the solution set $\{1, 2, 3, 4, 5, 6\}$ makes the sentence $n < 7$ true and satisfies the condition. Another way of writing $n < 7$ is $\{n \mid n < 7\}$. This is read "The set whose members are all natural numbers $n$ which satisfy the condition that $n$ is less than 7." The expression $\{n \mid \quad\}$ is called the *set-builder*.

EXAMPLE 4:

Write the following expression by using the set-builder and find the solution set:

The set of all natural numbers greater than 5.

*Solution:* The expression is written with the set-builder as $\{n \mid n > 5\}$; this is read "The set whose members are all natural numbers $n$ which satisfy the condition that $n$ is greater than 5."

*Solution set:* $\{6, 7, 8, \cdots\}$.

## SELECTED ACTIVITIES FOR PUPILS

1. Deciding whether a statement is true or false

    *Example:* True or false: $5 + 7 \neq 12$     $7 \times 9 < 50$     $25 - 9 = 15$

                $30 \div 6 > 3 \times 2$

2. Selecting the proper operation symbol

    *Example:* Write $+$, $-$, $\times$, or $\div$ in each of the circles to make the sentence true.

         $6 \bigcirc 3 = 18$     $9 \bigcirc 3 = 12$     $25 \bigcirc 15 = 10$     $25 \bigcirc 5 = 5$

3. Constructing mathematical sentences to fit a picture situation

    *Example:* Write as many mathematical sentences as you can which go with this picture.

Some possible solutions:

$6 + 2 = 8$

$8 - 2 = 6$

$2 \times 3 + 2 = 8$

4. Constructing a mathematical sentence which fits a given word problem

   *Example:* Write a mathematical sentence which fits this word problem: Ted had some marbles. After he lost 7 of them, he had 20 marbles left. How many marbles did Ted have to begin with?

5. Constructing a word problem to fit a given mathematical sentence

   *Example:* Write a word problem which fits this mathematical sentence.
   $5 \times 3 + 2 = 17$.

6. Replacing placeholders with numerals

   *Examples:* $U = \{1, 2, 3, \cdots\}$
   $$15 + \triangle = 23 \qquad \square + \square = 4 \qquad \square + \bigcirc = 5$$
   $$3 \times 12 = (3 \times \square) + (3 \times \bigcirc) = 36$$
   $$5 \times 7 + 3 = \triangledown \qquad \square \times 3 < 10$$

7. Using letters as placeholders

   *Example:* If $15 - 2n = 7$, then $n =$ _____.

8. Deciding whether a given sentence expresses an inequality

   *Example:* Underline each sentence which expresses an inequality.
   $$26 + 9 = 35 \qquad 6 \times 4 + 10 > 30$$
   $$45 + 15 \neq 55 \qquad 8 \div 4 + 3 < 8$$

9. Using relation symbols

   *Example:* Construct several mathematical sentences and use the symbols $=, \neq, >,$ and $<$.

10. Using punctuation symbols

    *Example:* Perform the indicated operations and explain why you obtained different solutions. You may want to use the number line.
    a) $5 \times 3 + 2 = \boxed{?}$
    b) $5 \times (3 + 2) = \boxed{?}$

## EXERCISES

1. Replace each frame by the symbol $=, >,$ or $<$ to make the sentence true.
   $$7 \times 12 \ \square \ 4 \times 21 \qquad 15 \times 121 \ \square \ 121 \times 15$$
   $$91 \div 7 \ \square \ 55 \div 5 \qquad 96 \div 8 \ \square \ 3 \times 4$$
   $$11 \times 22 \ \square \ 6 \times 41 \qquad 174 + 241 \ \square \ 241 + 174$$

2. Which of these sentences express an inequality?

$7 \times 9 = 63$          $319 + 11 = 11 + 319$          $8 \times 21 > 160$

$47 + 36 \neq 100$          $98 \div 7 \neq 13$          $100 - 63 < 31$

3. Give examples of open and closed mathematical sentences.

4. Complete these open sentences so that each expresses a true statement.

$127 + \underline{\hspace{1cm}} = 135$          $6 \times 23 = \underline{\hspace{1cm}}$          $95 \div \underline{\hspace{1cm}} = 19$

$243 - \underline{\hspace{1cm}} = 129$          $9 \times \underline{\hspace{1cm}} = 126$          $\underline{\hspace{1cm}} \div 7 = 15$

5. Solve:

$2n + 9 = 31$          $7n - 10 = 74$          $3n - 6 = 9$

$\dfrac{n}{7} - 2 = 3$          $5n + 12 = 57$          $9n + 13 = 148$

6. Translate these word phrases into mathematical phrases:
   a) A certain number divided by nine
   b) Four times the sum of ten and fifteen
   c) Nine less than three times a certain number

7. Eleven times what number is 132?

8. Bill has a total of 29 dimes and quarters. If Bill has 5 more dimes than quarters, how many of each does he have?

9. $U = \{1, 2, 3, \cdots, 10\}$.

   *Condition:*                                        *Solution set:*

   $7 + \square = 10$                                  $\underline{\hspace{2cm}}$

   $n < 6$                                             $\underline{\hspace{2cm}}$

   $n + 3 < 6$                                         $\underline{\hspace{2cm}}$

10. Read this expression: $\{n \mid n + 2 > 5\}$. The universe is the set of natural numbers.

## SELECTED REFERENCES

Aiken, D. J. and C. A. Beseman, *Modern Mathematics: Topics and Problems.* New York: McGraw-Hill, Inc., 1959, Topics II and III.

Briggs, J., F. Mettler, and R. Denholm, *Implementing Mathematics Programs in California.* Menlo Park, Calif.: Pacific Coast Publishers, n. d.

Heddens, J. W., *Today's Mathematics.* Chicago: Science Research Associates, Inc., 1964, Unit XVII.

Howard, C. F. and E. Dumas, *Basic Procedures in Teaching Arithmetic.* Boston: D. C. Heath & Company, 1963, Ch. XV.

Johnson, D. A. and W. A. Glenn, *Sets, Sentences, and Operations.* St. Louis: Webster Publishing Company, 1960.

Marston, H., *Worktext in Modern Mathematics.* New York: Harper & Row, Publishers, 1962, Ch. II.

Mueller, F. J., *Arithmetic—Its Structure and Concepts*, 2nd Ed. Englewood Cliffs, N.J.: Prentice-Hall, Inc., 1964, Unit XI.

National Council of Teachers of Mathematics, *Topics in Mathematics.* Washington, D.C.: the Council, 1964, Bklt. 8.

School Mathematics Study Group, *Studies in Mathematics, Vol. IX: A Brief Course in Mathematics for Elementary School Teachers.* Stanford: Leland Stanford Junior University, 1963, Ch. XII.

Stein, E. I., *Supplementary Units in Contemporary Arithmetic and Elementary Algebra.* Princeton, N.J.: D. Van Nostrand Co., Inc., 1960, Unit II.

Van Engen, H. *et al., Seeing Through Mathematics.* Chicago: Scott, Foresman and Company, 1962, Book I, Units I and II.

Ward, M. and C. E. Hardgrove, *Modern Elementary Mathematics.* Reading, Mass.: Addison-Wesley Publishing Company, Inc., 1964, Ch. X.

Williams, S. M., H. G. Read, and F. L. Williams, *Modern Mathematics in the Elementary and Junior High Schools.* Syracuse: The L.W. Singer Company, Inc., 1961, Unit X.

# 8

# GEOMETRY

GEOMETRY IS A branch of mathematics. The word, literally, means "land measurement." Geometric ideas were developed by early man when he observed and compared different shapes in his environment and when he was faced with the problem of measuring land. These ideas were gradually developed and organized into an orderly and logical pattern.

In modern elementary-school mathematics programs, more geometry is being introduced than was the case in traditional programs. In primary and intermediate grades informal geometry is emphasized. In informal geometry properties of geometric figures are studied by inductive reasoning through measuring and experimentation. Formal geometry, in which deductive reasoning is employed, and which leads to logical proofs, is predominantly dealt with in the secondary school.

The emphasis on the inductive approach in geometry at the elementary-school level does not exclude deductive reasoning, however. When concepts have been formed intuitively by experimentation and direct comparison of concrete materials, the generalizations formed should be used deductively in problem solving. As children accumulate more concepts and as concepts become more refined, the pupils will become better prepared for deductive reasoning.

## Points, Lines, and Planes

Geometry is the branch of mathematics that deals with points, lines, planes, and space. The terms "point," "line," "plane," and "space" are usually left undefined and are characterized by their properties.

A geometric point is an idea. It cannot be seen, because it has no size. It is represented on paper by a dot. Even the sharpest point of a needle contains

102

an infinite number of geometric points. ~~In mathematics, the set of all points is called *space*.~~

~~A *line* is also a mathematical idea, and is thought of as an infinite set of points.~~ In ~~geometry the term "line" is understood to mean a straight line.~~ The representation of a line on paper can be made with a straightedge and a pencil. Figure 8-1 represents a line. The arrowheads indicate that the line extends in opposite directions and that it has no end.

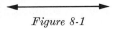

*Figure 8-1*

The direction and location of a line are determined by two different points on the line. Figure 8-2 depicts a line which is determined by the points $A$ and $B$. This line is named by the symbol $\overleftrightarrow{AB}$. $\overleftrightarrow{AB}$ is read "line $AB$." It

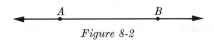

*Figure 8-2*

should be realized that the symbol $\overleftrightarrow{AB}$ indicates that the line under consideration passes through points $A$ and $B$ and that it extends endlessly.

~~A set of points whose members are two given points and all points on the line between these two points is called a *line segment*.~~ The line segment from point $A$ to point $B$ inclusive in Figure 8-2 is identified by the symbol $\overline{AB}$. $\overline{AB}$ is read "line segment $AB$." ~~The *endpoints* of the line segment are points $A$ and $B$.~~

~~Line segments which have the same length are *congruent* segments.~~ The symbol $\cong$ is used to express the idea of congruence. $\overline{AB} \cong \overline{CD}$ is read "line segment $AB$ is congruent to line segment $CD$."

~~A set of points containing the point of origin and all the points on the line extending in one direction from that point is called a *ray*.~~ In Figure 8-3 two rays are represented: ray $AB$ and ray $AC$ ($\overrightarrow{AB}$ and $\overrightarrow{AC}$). Point $A$ is the *origin* of both rays, thus the intersection of $\overrightarrow{AB}$ and $\overrightarrow{AC}$ is point $A$.

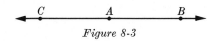

*Figure 8-3*

An infinite number of lines can pass through a single point. ~~If two or more lines have one single point of intersection, the lines passing through the given point are called *concurrent lines*.~~ Some concurrent lines are shown in Figure 8-4.

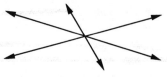

*Figure 8-4*

Lines that are in the same plane but have no point in common are called *parallel lines*. An illustration of two parallel lines is shown in Figure 8-5. Since parallel lines have no point in common, the intersection of such lines is the empty set.

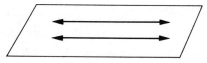

*Figure 8-5*

Lines that are not in the same plane and have no point in common are called *skew lines*. In Figure 8-6 a picture of skew lines is presented.

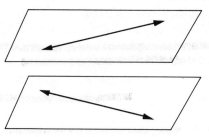

*Figure 8-6*

A *curve* is thought of as a continuous set of points passed through in going from one point to another. A curve, like a point and a line, is an idea and cannot be seen. Curves can be represented on paper. In Figure 8-7 several curves are illustrated.

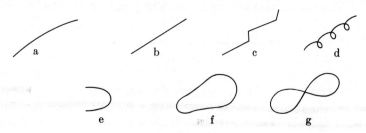

*Figure 8-7*

It should be noted that Figure 8-7(b), which is an illustration of a line segment, also represents a curve. A line segment is said to be a special kind of curve. Figure 8-7(c) represents a broken line curve. Figure 8-7(f) is an illustration of a curve that returns to the point where it started but does not cross itself. This is called a *simple closed curve*.

A *plane* is another mathematical idea. It is a set of points that can be thought of as a flat surface such as an extended table top. A plane contains an infinite set of points and an infinite set of lines, and is unlimited in extent. When a plane is pictured on paper only part of it is outlined, as in Figure 8-8.

*Figure 8-8*

## Angles

An *angle* is the union of two rays which have a common point of origin. The point of intersection is called the *vertex*. In Figure 8-9 an illustration of an

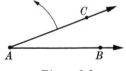

*Figure 8-9*

angle is presented. This angle is called angle $BAC$ or angle $CAB$ ($\angle BAC$ or $\angle CAB$). If $\overrightarrow{AC}$ in Figure 8-9 were to rotate in the direction of the arrow from the original position $\overrightarrow{AB}$ until it met $\overrightarrow{AB}$, it would have made a complete rotation. For measurement purposes, such a complete rotation is divided into 360 equal parts, each part of which is called a *unit angle*. The measure of a unit angle in degrees is 1, and the measure of a complete rotation in degrees is 360. The symbol for degree is °.

Figure 8-10 represents a *linear pair of angles*. These angles have one common side between them and a common vertex, and sides $AB$ and $AD$ form a line. The sum of the measures of $\angle DAC$ and $\angle BAC$ is 180°, and such angles are called *supplementary angles*. $\angle DAC$ is the supplement of $\angle BAC$ and $\angle BAC$ is the supplement of $\angle DAC$.

*Note*

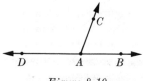

*Figure 8-10*

~~∠ *DAC* and ∠ *BAC* in Figure 8-11 have the same measure, and are there-~~
~~fore *congruent angles*. Each of these angles has a measure of 90°. An angle~~
~~which has a measure of 90° is called a *right angle*.~~

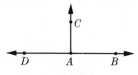

*Figure 8-11*

~~Two lines that intersect at right angles are~~ *perpendicular lines*. In Figure
8-12, $\overleftrightarrow{AB}$ and $\overleftrightarrow{CD}$ are perpendicular lines.

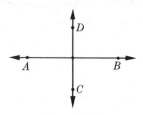

*Figure 8-12*

Examples of various angles are shown in Figure 8-13; their measures are
given below.

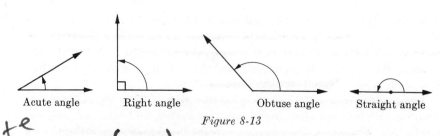

Acute angle        Right angle              Obtuse angle      Straight angle

*Figure 8-13*

*Note*

~~The measure of a *right angle* is 90°.~~
The measure of an *acute angle* is greater than 0° and less than 90°.

The measure of an *obtuse angle* is more than 90° and less than 180°. The measure of a *straight angle* is 180°.

*Note*

The measure of an angle may be approximated by using a protractor.

## Polygons

A *polygon* is a simple closed curve which is the union of more than two line segments. All the plane figures in Figure 8-14 are illustrations of polygons.

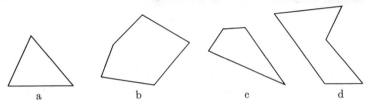

a      b      c      d

*Figure 8-14*

There are several special kinds of polygons. A *triangle* is a three-sided polygon. A *quadrilateral* has four sides. A *pentagon* has five sides. A *hexagon* has six sides. Plane figures having more than six sides usually are called polygons, for simplicity.

There are several special kinds of quadrilaterals. All the illustrations in Figure 8-15 represent quadrilaterals.

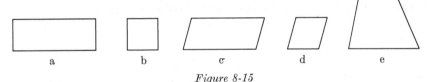

a      b      c      d      e

*Figure 8-15*

In Figure 8-15(a), all the four angles are right angles. This quadrilateral is called a *rectangle*. A special type of rectangle is one with four congruent sides, as in Figure 8-15(b). This type is called a *square*.

Figure 8-15(c) is an illustration of a *parallelogram*. In a parallelogram the pairs of opposite sides are parallel. It will be noticed that a rectangle is a parallelogram. If the four sides in a parallelogram are congruent, the figure is called a *rhombus*. Thus a square is a rhombus, but not all rhombuses are squares. A rhombus which is not a square is shown in Figure 8-15(d).

Figure 8-15(e) represents a *trapezoid*. A trapezoid is a quadrilateral in which one pair of opposite sides is parallel and the other pair is not parallel.

Figure 8-16 represents a *triangle*. The symbol for a triangle is △. The line segments are called *sides*. The point where two sides intersect is called a *vertex*. A triangle has three vertices.

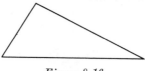

*Figure 8-16*

Figure 8-17(a) is an illustration of a triangle with three congruent sides. Such a triangle is called an *equilateral triangle*.

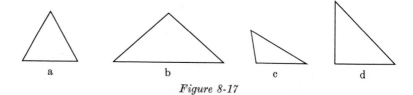

a                    b                    c                    d

*Figure 8-17*

Figure 8-17(b) illustrates an *isosceles triangle*. In an isosceles triangle at least two of the sides are congruent.

A triangle of which no two sides are congruent is called a *scalene triangle*. Such a triangle is represented in Figure 8-17(c).

Figure 8-17(d) shows a *right triangle*. In a right triangle one of the angles is a right angle.

*Congruent triangles* have the same size and the same shape as those shown in Figure 8-18. The fact that the triangles are congruent is indicated as follows: △ *BAC* ≅ △ *EDF*.

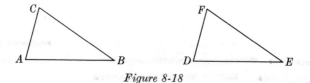

*Figure 8-18*

## Circles

A *circle* is a simple closed curve in a given plane, all the points of the curve being the same distance from a given point called the *center*.

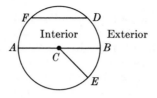

*Figure 8-19*

In Figure 8-19 an illustration of a circle is presented. Point *C* is called the center of the circle. A line segment that has both endpoints on the circle is called a *chord* of the circle. $\overline{FD}$ is a chord of circle *C*. A chord that passes through the center of the circle is a *diameter* of the circle. $\overline{AB}$ is a diameter of circle *C*. If one endpoint of a line segment is the center of the circle and the other endpoint is on the circle, the segment is called a *radius* of the circle. $\overline{CE}$ is a radius of circle *C*. $\overline{CA}$ and $\overline{CB}$ are also radii of circle *C*.

A circle divides a plane into the *interior* and the *exterior* of the circle. The circle itself is the boundary of these regions.

## SELECTED ACTIVITIES FOR PUPILS

1. Finding plane surfaces

   *Example:* Which objects in the classroom make you think of a geometric plane?

2. Identifying plane figures

   *Example:* Decide whether these cutouts have a rectangular, circular, or triangular form. (The teacher shows several cutouts.)

3. Finding plane figures

   *Example:* Find objects in the classroom that have a rectangular, circular, or triangular form.

4. Describing differences between different plane figures

   *Example:* Tell how a rectangle differs from a triangle.

5. Drawing different kinds of lines and curves

   *Examples:* a) Draw several lines through a given point.
   b) Draw a line segment and label it *KL*. Then draw another line segment that is congruent to $\overline{KL}$ and label it *MN*.
   c) Draw a line segment which has points *A* and *B* as endpoints; draw another line segment that is longer than $\overline{AB}$ and label it *CD*; finally draw a line segment that is longer than $\overline{AB}$ but shorter than $\overline{CD}$ and label it *EF*.

d) Draw a ray which has $R$ as point of origin.

e) Draw several different curves.

f) Draw a pair of parallel lines.

g) Draw a pair of perpendicular lines.

h) Draw a line, mark four dots on it, and label the dots $A$, $B$, $C$, and $D$. Then name as many different line segments as you can.

6. Drawing plane figures

*Example:* Draw four different kinds of quadrilaterals and name each one.

7. Working with angles

*Example:* Draw three different kinds of angles, label them, name each one, and measure the angles by using a protractor.

8. Working with triangles

*Example:* If, of three triangles, the first is congruent to the second, and the second is congruent to the third, what statement can you make about the first and the third triangles? Draw three such triangles, label them, and express your statement in mathematical symbols.

9. Working with circles

*Example:* Draw a circle. In it:

a) Draw a diameter.

b) Draw a radius.

c) Draw a chord.

d) Draw the largest chord possible.

e) Identify the interior or inside of the circle.

f) Identify the exterior or outside of the circle.

10. Working with polygons

*Example:* a) Draw a triangle, a quadrilateral, a pentagon, and a hexagon.

b) In each polygon draw a straight line segment from a given vertex to all other non-adjacent vertices. (These line segments are called *diagonals*.)

c) Complete this table:

| Kind of Polygon | Number of Sides | Number of Diagonals from One Vertex |
|---|---|---|
| Triangle | ———— | ———— |
| Quadrilateral | ———— | ———— |
| Pentagon | ———— | ———— |
| Hexagon | ———— | ———— |

d) Try to formulate a rule.

## EXERCISES

1. Draw a picture of a line which is determined by the points $A$ and $B$. Then:
   a) write the symbol for the line and read the symbol;
   b) identify line segment $AB$;
   c) write the symbol for line segment $AB$.

2. Read: $\overline{AB} \cong \overline{CD}$. Explain what the symbol means.

3. Explain what is meant by, and draw a picture representing:
   a) concurrent lines;
   b) parallel lines;
   c) skew lines;
   d) a curve (draw pictures of various curves).

4. Make drawings which represent:
   a) a line;
   b) a line segment;
   c) a ray;
   d) a broken line curve;
   e) a simple closed curve;
   f) an obtuse angle;
   g) an acute angle;
   h) a right angle;
   i) a rectangle;
   j) a parallelogram;
   k) a rhombus;
   l) a trapezoid;
   m) a hexagon;
   n) an isosceles triangle;
   o) an equilateral triangle;
   p) two congruent triangles.

5. Make five drawings which represent different kinds of quadrilaterals.

6. Explain why a square may be called a rectangle.

7. Draw an equilateral triangle $ABC$ and
   a) identify the vertices of the triangle;
   b) identify the angles of the triangle.

8. Draw a circle. Then draw:
   a) a radius;
   b) a diameter;
   c) a chord.

9. Explain why a rectangle may be called a parallelogram.

10. What does the word *polygon* mean?

11. Read: $\overline{AB}$; $\overleftrightarrow{AB}$; $\overrightarrow{AB}$; $\angle ABC$; $\triangle ABC$.

12. Draw four polygons: one with 3 sides, one with 4 sides, one with 5 sides, and one with 6 sides, and supply their special names.


## SELECTED REFERENCES

Barker, C. M., H. Curran, and M. Metcalf, *The "New" Math*. San Francisco: Fearon Publishers, Inc., 1964, Unit IX.

Bell, C., C. D. Hammond, and R. B. Herrera, *Fundamentals of Arithmetic for Teachers*. New York: John Wiley & Sons, Inc., 1962, Ch. XXI.

Briggs, J., F. Mettler, and R. Denholm, *Implementing Mathematics Programs in California*. Menlo Park, Calif.: Pacific Coast Publishers, n.d.

Brumfield, C. F. *et al.*, *Principles of Arithmetic*. Reading, Mass.: Addison-Wesley Publishing Company, Inc., 1963, Ch. XVI.

Corle, C. G., *Teaching Mathematics in the Elementary School*. New York: The Ronald Press Company, 1964, Ch. XII.

Dutton, W. H. and L. J. Adams, *Arithmetic for Teachers*. Englewood Cliffs, N.J.: Prentice-Hall, Inc., 1961, Ch. XIV.

Heddens, J. W., *Today's Mathematics*. Chicago: Science Research Associates, Inc., 1964, Units XIX and XX.

Howard, C. F. and E. Dumas, *Basic Procedures in Teaching Arithmetic*. Boston: D. C. Heath & Company, 1963, Ch. XV.

Mueller, F. J., *Arithmetic—Its Structure and Concepts*, 2nd Ed. Englewood Cliffs, N.J.: Prentice-Hall, Inc., 1964, Unit XXVI.

School Mathematics Study Group, *Studies in Mathematics, Vol. IX: A Brief Course in Mathematics for Elementary School Teachers*. Stanford: Leland Stanford Junior University, 1963, Chs. XIII, XIV, and XV.

Spooner, G., *Mathematics Enrichment*. New York: Harcourt, Brace & World, Inc., 1963, Program C, Part II.

Van Engen, H. *et al.*, *Seeing Through Mathematics*. Chicago: Scott, Foresman and Company, 1962, Book I, Unit VIII.

Ward, M. and C. E. Hardgrove, *Modern Elementary Mathematics*. Reading, Mass.: Addison-Wesley Publishing Company, Inc., 1964, Ch. VIII.

# III

## CONTENT, PROCEDURES, AND EVALUATION

# 9

---

# THE
# DEVELOPMENT
# OF
# NUMBER
# AND
# MEASUREMENT
# CONCEPTS

---

MATHEMATICS IS A special language that the child learns by observing his environment and participating in a variety of directed experiences involving number. As the child receives proper instruction and matures, he develops an understanding of basic number concepts and mathematical relations. ~~However, the formation of this understanding is a gradual process which can be fostered but not forced~~.

Some scholars have conducted important research on conceptual thinking in children and have attempted to determine how and when mathematical concepts are formed. Others have created devices which are intended to assist the child in the formation of such concepts. Resumés of research on the formation of mathematical concepts and descriptions of some structured materials used in the teaching of mathematics to young children are presented below. In the final part of this chapter suggestions are presented for the measurement and the development of basic mathematical concepts.

## Contributions of the Geneva School[1]

The French psychologist Jean Piaget, the leader of the Geneva School, has studied conceptual thinking in children for several decades. Though his findings have met with some criticism, they are so important that they should not be ignored by teachers of elementary-school mathematics. Several authors have interpreted his writings or have continued research in this area, and replications of his investigations generally corroborate his results.

Piaget distinguishes four stages in the development of concepts. The characteristics of these periods—as described by Piaget—are briefly presented below.

1. *The sensori-motor stage,* (from birth to two years of age.) This is the period before the child begins to use language. The initial simple reflexes become gradually modified. There is behavior which can be called intelligent, but intelligence is not yet operational[2] in the sense that the child can imagine or think an act before carrying it out; his behavior rests largely on performing actions. If the child, when striking an object with a stick, happens to move the object toward himself, and because of this effect repeats the action, he shows behavior that is intelligent, since he anticipates the same result. Transfer from observed effects to other situations is noticeable.

2. *The pre-operational stage,* (from two to six or seven years of age.) During this stage the child begins to represent something by means of something else, and he begins to imitate an object when it is not present. Thus actions become "internalized," since the child can use imagery. Signs are beginning to be understood, language is acquired, and the child plays symbolic games. The pre-operational stage is characterized by an absence of a knowledge of conservation, the fact that an object or relation remains unchanged even though there is a change in its perceivable features. If the child at this level observes beads being poured out of a wide glass into a taller, narrower one, he may state that there are more beads in the second glass than there were in the first, since the level of the beads is now higher; or he may say that

---

[1] This part of the chapter is based upon books and articles of Piaget and interpretations of and research reported by Anderson and Nelson; Berlyne; Bunt; Churchill; Coxford; Dienes; Duckworth; Lovell; Piaget, Inhelder, and Szeminska; Russell; Thomson; Van Engen; and Wallach. These writings are identified at the end of the chapter.

[2] Operations are considered to be actions which can be "internalized" by the child. If a child carries out a physical manipulation symbolically and thus "thinks" the action or carries it out in his mind, it is said that he has "internalized" the action.

there are fewer beads in the second glass, since it is narrower than the first. The child is unable to give reasons for his thinking, yet he may insist that he is right and point to the higher level of the beads in the second glass or to its narrower base. He concentrates on one of the features of the situation and reports only what he perceives. Such a lack of the understanding that a quantity is conserved if its units are rearranged indicates that the child has not yet grasped the group meaning of number, and fails to see, for example, the "threeness" of three.

In another experiment Piaget showed the child about 20 beads made of wood, most of which were brown and the remaining ones white. When the child at this level was asked whether there were more brown beads or wooden beads, the typical answer was that there were more brown beads. Piaget decided that the child at this age fails to see the relationship of the part to the whole, does not realize that a subclass has been included, and seems to reason on the basis of either the whole or the part. According to Piaget, the ability to solve a problem of inclusion appears around the seventh or eighth year of age.

3. *The stage of concrete operations,* from six or seven to eleven or twelve years of age.) During this stage the child becomes capable of classifying objects according to their similarities and differences. Piaget reports an example in which the child observes a bouquet of flowers, one half of which consists of daisies and the other half of other flowers. The child can now decide whether there are more flowers or more daisies. Thus he understands that the part is complementary to the rest and realizes that a subclass has been included. The relationship of one-to-one correspondence between elements of sets can now be seen, and the child becomes aware of conservation of discontinuous and continuous quantities. He can reverse his thinking; for example, without performing the operation itself he understands that a rearrangement of a set of objects may be reversed again to undo that rearrangement. This ability will enable him to understand that for an operation such as $2 + 1 = 3$ there is another operation, $3 - 1 = 2$, which undoes the original operation. The child is also capable of seriation, which means that he can place objects in a series according to their selected characteristics. For example, he can place rods of varying lengths in order from the shortest to the longest, and can arrange objects according to their weights.

Piaget believes that the child has now mastered the prerequisites for the formation of the concept of number, since he can classify objects and can put them in order of size. Now the child can learn to combine the operations of classification and seriation, and he can see the unit both as an element in a class and as an element within a series. Then he can make a statement about the collection as a whole and can identify any individual item. For

example, when counting three apples, he arrives at the cardinal number 3
and can identify the position of each apple in the series.

4. ~~The stage of formal operations~~ (after 11 or 12 years of age.) This is a period
of great progress, since the child starts to reason on the basis of hypotheses
or propositions and thus acquires a capacity for abstract thinking. An
example quoted by Piaget is the following: Children of different ages had to
compare the colors of the hair of three girls: Edith is fairer than Susan;
Edith is darker than Lilly; who is the darkest of the three? The thinking
required to solve such a problem is more complicated than the operational
thinking which can be applied to concrete operations that, of course, deal
with practical problems and concrete situations. ~~At the stage of formal
operations, concrete facts are no longer needed, and the child can make
logical deductions from hypotheses~~. He also begins to understand mathematical proportions in which two systems of reference are used at the same time.

Piaget, Inhelder, and Szeminska have conducted extensive research on the
development of concepts associated with length and measurement. Some of
their views and findings are presented in the following paragraphs.
~~Before the child can form the concept of measurement, he must realize
the conservation of distance and length~~.[3] He must understand that the
distance between two objects remains unchanged if a third object is placed
between them. He must also grasp the symmetrical character of distance:
$AB = BA$. Such understandings should help to bring about the concept of
conservation of length, and the child should discover that the length of an
object does not change when the object is moved. ~~Conservation of distance
and length was observed with children of seven to eight years of age~~.

Other prerequisites for measurement are the realization that the whole is
the sum of the component parts, and the understanding of the principles of
substitution and iteration. Selected measurement units may have to be
applied several times to the object or distance to be measured. The child of
seven to eight years of age realizes the need for several measurements in
locating points, and can subdivide line segments. When he is eight to nine
years old, he has attained the concept of unit iteration.

With the assistance of the background information presented above, the
student of mathematics will be able to appreciate the following experiment
reported by Piaget, Inhelder, and Szeminska.

The child was shown a model tower built on a table. He then had to
construct a similar tower on a table with a top higher or lower than the first
one, and he had to use blocks of a different size. The following observations
were made:

---

[3] *Distance* refers to the linear separation of objects or to "empty space"; *length*
refers to the size of "filled space" or to objects as such.

1. The child up to about four and a half years of age made comparisons only by visual transfer—that is, just by looking at the objects.

2. The child of about six years of age began using bodily transfer—that is, he used parts of his body such as his hands or arms as a measuring instrument. For example, he represented the height of the model tower by a distance between his hands and then went to the second tower to compare its height with that distance. Of course, the transferred length could hardly be kept constant.

3. The child of seven or eight years of age tended to use a measuring stick of the same length as or longer than the object to be measured. Thus he applied the principle: if $A = B$ and $B = C$, then $A = C$. If the measuring stick was longer than the object to be measured, the child marked the stick in order to transfer a constant length.

4. The child of eight or nine years of age became capable of operational measurement, since he could use a measuring stick which was shorter than the object to be measured. He realized that the whole equals the sum of the component parts, and used the principles of substitution and of unit iteration by applying the selected unit repeatedly to the object to be measured. Then he assigned a number to the object in terms of the selected unit of measure.

In an attempt to determine the awareness of conservation of area, the same authors conducted the following experiment: Two squares, a and b, were presented. The child realized the squares to be congruent. Square b

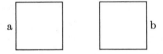

was divided into two congruent parts by means of a diagonal and the parts were arranged perpendicularly to one another, as in c. ~~Not until the child~~

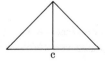

~~was seven or eight years old was there operational conservation of area~~. The child of eight to ten years of age could use the principle of unit iteration and thus apply units of area—for example, a model of the square inch—repeatedly, when measuring a total area.

~~The results of the work of the Geneva School suggest that, in the maturation of basic mathematical concepts, the child moves through a developmental pattern of stages which are clearly defined.~~ As Churchill[4] reports, Piaget stated that although further research may show that the general rate of progress through the stages may be accelerated or retarded by cultural or other factors, the sequence of stages is, in his opinion, invariant because maturation takes this form. The assumption of this uniformity for all individuals has met with some criticism. Churchill indicates that research conducted by other people resulted in findings which suggest that there are factors which make for differences in individual development not revealed in Piaget's approach. It has been shown that a child can be at the stage of concrete operations in one test but not in another. Children may arrive at concepts partly as a result of logical reasoning and partly because of experience with manipulating objects.

~~Piaget's implication that the general rate of progress through the stages may vary with individuals and with societies, and may be accelerated by certain factors,[5] probably will not be contradicted by many psychologists and educators.~~ Some findings of research indicate that skillful instruction may change the age at which children attain a stage. Coxford[6] reports, for example, that instruction given to a limited sample of exceptionally bright children resulted in significant gains in stage placement. This possibility places upon the teacher the responsibility to create an atmosphere in the classroom in which such acceleration is possible, even if not probable. His knowledge of the form which maturation takes and of the child's abilities and limitations should enable him to provide experiences which will assist the pupil in grasping basic mathematical concepts. The environment which the teacher creates should stimulate the child to participate in activities, manipulate, perform experiments, seek and verify his own answers, discover structures, and discuss problems with his classmates. The development of such a questioning mind should be one of the teacher's main objectives.

## Approaches to Initial Instruction in Mathematics

~~The approach to initial instruction in mathematics which uses the experiences the child has and the situations he meets in daily life has been called by~~

---

[4] E. M. Churchill, *Counting and Measuring* (Toronto: University of Toronto Press, 1961), pp. 89–90.

[5] E. Duckworth, "Piaget Rediscovered," *The Arithmetic Teacher*, November, 1964, pp. 496–99.

[6] A. F. Coxford, "The Effects of Instruction on the Stage Placement of Children in Piaget's Seriation Experiments," *The Arithmetic Teacher*, January, 1964, pp. 4–9.

Lovell[7] "the environment approach." It is claimed that incidental experiences which occur during the child's play and in class projects make the resultant learning meaningful, since there is a need for it in the situation which is encountered. In such situations children, individually or in small groups, count, match, combine, separate, compare, measure, and weigh. They engage in activities which they themselves have selected. Exercises with number devices are then introduced as the need arises.

Lovell states that few would disagree with the opinion that it is during play up to seven years of age that the foundations are laid for more complex forms of mental activity. However, he also warns that the flashes of insight or moments of understanding that children get in unstructured (or structured) situations are unstable and are not always transferred to other, more difficult situations, since the child's thinking is still very patchy and uncertain. Thus one may overestimate the quality of the child's thinking. Lovell rightly expresses the need for new, more extensive research in order to determine the long-range effectiveness of the environment approach, and also for research to investigate the effectiveness of this approach for the slow learner.

Most educators doubt the efficiency of the environmental method and do not want to rely upon it for the forming of the necessary mathematical foundations. Devices have been constructed for the purpose of providing structured number experiences for the beginning school child. These approaches provide, usually after some experimental play, directed work with the materials so that, from the beginning, the child is aided in abstracting number experiences. Two methods are described on the following pages.

## The Stern blocks[8]

The Stern blocks were devised by Catherine Stern in an attempt to provide concrete devices for the teaching of arithmetic, and the method which makes use of them is called "Structural Arithmetic." Influenced by Max Wertheimer, the founder of Gestalt Psychology, Stern built her method on the assumption that visual perceptual structures will lead to mental structures. When the physical structures are observed, compared, and measured, they will be fixed in mind so well that the child can still visualize them when they are not present.

---

[7] K. Lovell, *The Growth of Basic Mathematical and Scientific Concepts in Children* (London: University of London Press Ltd., 1961), pp. 40–45.

[8] The description of the Stern blocks is based upon the pamphlet *Structural Arithmetic*, published by Houghton Mifflin Company, Boston, Mass., and upon the following article: C. Stern, "The Concrete Devices of Structural Arithmetic," *The Arithmetic Teacher*, April, 1958, pp. 119–30.

The Stern method presents, in the kindergarten, the number series from 1 to 10, and all the basic concepts leading to mastery of addition and subtraction in the range from 1 to 10 in grade I, and from 1 to 100 in grade II. Initially only the concrete materials are used. When the workbook is introduced, the pupils find pictures of blocks and cubes resembling the configurations presented with the concrete materials. It is believed that the child reconstructs the pictures in his mind and thus visualizes the number relationships.

According to Stern, the devices show the properties of number. The blocks which represent the numbers fit into grooves in such a way that the pupil can discover that each block has a special place and that there is a sequence of block lengths. The pupils' experimenting with the blocks leads to their discovery of the fundamental operations. They estimate, compare, check, and correct their answers themselves.

In this method children do not develop their first number concepts by counting the elements of unstructured groups of objects, but by measuring structured materials, so that relationships can be discovered by the child himself as he fits the blocks into the grooves in various ways. During the first number games, number names and symbols are not used.

The *counting board*, illustrated in Figure 9-1, has ten grooves of different

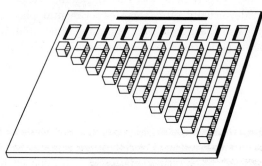

*Figure 9-1*

lengths, into which corresponding blocks fit. The game of placing the blocks into the grooves is self-corrective. The child learns to identify the place of each block on the counting board and gradually develops an awareness of the sequence of block lengths in the series. At a higher level of instruction, the board is equipped with a number guide which shows the symbols 1 to 10, which stand for the blocks. It is anticipated that the child discovers the names of the symbols by himself.

After the counting board, the ten *pattern boards* are introduced. There is a pattern board for each of the numbers 1 to 10. The child is to become familiar with the characteristic configurations or patterns by placing the required number of cubes in each pattern board.

Figure 9-2 is an illustration of the ~~unit box~~. The child's first experiences

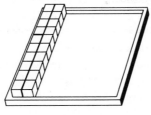

*Figure 9-2*

with the box consist of matching block pairs. This activity is also self-corrective. At a higher level of instruction, when the child can call the blocks by their names, the "story of 10" is introduced and the child is encouraged to make statements such as "the 6 needs 4 to make 10."

Finally the pupil should know what symbols stand for the blocks, and he should begin to use the plus and equal signs meaningfully. He is guided to express the block discoveries in number sentences such as $6 + 4 = 10$. The number question $5 + 4 = \square$ is solved by adding a 4-block to a 5-block and finding a single block of the same total length. The pupil discovers that there is only one block that satisfies this condition—the 9-block. Thus $5 + 4 = 9$. ~~Drill is not used at this stage and the child is not forced to recall answers to addition questions, since comprehension comes first and mastery will be attained later~~.

Subtraction is introduced by using the same principle, or by employing a device called the ~~number track~~. The numerals from 1 to 10 are painted on the track and the 10-block just fits into it. Since, for example, the 8-block reaches the figure 8, the child decides that if 2 is added, the combined blocks reach the total 10. If 2 is then subtracted, the result is again 8. Thus the child discovers that subtraction "undoes" what addition "does." For more advanced number work several sections of the number track can be joined.

Children seem to form concepts by the use of different methods. This places upon the teacher the responsibility to present various methods of solution and to have several visual aids available for use. The Stern method, if used properly, is an approach which the teacher may want to use along with other methods of teaching mathematics in the kindergarten and in the primary grades.[9]

---

[9] For a detailed explanation of the Stern method the student is referred to Stern's book, which is included in the selected references at the end of this chapter.

## The Cuisenaire rods[10]

The Cuisenaire rods, also known as *Numbers in Color*, were devised a few decades ago by George Cuisenaire, a Belgian schoolteacher, in an attempt to provide a new approach to the teaching of the early stages of arithmetic. Dr. Caleb Gattegno, an English mathematician, assisted Cuisenaire later in the further development of the method.

This method of teaching is based on the conviction that it is possible to perceive many mathematical relationships visually or through other sensory experiences. The child manipulates colored wooden rods, compares the resultant patterns, and should thereby discover relations, similarities, and differences. Discoveries of particular relationships are assumed to lead to generalizations and hypotheses whose validity may be directly investigated. The rods are not used for computational purposes. They are used to provide a basis in experience for understanding the particular facts and general laws of mathematics, and also to investigate, test, or prove mathematical statements.

The materials consist of sets of rods made of wood one square centimeter in cross-section and varying in lengths from one centimeter to 10 centimeters. Each of the ten different sizes of rods has a characteristic color, and each differently colored rod is represented by a letter symbol, as follows:

| Length of the Rod: | Color Name: | Letter Symbol: |
|---|---|---|
| 1 cm | white | w |
| 2 cm | red | r |
| 3 cm | light green | g |
| 4 cm | purple | p |
| 5 cm | yellow | y |
| 6 cm | dark green | d |
| 7 cm | black | k |
| 8 cm | brown | n |
| 9 cm | blue | u |
| 10 cm | orange | o |

The Cuisenaire rods are introduced in four stages:

1. *The stage of free play.* During this stage the pupil makes any arrangement with the rods he wants to and no restrictions are imposed upon him. Gattegno calls free play a dialogue between the child and the rods, since the rods suggest

---

[10] The description of the Cuisenaire rods is based upon C. Gattegno, *A Teacher's Introduction to Cuisenaire-Gattegno Methods* (New York: Cuisenaire Company of America, Inc., 1961).

questions as well as answers. The time allocated for free play will depend upon the maturity of the pupils. If the rods are introduced in the kindergarten, several months may have to be spent in free play activities. But if they are first introduced in the primary grades, only a few weeks may suffice.

2. *The stage of free play and directed activities without written notation.* During this period the teacher suggests specific arrangements of the rods that bring out basic mathematical ideas and relationships. The child arranges the rods as directed and reports what he sees and discovers.

3. *The stage when written signs and symbols are introduced.* Letter symbols representing the length of the rods are used and the symbols $+$, $-$, $\times$, $\div$, $=$, and $\square$ are introduced. Sentences are written such as $r = w + w$; $r - w = w$; $g - r = w$.

4. *The stage when number values are assigned to the rods.* During this stage the pupils treat the rods as models of numbers. Appropriate number values are assigned to each rod and operations are performed. Any rod can be selected as the basic measuring unit. Thus the numerical value of a rod will change as different rods are selected as basic measuring rods. For example, if the length of the purple rod is the measuring rod and is called one, then the red rod is called $\frac{1}{2}$ and the yellow rod $\frac{5}{4}$.

Since any equation made with the rods can be thought of as addition or as subtraction, these two operations are both dealt with at the same time.

*Example:* The drawing shown below represents an arrangement of black, yellow, and red rods and suggests these sentences:

$$7 = 5 + 2; \; 7 - 5 = 2; \; 7 = 2 + 5; \; 7 - 2 = 5.$$

| 7 | |
|:---:|:---:|
| 5 | 2 |

Exercises with the rods have been provided not only for the primary grades, but also for older children.

Some research has been conducted to determine the effectiveness of the Cuisenaire method in the teaching of grade III arithmetic.[11] More research, at various grade levels, seems to be advisable.

---

[11] The student is referred to: W. H. Lucow, "Testing the Cuisenaire Method," *The Arithmetic Teacher*, November, 1963, pp. 435–38; R. A. Passy, "The Effect of Cuisenaire Materials on Reasoning and Computation," *The Arithmetic Teacher*, November, 1963, pp. 439–40; and L. T. Root, "One School's Experience with Cuisenaire-Gattegno Mathematics Instruction," *New York State Mathematics Teachers Journal*, January, 1963, pp. 24–27.

The Cuisenaire method, if used properly, appears to be an approach which the teacher may use together with other approaches in the teaching of mathematics in the kindergarten and in the primary grades.

## The Measurement and Development of Basic Mathematical Concepts

*Note*

The child's first experiences with number should be the manipulation of objects. Piaget emphasizes that concepts are not derived from the materials themselves, but from the operations performed on the materials. As the child manipulates, classifies, and rearranges the objects, he observes the transformations and gradually acquires ability to work the operations mentally and to "think" the transformations.

In order to assist the pupil in the formation of proper mathematical concepts, the teacher should provide a variety of instructional materials in the classroom. For equipment in the primary grades a selection may be made from items such as blocks of different sizes and shapes, rods, disks, sets of plastic cubes for building towers and making staircases, pegboards and colored rubber bands, a hundred board, counting frames, abaci, beads, balls of different sizes, tongue depressors, dominoes, a flannel board, containers, measuring cups and spoons, measuring sticks, tape measures, toy cars, a clock and clock faces, a thermometer, a rain gauge, egg cartons, toy money, number lines, a calendar, picture books, modeling clay, geometric figures, templates, cutouts representing fractional parts, games, jigsaw puzzles, balance scales, and weights—for example, small bags filled with sand, or bean bags. On the playground there should be suitable equipment such as sandboxes, plastic pails, and big blocks of wood.

The teacher will determine when the child is ready to be introduced to processes illustrated in the books and on the worksheets. Arithmetic books and workbooks should contain illustrations of mathematical processes, and the teacher should engage each pupil actively in the solution of problems presented. Processes illustrated in the arithmetic books should be frequently performed by the child on concrete materials, and he should give evidence that he understands the process developed in the book. The goal is for the child finally to reach the stage when he can dispense with the practice of manipulating objects and no longer needs illustrations or diagrams. At this level the pupil can form mental pictures of physical manipulations, and thus he will gradually become independent of visual aids.

The extensiveness of mathematical skills, as well as the quantity and quality of the number concepts which school entrants have already acquired, vary widely with different children. (Resumés of studies which have attempted to determine how much arithmetic is known by school beginners were presented in Chapter 3.) Concepts and skills are therefore assessed before the teacher plans foundation experiences in mathematics. Though commercial readiness tests are available, the teacher himself can construct an instrument which fits his specific situation.

To assist the teacher in the preparation of such a test, several items are suggested below. Some of these items are to be used in testing skills, and the teacher will need to record the extent to which each pupil has mastered the skill tested. Concepts are tested by means of simple experiments in which the child is to react to situations. When interpreting the responses, the teacher must realize that a correct answer is no guarantee that the concept which is tested has been fully acquired. The child who happens to be at an intermediate stage of development may supply the correct response, but may still be very uncertain. Thus if the teacher considers the child's understanding of the situation to be unstable, he should continue his investigation by presenting additional questions and conducting more experiments which test the same concept.

When the child has given evidence of possessing a mathematical skill, the teacher should ascertain that the process has been understood. Many school entrants can count by rote but do not understand the "threeness" of three, since they associate number with the size or with another physical characteristic of the objects under consideration. They may see number not as a quantity but as a quality of things, and consider it as they do other qualities of an object such as color or shape. Such pupils need an abundance of varied experiences with the manipulation of objects, so that they will grasp the idea that the number which is attached to a group is independent of the physical characteristics of the objects.

## SUGGESTIONS FOR A NUMBER READINESS TEST

1. Rote counting to _____.
   *Note:* The teacher should decide how far the child's counting ability will be tested.

2. Rational counting to _____.

3. Recognition of numerals to _____.
   *Note:* The order of the presented numerals should be out of sequence.

4. Ability to write numerals to _____.

5. Ability to recognize one half of an object. _____ (yes or no).

6. Ability to identify a group of _____ objects.

   *Suggested experiment:* The teacher presents the child three cards, on which different groups of similar objects are shown—for example, stars. He asks: "On which card are there five stars?" This experiment is repeated with a larger group if the child supplies the correct answer.

7. Ability to reproduce a group of _____ objects.

   *Suggested experiment:* The teacher shows the child several groups of objects in succession, and asks him each time to place an equal number of disks next to the group shown. The numbers which represent the presented groups should not form a sequence.

8. Awareness of conservation of discontinuous quantities.

   *Suggested experiment:* The teacher places 24 pennies in two rows of 12 pennies each. He asks the child to match each penny in the first row with one in the second row until all the pennies have been placed in pairs. As a result, the child should agree that there are just as many pennies in the first row as there are in the second. Then the teacher places one of the rows of pennies in a pile and spreads the other row of pennies out so that it becomes longer. He asks the child: "If you needed money to buy a box of crayons, which group of pennies would you rather have?"

9. Awareness of conservation of continuous quantities.

   *Suggested experiment:* Two glasses of the same shape and size are partly filled with water, so that the child readily agrees that there is just as much water in one glass as there is in the other. The teacher then directs the child to pour the water from one of the glasses into a narrower, taller glass. Then he asks: "If you were very thirsty, which glass of water would you rather have?"

10. An understanding of the part-whole relationship.

    *Suggested experiment:* The teacher shows the child a number of beads— for example, 15—all of which are made of wood and most of which— for example, 12—are white and the remainder red. The teacher asks: "Are there more white beads or are there more wooden beads?"

11. Capability of seriation.

    *Suggested experiment:* The child is to place rods of different lengths in a series, from the shortest to the longest rod.

12. Ability to use ordinal numbers to _____.

    *Suggested experiment:* The teacher shows the child a set of blocks of different lengths, arranged in the form of a staircase. He points to the bottom step and says: "If this step is number one, point to the step which is number four."

Other experiments may be devised and conducted to appraise the child's concepts of measurement, time, money, and geometric concepts.

## SUGGESTED FOUNDATION ACTIVITIES

The teacher who is in need of additional activities for the purpose of developing basic mathematical concepts may want to make a selection from the following list.

1. Manipulating materials such as the Cuisenaire rods and the Stern blocks

2. Matching objects

   *Examples:* Get a cup for each of these saucers.
   If you can get one block for one (toy) penny, get as many blocks as you can for the pennies you have.
   Take as many pennies as you have fingers on one hand.

3. Ordering sets of objects

   *Examples:* Put all the long rods in this box.
   Take all the red disks out of the box and put them on the table.

4. Comparing objects

   *Examples:* Who is the taller, Bill or Tom?
   Who has more milk left in her glass, Susan or Mary?
   Of these two rocks, which is the heavier?

5. Comparing quantities

   *Example:* In which of these groups of disks are many disks and in which group are few disks?

6. Determining the positional relationship between objects

   *Examples:* Put this disk between the two balls.
   Point to the book which is under the table.
   Point to the desk at your right.

7. Constructing models

   *Examples:* Building a house from blocks.
   Building a tower according to a model.
   Fitting together the pieces of a jigsaw puzzle.

8. Arranging objects in a predetermined order

   *Examples:* Put all these rods in order from the shortest to the longest.
   Stack the trays in a nest.

9. Changing the form but not the volume of an object

   *Example:* Activities with a batch of modeling clay which is formed into
   different shapes.

10. Using number rhymes to learn the number names in order (When saying
    such rhymes, the children are encouraged to use their fingers.)

11. Counting to determine how many elements there are in a given set

    *Examples:* How many disks are there on the table?
    How many beads are there on this string?

12. Supplying missing number names in a sequence

    *Examples:* 1, 2, 3, 4, _____, _____.
    5, 6, 7, _____, _____, _____.
    5, 4, _____, _____, _____.

13. Identifying the place which a given element occupies in a series

    *Examples:* Point to the fifth disk in this row, starting from the left.

14. Working with sets of objects

    *Examples:* Joining sets.
    Separating a set into subsets.
    Placing the objects of equivalent sets in one-to-one correspondence.
    Rearranging the objects in a set and determining whether the number
    has changed.
    Drawing a picture of a set that has three members.

15. Arranging numerals in order

    *Examples:* The numerals 1 to 10 are written on cards, one numeral on a
    card. The child is to arrange the numerals in order, beginning with 1.

16. Arranging groups in order

    *Example:* The child is to arrange cards in order, according to the number
    of pictures on the cards.

17. Working with the number line
    The line can be used with such activities as teaching the number
    sequence, determining the cardinal number of a group of successive
    intervals, multiple counting, identifying numerals, and writing numerals.
    In the kindergarten room, a number line is often reproduced on the
    floor with masking tape. The points marked on the tape should be
    approximately one step apart. The child starts on zero and counts the
    steps he takes.

18. Multiple counting

    *Example:* Count by twos, starting with 4.

19. Identifying fractional parts

    *Examples:* Exercises in tearing or cutting a sheet of paper into two or more parts of approximately the same size.
    Exercises with rods of different lengths.

20. Recognizing coins

    *Example:* Take a nickel from the desk.

21. Measuring lengths and distances

    *Examples:* Exercises with rods of different lengths.
    Measure the two bulletin boards and decide which one is the longer.
    Draw a line 1 yard long on the chalkboard, and measure how many feet it is.

22. Weighing

    *Examples:* Which of these two books is the heavier?
    How many beads do you have to put on the scale to make balance with this block?

23. Measuring capacity

    *Examples:* How many spoonfuls of sand are needed to fill this cup?
    How many cups of water are needed to fill a quart?
    How many pints of water are needed to fill a gallon?

24. Playing games which require the use of mathematical skills which the child has acquired

    *Example:* Playing the game of dominoes, in which equivalent sets of dots are matched.

25. Conducting projects

    *Example:* Baking a cake with the kindergartners. (Many mathematical skills have to be used in such a project: reading and interpreting number names, weighing and measuring ingredients, counting, dividing, measuring time, etc.)

26. Using the calendar

    *Examples:* Locating dates.
    Deciding how many days it is until an important event.
    Supplying the numerals on a blank calendar.
    Teaching the meaning of ordinal numbers.

27. Telling time
    The teacher uses a large model of a demonstration clock and each pupil works with a small clock face.

28. Working with simple geometric forms

    *Examples:* Identifying frequently used geometric forms.
    Connecting several given points.
    Drawing frequently used geometric figures.
    Comparing sizes of line segments and areas of figures.

29. Assigning numbers to parts of a whole

    *Example:* Find the number of each part:

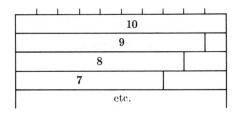

30. Buying articles in the play shop
    *Note:* The price of each article is shown on a tag. Initially, the price of each article is one cent.

## SELECTED RESEARCH

Brownell. W. A. *et al.*, *Arithmetic in Grades I and II: A Critical Summary of New and Previously Reported Research*. Duke University Research Studies in Education, No. 6. Durham, N.C.: Duke University Press, 1941.

Brownell made an extensive study of arithmetic known by school beginners and summarized several investigations already made in this area. A summary of the important findings of these studies is presented in Chapter 3.

The student is urged to acquaint himself with these volumes: Piaget, J., *The Child's Conception of Number*; and Piaget, J., B. Inhelder, and A. Szeminska, *The Child's Conception of Geometry*. These books contain reports of several experiments which were conducted to determine the child's concepts of number and geometry.

## EXERCISES

1. Which stages does Piaget distinguish in the development of a concept? Describe the characteristics of these stages.

2. Explain what is meant by the "internalization" of an action.

3. Describe an experiment conducted to determine whether the child is aware of conservation of discontinuous quantities.

4. How can you determine whether the child is capable of seriation?

5. Give examples of cardinal numbers and of ordinal numbers.

6. Explain what Lovell means by the "environment approach."

7. Should the primary-grade teacher use the "environment approach" exclusively? Give reasons for your answer.

8. Describe the important characteristics of the Cuisenaire method.

9. Describe some of the devices used in the Stern method.

10. What is meant by the statement: "Visual perceptual structures will lead to mental structures"?

11. Select, from the foundation experiences suggested in this chapter, several which you would recommend for the kindergarten program.

12. Describe some activities which can introduce the child to the concept of a set.

### For advanced students

13. Prepare a demonstration lesson with the Cuisenaire rods.

14. Prepare a demonstration lesson with the Stern blocks.

15. As assigned by the instructor of the course, report on and give an evaluation of one or more of the following articles:
    a) Akins, T. S., "Let Them Discover." *The Arithmetic Teacher*, January, 1962, pp. 26–28.
    b) Beard, V., "Mathematics in Kindergarten." *The Arithmetic Teacher*, January, 1962, pp. 22–25.
    c) Brownell, W. A., "Arithmetic Abstractions—Progress Toward Maturity of Concepts Under Differing Programs of Instruction." *The Arithmetic Teacher*, October, 1963, pp. 322–29.
    d) Campbell, D., "Kindergartners Learn Arithmetic." *The Arithmetic Teacher*, April, 1958, pp. 137–39.
    e) Coxford, A. F., "The Effects of Instruction on the Stage Placement of Children in Piaget's Seriation Experiments." *The Arithmetic Teacher*, January, 1964, pp. 4–9.

f) Erickson, L. H., "Color As an Aid in Teaching Concepts." *The Arithmetic Teacher*, February, 1958, pp. 10–14.
g) Félix, L., "Modern Mathematics Begins in the Elementary School." Translated by H. Kavett and P. F. Kavett. *The Arithmetic Teacher*, January, 1962, pp. 32–36.
h) Heard, I. M., "Developing Concepts of Time and Temperature." *The Arithmetic Teacher*, March, 1961, pp. 124–26.
i) Kolson, C. J., "The Oral Arithmetic Vocabulary of Kindergarten Children." *The Arithmetic Teacher*, February, 1963, pp. 81–83.
j) Lucow, W. H., "Testing the Cuisenaire Method." *The Arithmetic Teacher*, November, 1963, pp. 435–38.
k) Mascho, G., "Familiarity with Measurement." *The Arithmetic Teacher*, April, 1961, pp. 164–67.
l) Passy, R. A., "The Effect of Cuisenaire Materials on Reasoning and Computation." *The Arithmetic Teacher*, November, 1963, pp. 439–40.
m) Priore, A., "Achievement by Pupils Entering the First Grade." *The Arithmetic Teacher*, March, 1957, pp. 55–60.
n) Stutler, M. S., "Arithmetic Concepts in First Grade." *The Arithmetic Teacher*, February, 1962, pp. 81–85.

## SELECTED REFERENCES

Andrews, E. E. and L. D. Nelson, "Beginning Number Experiences and Structured Materials." *The Arithmetic Teacher*, October, 1963, pp. 330–33.

Berlyne, D. E., "Recent Developments in Piaget's Work." *British Journal of Psychology*, February, 1957, Part I, pp. 1–12.

Brownell, W. A. *et al.*, *Arithmetic in Grades I and II: A Critical Summary of New and Previously Reported Research*. Duke University Research Studies in Education, No. 6. Durham, N. C.: Duke University Press, 1941.

Bruner, J. S., *The Process of Education*. Cambridge: Harvard University Press, 1960.

Bunt, L. N. H., *The Development of the Ideas of Number and Quantity According to Piaget*. Groningen, The Netherlands: J. B. Wolters, 1951.

Churchill, E. M., *Counting and Measuring*. Toronto: University of Toronto Press, 1961.

Coxford, A. F., "Piaget: Number and Measurement." *The Arithmetic Teacher*, November, 1963, pp. 419–27.

Dienes, Z. P., *Building Up Mathematics*. London: Hutchinson Educational Ltd., 1960, Chs. I–III.

Duckworth, E., "Piaget Rediscovered." *The Arithmetic Teacher*, November, 1964, pp. 496–99.

Dutton, W. H., *Evaluating Pupils' Understanding of Arithmetic.* Englewood Cliffs, N.J.: Prentice-Hall, Inc., 1964.

Gattegno, C., *A Teacher's Introduction to Cuisenaire-Gattegno Methods.* New York: Cuisenaire Company of America, Inc., 1961.

Grossnickle, F. E. and L. J. Brueckner, *Discovering Meanings in Elementary School Mathematics.* New York: Holt, Rinehart & Winston, Inc., 1963, Ch. V.

Hollister, G. E. and A. G. Gunderson, *Teaching Arithmetic in the Primary Grades.* Boston: D. C. Heath & Company, 1964.

Joyce, B. and E. Joyce, "Studying Issues in Mathematics Instruction." *The Arithmetic Teacher*, May, 1964, pp. 303–7.

Lee, J. J., *Suggestions for Teaching Arithmetic in Infant Classes.* Wellington: Department of Education, 1963.

Lovell, K., *The Growth of Basic Mathematical and Scientific Concepts in Children.* London: University of London Press Ltd., 1961.

Piaget, J., *The Child's Conception of Number.* Translated by C. Gattegno and F. M. Hodgson. London: Routledge and Kegan Paul Ltd., 1961.

———, "How Children Form Mathematical Concepts." *Scientific American*, November, 1953, pp. 74–79.

———, "The Stages of the Intellectual Development of the Child." *Bulletin of the Menninger Clinic*, May, 1962, pp. 120–28.

Piaget, J., B. Inhelder, and A. Szeminska, *The Child's Conception of Geometry.* Translated by E. A. Lunzer. New York: Basic Books, Inc., 1960.

Rosenquist, L. L., *Young Children Learn to Use Arithmetic.* Boston: Ginn and Company, 1949.

Russell, D. H., *Children's Thinking.* Boston: Ginn and Company, 1956, Chs. V and VIII.

Smith, T., *Number.* Oxford: Basil Blackwell, 1960.

Spitzer, H. F., *The Teaching of Arithmetic.* Boston: Houghton Mifflin Company, 1961, Ch. II.

———, "Arithmetic in Kindergarten and Grades 1 and 2." *Twenty-fifth Yearbook of the National Council of Teachers of Mathematics.* Washington, D. C.: the Council, 1960, pp. 94–120.

Stern, C., *Children Discover Arithmetic.* New York: Harper & Row, Publishers, 1949.

———, "The Concrete Devices of Structural Arithmetic." *The Arithmetic Teacher*, April, 1958, pp. 119–30.

Thomson, R., *The Psychology of Thinking.* Baltimore: Penguin Books, Inc., 1959, Ch. V.

Thorpe, C. B., *Teaching Elementary Arithmetic.* New York: Harper & Row, Publishers, 1962, Ch. X.

Van Engen, H., "The Child's Introduction to Arithmetic Reasoning." *School Science and Mathematics*, May, 1955, pp. 358–63.

Wallach, M. A., "Research On Children's Thinking." *Sixty-second Yearbook of the National Society for the Study of Education.* Chicago: University of Chicago Press, 1963, Part I, Ch. VI.

# 10

# ADDITION

CHAPTER 9 OFFERED suggestions relative to helping the pupil build the background required for profiting from instruction in addition and subtraction. The present chapter describes in some detail the instruction to be given in the addition of whole numbers and deals in a few paragraphs with addition involving negative integers.

## Meaning and Terms

Addition is an operation on two numbers resulting in a single number which is called the *sum.* In 7 + 5 = 12, 7 and 5 are the *addends* and 12 is the *sum.* The operation is *binary* in nature because only two numbers are added at a time. If there are three or more addends, first two of these are added, then the third is added to the result of the first operation, etc.

In set language, addition of whole numbers can be described as the operation by which the cardinal number of a single set of objects is determined when that set contains two disjoint sets of objects of which the cardinal numbers are known. Hence, if the cardinal numbers of the disjoint sets $A$ and $B$ are 2 and 3, the cardinal number of the set $A \cup B$ is the sum of 2 and 3, which is 5. It should be emphasized that this result is obtained only when the sets are disjoint so that $A \cap B$ is empty. In the operation described, the union of set $A$ and set $B$—not of the cardinal numbers—is formed, and the cardinal numbers—not the sets—are added.

*Example:*
If $A = \{\bigcirc, \square\}$ and $B = \{\triangle, \bigcirc, \square\}$, then $A \cup B = \{\bigcirc, \square, \triangle, \bigcirc, \square\}$. The cardinal number of $A$ is 2 and that of $B$ is 3, and $A$ and $B$ are disjoint sets. Thus the cardinal number of $A \cup B$ is $2 + 3 = 5$, or $n(A \cup B) = 5$.

If two sets are not disjoint sets, the cardinal numbers of the sets cannot be added to find the cardinal number of the union of the sets. This is shown in the following example: If $A = \{$Sun, Moon, Venus$\}$ and $B = \{$Sun, Moon, Mars, Earth$\}$, then $A \cup B = \{$Sun, Moon, Venus, Mars, Earth$\}$. The cardinal number of $A \cup B$ is 5, and not 7. The operation can be illustrated in a Venn diagram:

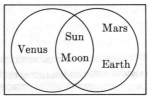

In this diagram it is also shown that $A \cap B = \{$Sun, Moon$\}$.

The meaning of the equal sign in a mathematical sentence such as $3 + 2 = 5$ should be clearly understood. The sign indicates that the total of the numbers expressed by the symbols to its left equals the number expressed by the symbol to its right. Consequently, before the operation of addition takes place, two specific groups are considered, and after the operation has taken place, a single group is considered, the cardinal number of which is the total of those of the two original groups.

## Properties

Several properties which apply to the addition of whole numbers were presented in Chapter 4. The student should state what is meant by and give an example of each of these properties of addition: commutation, association, closure, and the identity element for addition. *Note*

Young children should acquire inductively a functional knowledge of these properties. They do not yet need to know the terms and definitions of the various properties.

## Grade Placement of Addition Topics

In contemporary textbooks, the introduction of the key (or basic) addition facts and the study for mastery of these facts are usually spread over several years. Typically, addition facts with sums not larger than 10 are introduced in grade I, and the remaining facts with sums through 18 in grade II. The study for mastery of these facts is usually started in grade II and finished in grade III. ~~Regrouping (traditionally called carrying) in addition is, as a rule, not undertaken before grade III. Addition of two-digit numbers is occasionally introduced in grade II, but usually taught in grade III.~~ Multi-digit numbers are added in grade III, and at higher grade levels the difficulty of such exercises increases.

Many arithmetic materials which have been published recently present addition topics earlier. Findings of research as reported in Chapter 3, as well as the consensus of many experienced teachers, support this trend. ~~The new emphasis on mathematics has also stimulated educators to determine whether some topics can be efficiently introduced at lower grade levels, since the addition of new topics in the middle and upper grades makes the already overburdened mathematics curriculum of these grades heavier~~. It is therefore recommended that the placement of addition topics as presented below be considered for average pupils.

Grade I:
1. Readiness activities for addition (presented in Chapter 9).
2. Introduction of the key addition facts and of the related facts, with sums not greater than 20.
3. Addition of more than two 1-digit numbers in equation and in column form.
4. Introduction of the ideas of commutation and association.

Grade II:
1. Maintenance and extension of topics introduced in grade I.
2. Mastery of the key addition facts.
3. Addition of a 1- and a 2-digit number.
4. Addition of two 2-digit numbers without regrouping.
5. Addition of two 3-digit numbers without regrouping.
6. Addition of two 2-digit numbers with regrouping.
   *Note:* Cases should be presented both in equation and in column form.

Grade III:
1. Maintenance and extension of topics introduced at lower grade levels.
2. Column addition of 3- and 4-digit numbers with regrouping.

Grades IV and up:
1. Maintenance and extension of topics introduced at lower grade levels.
2. Column addition with multi-digit numbers and with an increasing number of addends.

## The Key Addition Facts

*Note*

The *key addition facts*, also called the *basic* addition facts, comprise all the possible two-term addition facts which can be formed by using the figures 0 through 9. A *fact* includes the sum. If the sum is not given, the addition pair is called a *combination*. There are 100 key addition facts, as presented on page 140.

The length of the readiness program preceding the introduction of the key addition facts depends upon the maturity of the pupil and the number sense he has acquired. As described in the previous chapter, such readiness activities should include matching, counting, grouping, combining, separating, and exercises to acquaint the pupil with the necessary vocabulary and symbols.

There is no agreement concerning the order in which the key facts should be presented, nor is there a definite rule as to whether a key subtraction fact should be presented immediately after the related addition fact has been introduced. In some textbooks the key addition facts and the key subtraction facts are presented simultaneously, whereas in others the presentation of a few addition facts is followed by the introduction of the related subtraction facts. Some authorities advocate the presentation of the so-called "easy" addition facts (those which have a sum of 10 or less) first, and the so-called "hard" facts later. There are other authors[1] who present the facts in stages, according to the assumed degree of difficulty.

The key facts in which zero is added, and which are called the zero facts, are also treated differently. In some books the zero facts are omitted and are taught later as a generalization in situations requiring the addition of 2-digit numbers. In other books the zero facts are introduced together with the other key addition facts. The latter point of view seems to be preferable. Occasionally situations arise in grade I in which zero must be added—for example, when the total number of pupils absent during the morning and afternoon periods of a schoolday has to be determined, if 2 pupils were absent during the morning and none during the afternoon. Moreover, since children are to develop the idea that the operation of subtraction is the inverse of addition, and since there are several situations resulting in a fact such as $4 - 4 = 0$, children should be able to write the sentence: since $4 - 4 = 0$, $0 + 4 = 4$. The zero facts may cause some difficulty for pupils just beginning the study of the key addition facts. It is therefore recommended that the zero facts be introduced only after some of the other facts have been presented.

---

[1] E. H. Taylor and C. N. Mills, *Arithmetic for Teacher-training Classes* (New York: Holt, Rinehart & Winston, Inc., 1955), pp. 41–42.

| | | | | | | | | | |
|---|---|---|---|---|---|---|---|---|---|
| 9 + 0 = 9 | 8 + 0 = 8 | 7 + 0 = 7 | 6 + 0 = 6 | 5 + 0 = 5 | 4 + 0 = 4 | 3 + 0 = 3 | 2 + 0 = 2 | 0 + 1 = 1 | 0 + 0 = 0 |
| 9 + 1 = 10 | 8 + 1 = 9 | 7 + 1 = 8 | 6 + 1 = 7 | 5 + 1 = 6 | 4 + 1 = 5 | 3 + 1 = 4 | 2 + 1 = 3 | 1 + 1 = 2 | 0 + 1 = 1 |
| 9 + 2 = 11 | 8 + 2 = 10 | 7 + 2 = 9 | 6 + 2 = 8 | 5 + 2 = 7 | 4 + 2 = 6 | 3 + 2 = 5 | 2 + 2 = 4 | 2 + 1 = 3 | 0 + 2 = 2 |
| 9 + 3 = 12 | 8 + 3 = 11 | 7 + 3 = 10 | 6 + 3 = 9 | 5 + 3 = 8 | 4 + 3 = 7 | 3 + 3 = 6 | 2 + 3 = 5 | 3 + 1 = 4 | 0 + 3 = 3 |
| 9 + 4 = 13 | 8 + 4 = 12 | 7 + 4 = 11 | 6 + 4 = 10 | 5 + 4 = 9 | 4 + 4 = 8 | 3 + 4 = 7 | 2 + 4 = 6 | 4 + 1 = 5 | 0 + 4 = 4 |
| 9 + 5 = 14 | 8 + 5 = 13 | 7 + 5 = 12 | 6 + 5 = 11 | 5 + 5 = 10 | 4 + 5 = 9 | 3 + 5 = 8 | 2 + 5 = 7 | 5 + 1 = 6 | 0 + 5 = 5 |
| 9 + 6 = 15 | 8 + 6 = 14 | 7 + 6 = 13 | 6 + 6 = 12 | 5 + 6 = 11 | 4 + 6 = 10 | 3 + 6 = 9 | 2 + 6 = 8 | 6 + 1 = 7 | 0 + 6 = 6 |
| 9 + 7 = 16 | 8 + 7 = 15 | 7 + 7 = 14 | 6 + 7 = 13 | 5 + 7 = 12 | 4 + 7 = 11 | 3 + 7 = 10 | 2 + 7 = 9 | 7 + 1 = 8 | 0 + 7 = 7 |
| 9 + 8 = 17 | 8 + 8 = 16 | 7 + 8 = 15 | 6 + 8 = 14 | 5 + 8 = 13 | 4 + 8 = 12 | 3 + 8 = 11 | 2 + 8 = 10 | 8 + 1 = 9 | 0 + 8 = 8 |
| 9 + 9 = 18 | 8 + 9 = 17 | 7 + 9 = 16 | 6 + 9 = 15 | 5 + 9 = 14 | 4 + 9 = 13 | 3 + 9 = 12 | 2 + 9 = 11 | 9 + 1 = 10 | 0 + 9 = 9 |

The following sequence for the study of addition facts is suggested:

1. The facts with sums of 2, 3, 4, and 5 consecutively.

2. The zero facts with a sum of 0, 1, 2, 3, 4, and 5.

3. The facts with sums of 6, 7, 8, 9, and 10 consecutively.

4. A thorough study of the component parts of 10—for example, $4 + \square = 10$, $10 = 7 + \square$. This will prepare the pupils for addition of facts with sums greater than 10 when the second number must be renamed as the sum of two numbers, one being the complement of the first addend. For example,

$$7 + 5 = 7 + (3 + 2)$$
$$= (7 + 3) + 2$$
$$= 10 + 2$$
$$= 12.$$

5. A presentation of related facts such as $10 + 1 = 11$, $10 + 2 = 12$, etc. An understanding of these facts will help the pupils to work exercises such as $7 + 5 = \square$ as illustrated above.

6. The facts with sums of 11, 12, 13, 14, 15, 16, 17, and 18 consecutively.

7. Related facts in which a 1-digit number is added to 11 through 20, the sum being not greater than 20. *Example:* $12 + 6 = 18$.

It is recommended that the key subtraction facts with minuends of 2, 3, 4, and 5 be introduced after the key addition facts with sums of 2, 3, 4, and 5 are understood. The presentation of each key subtraction fact with a minuend greater than 5 should, in like manner, follow the related addition fact. This sequence will enable the children to understand that the operation of subtraction is the inverse of addition, and it will contribute toward understanding of the so-called "number families."

## Introducing the Key Addition Facts

When the pupils have acquired the basic concepts of addition and subtraction and have obtained some skill in finding answers meaningfully to easy basic number questions, the key addition facts are introduced in sequential order. This is often done in "number families." The number family of six, for example, comprises all the addition facts with sums of 6 and all the subtraction facts with minuends of 6. The complete family of six consists of the following facts:

*Note*
*H*

|  |  |
| --- | --- |
| 6 + 0 = 6 | 6 − 0 = 6 |
| 5 + 1 = 6 | 6 − 1 = 5 |
| 4 + 2 = 6 | 6 − 2 = 4 |
| 3 + 3 = 6 | 6 − 3 = 3 |
| 2 + 4 = 6 | 6 − 4 = 2 |
| 1 + 5 = 6 | 6 − 5 = 1 |
| 0 + 6 = 6 | 6 − 6 = 0 |

When a new family is introduced, the pupils should have sufficient opportunity to discover the facts and to form their own generalizations. The teacher assumes an active role in this process by asking proper guide questions and by encouraging the pupils to engage in activities leading to the formation of the desired concepts.

Many activities can be suggested for a meaningful introduction of the facts and "families." The teacher may want to include in the program several of those described below. The selection will depend upon the background and ability of the pupils.

1. Pupils who still need to work with concrete materials are encouraged to manipulate objects such as counters, blocks, and beads on a counting frame. When the family of seven is introduced, the children form as many different groups as possible by using 7 objects. They are led to decide that a group of 7 beads can be separated into a group of 5 beads and one of 2 beads, or into a group of 4 beads and one of 3 beads, etc. The Cuisenaire rods and the Stern blocks are useful for this purpose.

2. The facts are developed by the teacher on the flannel board or on the magnetic board while he leads the class discussion. The group under consideration is separated into component parts, and number questions and number facts are presented. A board illustrating the family of three in addition is depicted below.

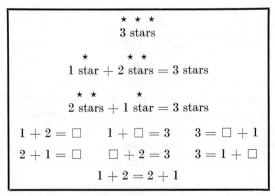

3. Cards with dots, pictures, or stars showing the possible component parts of the group under consideration can be prepared by the teacher or, if time allows, by the children. These cards can be prepared in such a way that the commutative property is suggested:

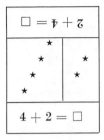

For the family of six there are four cards: (1) for $6 + 0$ and $0 + 6$; (2) for $5 + 1$ and $1 + 5$; (3) for $4 + 2$ and $2 + 4$; and (4) for $3 + 3$.

4. The pupils draw circles on a line representing beads on a rod, and write number sentences which can be derived from such a pattern:

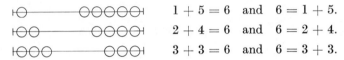

$1 + 5 = 6$ and $6 = 1 + 5.$
$2 + 4 = 6$ and $6 = 2 + 4.$
$3 + 3 = 6$ and $6 = 3 + 3.$

5. The number line is used:

0  1  2  3  4  5  6

$6 = 5 + 1$ and $5 + 1 = 6.$

0  1  2  3  4  5  6

$6 = 4 + 2$ and $4 + 2 = 6.$

The number line is an excellent device to illustrate the commutative property:

0  1  2  3  4  5  6

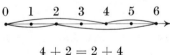

$4 + 2 = 2 + 4$

After some number families have been introduced and the patterns have been properly discussed, the pupils are guided toward the discovery of similarities. The teacher's questions should stimulate the children to form these important generalizations:

1. If 1 is added to a given number, the answer is the next larger number.

2. If zero is added to a number, the answer is the same number.

3. Changing the order of two addends does not change the sum.

*} Note*

Before the addition facts with sums of more than 10 are introduced, the teacher should: (1) ascertain that the pupils can find the different component parts of 10; (2) make sure that the children understand the principle of place value; and (3) introduce the case in which ones are added to 10, as in $10 + 5 = 15$. These skills assist the children when adding, for example, $8 + 7$:

$$8 + 7 = 8 + (2 + 5)$$
$$= (8 + 2) + 5$$
$$= 10 + 5$$
$$= 15.$$

An understanding of the principle of place value is essential for meaningful addition of ones to 10. If this principle is understood, the pupils will be able to complete sentences such as these:

$$12 = 10 + \square$$
$$12 = \square + 2$$
$$10 + 2 = \square$$
$$10 + \square = 12$$
$$\square + 2 = 12$$

Here again the number line is a useful device:

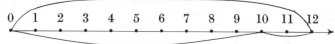

If the pupils can add a 1-digit number to 10, they will not encounter much difficulty later when adding a 1-digit number to a multiple of ten, as in $30 + 5 = 35$.

## Developing and Anchoring Skills

The sequential nature of mathematics requires that skills be developed and anchored after a process has been understood. Therefore, during and after the activities described above, the teacher should continuously strive to improve the pupils' skill in supplying answers to addition questions. The final goal should be that the pupils master the facts to perfection. The presentation of various kinds of exercises and of carefully selected devices will reduce the chance of the children losing interest. Descriptions of several exercises and devices from which a selection can be made are presented below.

1. Exercises presented in the pupil's textbook and workbook and those provided by the teacher, including:

a) Finding a missing addend. *Example:* $3 + \square = 7$. Though this missing addend can be easily found by subtracting the given addend from the sum, the pupils should also find the answer by thinking from 3 to 7.

b) Renaming a number as the sum of two numbers, one of which is given. *Example:* $7 = 4 + \square$.

c) Finding doubles. *Example:* $\square + \square = 4$. The same shape of the frames in this example suggests that the missing addends are identical.

d) Finding several different facts with the same sum. *Example:* $\square + \triangle = 10$. The different shape of the frames suggests that the addends are different.

e) Working exercises which involve the principle of place value. *Example:* For 13 pennies you can buy the same as you can for 1 dime and $\square$ pennies. So $13 = 1$ ten and $\square$ ones, or $13 = 10 + \square$.

f) Finding different names for the number 10.

g) Drawing a picture to fit a given number sentence. *Example:* Draw a picture of a set that shows that $3 + 2 = 5$.

2. Different presentations of number questions. *Examples:*

a)   $10 =$

| 6 | + | $\square$ |
|---|---|---|
| $\square$ | + | 8 |
| 3 | + | $\square$ |
| $\square$ | + | 1 |

b)

| How much? |
|---|
| 6 |
| 4 |
| 3 |
| 1 |

c)

| Just as much: | |
|---|---|
| $4 + 2$ | $3 + \square$ |

d) The total should be 12:

$$\boxed{8 + \square} \qquad \boxed{3 + \square}$$

e)

| | Add 3: |
|---|---|
| 14 | $\square$ |
| 9 | $\square$ |
| 10 | $\square$ |
| 12 | $\square$ |

f) Make it 10 each. The first one has been done.

| 4 | 5 | 7 | 9 | 2 |
|---|---|---|---|---|
| 6 | | | | |

g) Count the number of boxes. Decide how many are shaded. Then write the addition facts. The first one has been done.

$$\boxed{2 + 1 = 3}$$

h) Draw the missing stars and write the numeral:

$$\square + 2 = 5$$

i) Write the answers. The first one has been done.

| | | 6 | 3 | 9 | 10 | 2 | 14 | 11 |
|---|---|---|---|---|---|---|---|---|
| $+\,4$ | 10 | | | | | | | |

3. The reading and writing of addition facts from illustrations on number iines. *Example:*

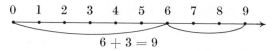

$$6 + 3 = 9$$

4. The preparation of an addition table. The numbers named in the left column are added to those in the top row or vice versa. A few examples have been given.

| + | 0 | 1 | 2 | 3 | 4 | 5 | 6 | 7 | 8 | 9 |
|---|---|---|---|---|---|---|---|---|---|---|
| 0 | | | | | | | | | | |
| 1 | | | | | | | | | | |
| 2 | | | | | | | | | | |
| 3 | | | | 5 | | | | | | |
| 4 | | | | | | | | | | |
| 5 | | | | | | 9 | | | | |
| 6 | | | | | | | | | | |
| 7 | | | | | | | | | | |
| 8 | | | | | | | | | | |
| 9 | | | | | | | | | | |

For addition facts with sums not greater than 10, only a part of the table is needed:

| + | 0 | 1 | 2 | 3 | 4 | 5 | 6 | 7 | 8 | 9 | 10 |
|---|---|---|---|---|---|---|---|---|---|---|----|
| 0 | | | | | | | | | | | |
| 1 | | | | | | | | | | | |
| 2 | | | | | | | | | | | |
| 3 | | | | | | | | | | | |
| 4 | | | | | | | | | | | |
| 5 | | | | | | | | | | | |
| 6 | | | | | | | | | | | |
| 7 | | | | | | | | | | | |
| 8 | | | | | | | | | | | |
| 9 | | | | | | | | | | | |
| 10 | | | | | | | | | | | |

The addition facts can also be presented in similar form, as in the first table, with the addends not arranged in order. The teacher may supply mimeographed or dittoed exercises to pupils who need extra practice.

5. Exercises with flashcards. On one side of an addition flashcard the number question is presented, and on the other side the fact is given so that the pupils can check their answers. In individual use, cards to which incorrect responses are given are put aside for restudy. Since horizontal presentation of mathematical sentences is important, the questions and the facts are presented on the flashcards in horizontal form, as shown in the following example. They are presented vertically on a different set of flashcards, in order to prepare the pupils for column addition.

Front       Back

6. Exercises with the addition wheel. The addition wheel is illustrated below. One of the addends is presented on a rectangular piece of oak tag which is hung in the center on a bolt. This part can be removed and replaced by other pieces showing different numerals. The second addend appears through a window in the front board. Other addends appear in turn when the back board is rotated. This device presents the addition questions in horizontal form.

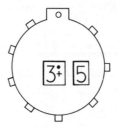

7. Pupils of at least average ability engage in writing sentences such as $6 + 0 = 5 + 1 = 4 + 2$, etc. These pupils are also encouraged to complete number sentences by supplying the symbol $=$, $>$, or $<$ in sentences of the following kind:

$$6 + 0 \bigcirc 4 + 2$$

$$4 + 1 \bigcirc 2 + 2$$

$$4 + 1 \bigcirc 3 + 3$$

8. Writing and memorizing facts.

9. Devising and solving verbal problems to fit given open mathematical sentences.

## Addition of More Than Two 1-digit Numbers

When the key addition facts with sums through 10 have been developed, additions with three and more 1-digit numbers should be introduced. In such additions no combinations are included which have not yet been presented.

*Example:* $4 + 3 + 2 = \square$.

When the pupils find the answer to this number question, they do not see the numeral which represents the sum of 4 and 3. If this results in a difficulty, the teacher encourages the children to work several exercises in two steps, as follows: $4 + 3 = 7$, and $7 + 2 = 9$. The number line can also be used to illustrate the process and to allow the pupils to see the numeral which represents the sum of the first two addends:

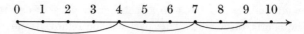

When illustrating $3 + 2 + 1 = 6$ on the flannel board or on the magnetic board, the teacher presents the objects in different groupings and has the children determine the sum. After several exercises have been illustrated, the pupils should discover that a different grouping of the addends does not change the sum (associative property). Then the pupils will do exercises such as:

$$(3 + 2) + 1 = \qquad 3 + (2 + 1) =$$
$$\Box + 1 = \Box \qquad 3 + \quad \Box \quad = \Box$$

and they will finally write:

$$(3 + 2) + 1 = 5 + 1 = 6$$

and 
$$3 + (2 + 1) = 3 + 3 = 6,$$

so 
$$(3 + 2) + 1 = 3 + (2 + 1).$$

The associative property is applied frequently at later stages, when exercises are presented in which pairs of addends total 10 or a multiple of 10.

*Examples:* $3 + 6 + 4 = 3 + (6 + 4) = 3 + 10 = 13.$

$9 + 1 + 7 + 3 = (9 + 1) + (7 + 3) = 10 + 10 = 20.$

After understanding the equation form, the pupils will rapidly acquire skill in adding 1-digit numbers presented in vertical arrangement. These column additions are checked by adding in the direction opposite to the original one. Both the commutative and the associative properties are applied when column addition which was originally added up is checked by adding down:

$$
\begin{array}{r}
4 \\
5 \\
6 \\
\hline
+15 \\
\end{array}
$$

When adding up, the order is: $6 + 5 + 4 = 15.$

When adding down, the order is: $4 + 5 + 6 = 15.$

This can be justified as follows:

$$(6 + 5) + 4 = 4 + (6 + 5) \qquad \text{commutative property}$$
$$= 4 + (5 + 6) \qquad \text{commutative property}$$
$$= (4 + 5) + 6 \qquad \text{associative property}$$

As in horizontal addition of more than two 1-digit numbers, in column addition the case of the "unseen" sum and addend presents itself. In the example shown, the addition of 5 to 4 results in the unseen sum 9, which is an addend in the next addition question $9 + 6 = \Box$. The number 9 is not expressed on paper, so it must be remembered. If the pupil has received proper instruction in horizontal addition of more than two 1-digit numbers and has been encouraged to illustrate the process on the number line, he should not experience much difficulty with simple column additions. If difficulties still arise, the child should be encouraged to work additional exercises in horizontal form, as illustrated above.

Addition exercises with more than two 1-digit numbers include those in which a missing addend must be found.

*Examples:*

$$5 + \square + 2 = 9$$
$$\square + 1 + 1 = 6$$
$$9 = 6 + 1 + \square$$

$$\begin{array}{r} 5 \\ 1 \\ \square \\ + \underline{\phantom{8}} \\ 8 \end{array}$$

At a later stage, additions consisting of more than two 1-digit numbers with sums greater than 10 are introduced. Although the pupils are then supposed to know the key addition facts involved, they continue to work exercises by using the component parts of 10.

*Example:* $4 + 7 = 4 + \square + 1 = \bigcirc + 1 = \triangle.$

## Suggested Sequence for Addition Cases

Theoretically a child can add any two numbers if he has mastered the key facts and knows how to regroup in addition. However, leading the pupil from the stage of the key facts, with a minimum of practice, to the stage in which he adds multi-digit numbers presented in a column would not enable him to develop an understanding of the mathematical processes involved. Instead, the different cases which can be distinguished in addition must be presented in a logical sequence, while previously taught skills are utilized and practised. This will gradually develop a deeper understanding of the processes.

A new case should be presented in equation form, so that the pupil is encouraged to find the answer by mental computation. If the addition question is too difficult to be computed mentally, or if there are too many addends, the numerals can be arranged vertically.

The recommended sequence for the introduction of the addition cases with sums not greater than 100 is as follows:

1. The key addition facts, interrupted by the case in which ones are added to 10, as previously described. Addition of three or more 1-digit numbers is undertaken simultaneously, or after the key facts have been developed.

2. Addition of multiples of ten with sums not greater than 100.

   *Example:* $30 + 20 = \square.$

3. Addition of a multiple of ten and ones.

   *Example:* $40 + 6 = \square.$

4. Higher decade addition not requiring bridging the decade.

   *Example:* 25 + 3 = □.

5. Addition of a 2-digit number to ten or to a multiple of ten.

   *Example:* 20 + 15 = □.

6. Addition of 10 or a multiple of ten to a 2-digit number.

   *Example:* 25 + 10 = □.

7. Addition of a 2-digit number to a 2-digit number without regrouping.

   *Example:* 25 + 12 = □.

8. Higher decade addition requiring bridging the decade.

   *Example:* 25 + 8 = □.

9. Addition of a 2-digit number to a 2-digit number with regrouping.

   *Example:* 25 + 17 = □.

The grade placement of addition cases with sums greater than 100 should also be based upon a logical sequence. Cases which can precede addition of two 2-digit numbers with regrouping are: (1) Addition of multiples of ten with sums greater than 100; (2) Addition of multiples of 100 with sums not greater than 1000; and (3) Addition of a 1-, 2-, or 3-digit number to a 3-digit number without regrouping. Simple exercises with more than two addends are included. Of great importance are the exercises in which a multiple of ten and ones must be added to 100 or to a multiple of 100, as in 200 + 40 + 5 = □.

## Addition of Multiples of Ten

In teaching addition of multiples of ten, previously acquired knowledge and skills are utilized. If, as is recommended, this case immediately follows the addition exercises with sums through 20, the pupils will already have added 10 to 10 by using counters, beads, or the number line. They can count by tens to 100, they are acquainted with the place of the tens on the hundred board, and they should be able to handle the key addition facts. Consequently, the addition of multiples of ten with sums not greater than 100 is a comparatively easy case. Several procedures can be followed in the introduction of this case of addition. The teacher should select the procedures which are most suitable for his pupils.

EXAMPLE:

*Problem:* Dave had 30 baseball cards. He got 20 cards from his friend. How many cards did Dave then have in all?

*Number question:* $30 + 20 = \square$.

*Some possible solutions:*

1. Multiple counting

   $20$ = two tens. Count two tens after 30: 30   40   50.

$$30 + 20 = 50$$

*Note:* When the pupil computes the answer, he works with numbers. Thus, when the equation has been solved, the answer must be interpreted. The interpretation of the answer in the example under consideration is: Dave had 50 cards in all. In many examples in this volume the interpretation of the answer has been left out.

2. Using the tens blocks:

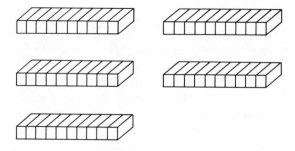

The pupils reason as follows:

$3 + 2 = 5$, and 3 tens $+ 2$ tens $= 5$ tens.

Thus $30 + 20 = 3$ tens $+ 2$ tens $= 5$ tens $= 50$. $30 + 20 = 50$.

~~$3 + 2 = 5$ and $30 + 20 = 50$ are called *related facts*.~~

At a later stage the pupils will learn additional facts which are related to basic facts such as $3 + 2 = 5$:

$$
\begin{aligned}
3 + \phantom{000}2 &= \phantom{000}5 \\
30 + \phantom{00}20 &= \phantom{00}50 \\
300 + \phantom{0}200 &= \phantom{0}500 \\
3000 + 2000 &= 5000
\end{aligned}
$$

etc.

3. Using the hundred board:

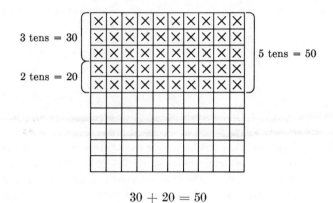

3 tens = 30

2 tens = 20

5 tens = 50

$$30 + 20 = 50$$

4. Using the number line:

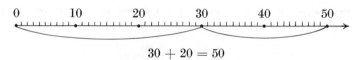

$$30 + 20 = 50$$

Exercises in which three or more multiples of ten are added and those in which a missing addend is found follow the kind presented above.

*Examples:*

$$20 + 20 + 10 = \square$$

$$30 + 10 + \square = 70$$

$$100 = 50 + 20 + \square$$

$$40 + \square = 70$$

$$\square + 20 = 60$$

$$100 = 70 + \square$$

## Addition of a Multiple of Ten and a 1-digit Number

Addition of multiples of ten and 1-digit numbers is performed meaningfully if the principle of place value is understood. Therefore, pertinent exercises must be presented and discussed. These exercises are intended to develop the ability to answer such number questions as $20 + 7 = \square$.

*Examples:*          27 = □ tens and ○ ones

2 tens and 7 ones = 20 + □

2 tens + 7 ones = 20 + 7 = □

27 = 20 + □

27 = □ + 7

20 + 7 = □

~~It is recommended that the number line or the hundred board with movable disks be used by those pupils who need additional help~~.

When a multiple of ten must be added to a 1-digit number, as in 7 + 20, the commutative property can be applied: $7 + 20 = 20 + 7 = 27$. When the pupils have worked several similar exercises, they will not consciously apply the commutative property any more, but will supply the answer automatically.

These exercises are also presented in vertical arrangement. ~~The identity element is then stressed by demonstrating the addition of zero to a number.~~

$$\begin{array}{r} 20 \\ +\ 4 \\ \hline 24 \end{array} \qquad \begin{array}{r} 4 \\ +20 \\ \hline 24 \end{array}$$

## Decade Addition

~~A decade addition combination consists of a 2-digit addend and a 1-digit addend~~. There are two types of these combinations: (1) Those which result in a sum which is in the same decade as the 2-digit addend, *e.g.* 24 + 5; and (2) ~~Those which require bridging the decade, *e.g.* 24 + 9~~. In the second example the 2-digit addend is in the third decade (20–29) and the sum is in the fourth decade (30–39).

Decade addition not involving bridging presents no special difficulty for pupils who have mastered the key addition facts. The teacher should present several related facts such as

$$3 + 2 = 5$$
$$13 + 2 = 15$$
$$23 + 2 = 25$$
$$33 + 2 = 35,$$

and guide the pupils to see that, in all these examples, the key fact $3 + 2 = 5$

is applied. After a sufficient amount of practice, the children should know immediately the answer to such a question when it is presented.

Exercises involving bridging are more difficult and are introduced at a later stage. When finding the answer to a question such as $27 + 8 = \square$, some pupils may think: $7 + 8 = 15$, and $20 + 15 = 35$. A more mature procedure is, first, to add enough to 27 to get 30, and then to add the remainder to 30, as follows:

$$27 + 8 = 27 + (3 + 5)$$
$$= (27 + 3) + 5$$
$$= 30 + 5$$
$$= 35$$

This procedure can be shown on the number line:

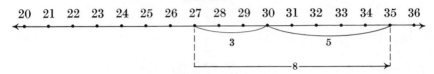

~~This method is especially recommended as a foundation for mental computa-tion.~~ The final goal is for pupils to say the answer almost immediately whenever they look at a question. To reach this goal, most children will have to do a great amount of practice in decade addition, including oral exercises.

## Addition of a 2-digit Number to a Multiple of Ten

EXAMPLE:
*Problem:* Ted had 20 baseball cards. He got 12 more cards. How many cards did Ted then have in all?
*Number question:* $20 + 12 = \square$.
*Suggested solutions:*

1. If the previously discussed cases have been understood, the pupils will be able to solve this number question as follows:

$$12 = 10 + 2. \text{ Thus:}$$
$$20 + 12 = 20 + (10 + 2)$$
$$= (20 + 10) + 2$$
$$= 30 + 2$$
$$= 32$$

These steps can be illustrated on the number line:

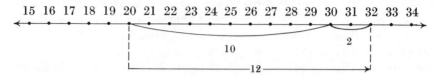

2. The process is illustrated on an abacus, with 9 beads on each rod:

Step 1

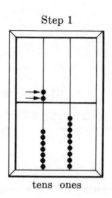

tens  ones

2 tens are shown

1 ten and 2 ones are moved up

Step 2

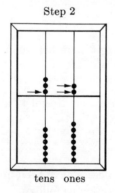

tens   ones

The abacus shows 3 tens and 2 ones, or 32.

3. On the hundred board with movable disks, first two rows of 10 are turned over. Then one row of 10 and 2 ones are turned over and it is decided that a total of 3 rows of 10 and 2 ones have been turned over. 3 tens + 2 ones = 32.

4. Vertical addition should follow the meaningful presentations described above.

## Addition of a Multiple of Ten to a 2-digit Number

EXAMPLE:

*Problem:* Linda had 22 cards. She got 20 more cards. How many cards did Linda then have in all?

*Number question:* $22 + 20 = \square$.

*Suggested solutions:*

1. The answer is found by applying the commutative property:

$$22 + 20 = 20 + 22$$
$$\text{and } 20 + 22 = 20 + (20 + 2)$$
$$= (20 + 20) + 2$$
$$= 40 + 2$$
$$= 42$$

In this solution use is made of a previous case in which a 2-digit number was added to a multiple of 10. The 2-digit number 22 is renamed $20 + 2$. The associative property is applied: first 20 is added to 20, and then 2 is added to 40.

2. Previously learned cases are applied. The pupil is led to reason as follows: Since $20 + 20 = 40$, $22 + 20 = 42$.

3. ~~The addends are written in vertical arrangement, and are expressed in expanded notation~~. Then vertical addition takes place:

$$22 = 2 \text{ tens and } 2 \text{ ones} = 20 + 2$$
$$+\underline{20 = 2 \text{ tens} \qquad\qquad = 20}$$
$$4 \text{ tens and } 2 \text{ ones} = 40 + 2 = 42.$$
$$\text{So: } 22 + 20 = 42.$$

4. The number question is solved by using the ~~standard algorism~~:

$$\begin{array}{r} 22 \\ +20 \\ \hline 42 \end{array}$$

*A pattern of procedure followed in finding the answer to a number question*

## Addition of Two 2-digit Numbers without Regrouping

EXAMPLE:

*Problem:* Joan sold 32 Christmas cards on Monday and 23 on Tuesday. How many cards did Joan sell those two days in all?

*Number question:* $32 + 23 = \square$.

*Suggested solutions:*

1. This case is considered an extension of the case in which a multiple of ten is added to a 2-digit number, as in $32 + 20$. The extension is that 3 ones are added to the obtained sum. Twenty-three is renamed as follows: $23 = 20 + 3$. Then 20 is added to 32 and 3 is added to that sum:

$$32 + 23 = 32 + (20 + 3)$$
$$= (32 + 20) + 3$$
$$= 52 + 3$$
$$= 55$$

The process should be illustrated on the number line.

2. The tens and ones are isolated and then added: $32 + 23 = (30 + 20) + (2 + 3) = 50 + 5 = 55$. The mathematical justification for this procedure is presented later in this chapter.

3. The answer to the number question is found by using the abacus. First, 3 tens and 2 ones are isolated. Then 2 tens and 3 ones are moved up. Finally the total is determined.

4. The answer is found by vertical addition. This presentation should follow the equation form. The pupils will then be able to perform the operation meaningfully as follows:

$$\begin{array}{ll} \quad 32 & \text{or:} \quad 32 \\ +\underline{\quad 23} & \quad\;\; +\underline{\quad 23} \\ \quad 50\;(30 + 20 = 50) & \quad\quad 5\;(2 + 3 = 5) \\ +\underline{\quad\; 5}\;(2 + 3 = 5) & \quad +\underline{\;\; 50}\;(30 + 20 = 50) \\ \quad 55 & \quad\quad 55 \end{array}$$

When this process is understood, the teacher suggests to write the final answer immediately, without first writing the sum of the tens and the sum of the ones separately:

$$\begin{array}{r} 32 \\ 23 \\ +\underline{\phantom{0}} \\ 55 \end{array}$$

## Addition of Two 2-digit Numbers with Regrouping

EXAMPLE:

*Problem:* Ray had 28 postcards from foreign countries. During his vacation he collected 23 more cards. How many cards did Ray then have in all?

*Number question:* $28 + 23 = \Box$.
*Suggested solutions:*

1. The process involved in this addition is a combination of two cases previously learned: (1) Addition of a multiple of ten to a 2-digit number, and (2) Addition of a 1-digit number to a 2-digit number involving bridging. Therefore, when solving the number question, 23 is renamed as follows: $23 = 20 + 3$. First, 20 is added to 28, then 3 is added to the obtained sum:

$$28 + 23 = 28 + (20 + 3)$$
$$= (28 + 20) + 3$$
$$= 48 + 3$$
$$= 51$$

The following sequence of exercises is recommended for leading the pupils to this method of solution:

$$18 + 10 = \Box, \quad \text{and } 28 + 7 = \Box, \quad \text{so } 18 + 17 = \Box.$$

2. The tens and the ones in each of the two addends are isolated and added separately:

$$28 + 23 = (20 + 20) + (8 + 3) = 40 + 11 = 51.$$

3. The process is illustrated on the abacus:

Step 1

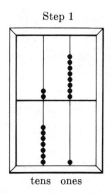

tens   ones

2 tens and 8 ones are isolated

$23 = 20 + 3$, or 2 tens and 3 ones
First, 3 ones are added.
8 ones + 3 ones = 11 ones, or 1 ten, 1 one.
Thus 1 ones bead is isolated and 1 ten is moved up on the tens rod.

Step 2

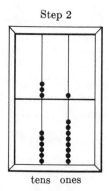

tens   ones

The abacus now shows 3 tens and 1 one, or 31.
20 must be added
Thus 2 tens are moved up

Step 3

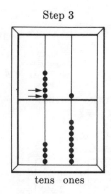

tens  ones

The abacus shows 5 tens and one 1, or 51.

4. The process is made meaningful by creating a money situation and illustrating it with dimes and pennies on the magnetic board, or with toy money on the flannel board.

5. After the process of adding 28 and 23 has been developed meaningfully as described above, the addends are presented in vertical arrangement.
*Step 1:* 28 and 23 are written in expanded notation and the addition is performed:

$$28 = 20 + 8$$
$$23 = 20 + 3$$
$$+\overline{\phantom{xx}40 + 11 = 51}$$

*Step 2:* The pupils determine that in

$$\begin{array}{r} 28 \\ +\underline{23}, \end{array} \quad 3 + 8 = 11,$$

which equals 1 ten and 1 one. They write down the
1 one and "remember" the 1 ten, which is then
added to the total of the tens column. In the
beginning stages, the pupils are allowed to write
the 1 (for 1 ten) above the digits which stand for
the tens, as shown at the right.

$$\begin{array}{r} 1 \\ 28 \\ +\underline{23} \\ 51 \end{array}$$

Addition of multi-digit numbers and columns with several addends
should not be started before the pupils understand the process of regrouping
clearly. Much practice is necessary before the children can perform column
additions with several addends accurately.

## Addition Involving Negative Integers

Occasionally the elementary-school child meets situations which involve
negative numbers—for example, in weather reports. Such situations should
be utilized when the number line is extended to include negative integers.

Addition exercises in which the first addend has a negative and the
second addend a positive value need not be difficult for pupils of average
ability. Exercises in which the second addend has a negative value, thus
resulting in an answer which is less than the first addend, may prove to be
quite difficult for many children. The teacher may want to introduce this
case to rapid learners.

It is recommended that the thermometer be used in initial exercises and
that, later on, simple problems be worked with the help of the horizontal
number line.

### Properties and terms

The properties which apply to the addition of whole numbers hold for the
addition of integers. The integers also have the property of the additive
inverse which is presented below.

If a number line extends both left and right, the points on the line to the
right of zero—which is called the origin—represent by convention *positive
numbers* and their names are preceded by a *positive sign*, whereas the points
on the line to the left of zero represent *negative numbers* and their names are

*Note*

preceded by a *negative sign.* Such numbers are called *directed* or *signed numbers.* ~~With the exception of zero, an integer is either positive or negative.~~ Mathematicians have agreed that a numeral which does not have a positive or negative sign is considered to represent a positive number.

The marks on the number line shown below represent integers. The set of all integers is tabulated as follows:

$$\{\cdots, \,^-3, \,^-2, \,^-1, \, 0, \,^+1, \,^+2, \,^+3, \cdots\}.$$

The symbol $^+1$ is read "positive one," the symbol $^-2$ "negative 2," etc. Since the number line extends in opposite directions from zero, each integer except zero has an opposite or an additive inverse. That is, to each positive or negative integer there corresponds a second integer such that the sum of these two integers is zero. For example: the *additive inverse* of $^+1$ is $^-1$, since $^+1 + \,^-1 = 0$; the *opposite* of $^-5$ is $^+5$, since $^-5 + \,^+5 = 0$, etc.

$$^-5 \quad ^-4 \quad ^-3 \quad ^-2 \quad ^-1 \quad 0 \quad ^+1 \quad ^+2 \quad ^+3 \quad ^+4 \quad ^+5$$

Examples of addition exercises in which the second addend is a negative integer are presented below.

EXAMPLE 1:
*Number question:* $5 + \,^-2 = \square.$
*Solution 1:*

$$^-6 \quad ^-5 \quad ^-4 \quad ^-3 \quad ^-2 \quad ^-1 \quad 0 \quad ^+1 \quad ^+2 \quad ^+3 \quad ^+4 \quad ^+5 \quad ^+6$$

sum

a) Draw an arrow from 0 to $^+5$ (we draw the arrows above or below the number line). This line segment represents the first addend.
b) Draw an arrow from $^+5$ to the point 2 units to the left. This line segment represents the second addend. The sum of 5 and $^-2$ is 3.

$$5 + \,^-2 = 3$$

*Solution 2:*

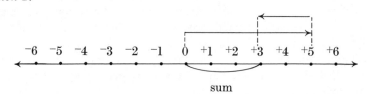

Since $5 = 3 + 2$, $5 + \,^-2 = (3 + 2) + \,^-2$     renaming ✔

$\qquad\qquad\qquad\quad = 3 + (2 + \,^-2)$     associative property ✔

$\qquad\qquad\qquad\quad = 3 + 0$     additive inverse property ✔

$\qquad\qquad\qquad\quad = 3$     identity element for addition ✔

Note #

EXAMPLE 2:
*Number question:* $4 + {}^-6 = \square$.
*Solution:*

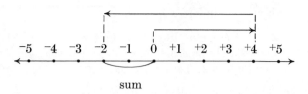

sum

a) Draw an arrow from 0 to $^+4$. This line segment represents the first addend.
b) Draw an arrow from $^+4$ to the point 6 units to the left. This line segment represents the second addend. The sum of 4 and $^-6$ equals $^-2$.

$$4 + {}^-6 = {}^-2$$

EXAMPLE 3:
*Number question:* ${}^-4 + {}^-2 = \square$.
*Solution:*

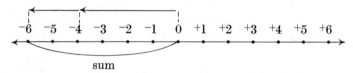

sum

a) Draw an arrow from 0 to $^-4$. This line segment represents the first addend.
b) Draw an arrow from $^-4$ to the point 2 units to the left. This line segment represents the second addend. The sum of $^-4$ and $^-2$ is $^-6$.

$$^-4 + {}^-2 = {}^-6$$

## Miscellaneous Practice Exercises

The pupils' textbook and the accompanying workbook usually provide a sufficient amount of exercises in vertical addition. In many cases the teacher will have to provide extra practice in horizontal addition and oral addition, and sometimes in vertical addition. He may also have to supply enrichment exercises in addition for the rapid learners. Several books with enrichment exercises are available. The following exercises for oral and written work may also be considered for grade levels to be determined by the teacher, according to the mathematical maturity of the pupils.

1. Counting by multiples.

*Examples:* Counting by 11's, 12's, 13's, etc.

2. Adding numbers according to a specified pattern.

*Example:* 1— 2— 4— 7—, etc. In this example each successive addend is 1 more than the immediately preceding one. (The difference between 2 and 1 is 1; between 4 and 2 it is 2; between 7 and 4 it is 3; etc.)

3. Adding mentally numbers called out by the teacher.

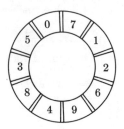

4. Adding in a ring. The teacher writes in a ring on the chalkboard several numerals. The pupils have to add the numbers expressed by the numerals he points to. An example of such a ring is shown above. An exercise might be: 5 + 2 + 1 + 3 + 7 + 5, etc.

5. Adding numbers expressed in columns, as illustrated below.

*Example:*

$$
\begin{array}{r}
45 \\
36 \\
27 \\
+\ \underline{48} \\
\end{array}
$$

$$48 + 27 = 48 + (20 + 7) = (48 + 20) + 7$$
$$= 68 + 7 = 75$$
$$75 + 36 = 75 + (30 + 6) = (75 + 30) + 6$$
$$= 105 + 6 = 111$$
$$111 + 45 = 111 + (40 + 5) = (111 + 40) + 5$$
$$= 151 + 5 = 156$$

6. Adding the numbers named in a magic square.

*Example:* In the magic square shown below, the sum of the numbers named in each row, column, and longest diagonal equals 12:

| 1 | 6 | 5 |
|---|---|---|
| 8 | 4 | 0 |
| 3 | 2 | 7 |

$$1 + 6 + 5 = 12, \quad 1 + 8 + 3 = 12, \quad 1 + 4 + 7 = 12, \text{ etc.}$$

The pupils should construct other magic squares. This can be done by adding an equal amount to the number represented in each box or by multiplying them by the same number:

| 3 | 8 | 7 |
|---|---|---|
| 10 | 6 | 2 |
| 5 | 4 | 9 |

The numbers named in the original square have been increased by 2.

$$3 + 8 + 7 = 18, \qquad 7 + 2 + 9 = 18, \qquad 7 + 6 + 5 = 18, \text{ etc.}$$

| 10 | 60 | 50 |
|----|----|----|
| 80 | 40 | 0 |
| 30 | 20 | 70 |

The numbers named in the original square have been multiplied by 10.

$$10 + 80 + 30 = 120, \qquad 30 + 20 + 70 = 120, \text{ etc.}$$

7. Adding in rows and columns. The teacher expresses in the boxes any numbers he selects. Then the pupils add the rows and the columns. Practice is provided in both horizontal and vertical addition. The grand total expressed in the bottom box at the right must be the total for both the sums of the columns and the sums of the rows.

*Example:*

| 25 | 16 | 9 | 14 | |
|----|----|----|----|---|
| 30 | 21 | 13 | 8 | |
| 16 | 9 | 5 | 10 | |
| | | | | |

8. Adding a given set of numbers—for example, the odd numbers from 5 through 25, or the even numbers from 10 through 40.

9. Adding dollars and cents, both by mental and written computation.

## Mathematical Justification of a Selected Procedure

When working an exercise such as $32 + 24$, the pupil may decide to add first the tens, and then the ones, and find the total of these sums. In this simple procedure several properties are applied. Young children should not be required to show all the steps and state all those properties. They simply work the exercise as follows:

$$32 + 24 = (30 + 20) + (2 + 4) = 50 + 6 = 56.$$

Pupils who are mathematically more mature can understand the mathematical justification of the procedure as presented below.

$$
\begin{aligned}
32 + 24 &= (30 + 2) + (20 + 4) &\quad \text{renaming}\\
&= [(30 + 2) + 20] + 4 &\quad \text{associative property}\\
&= [30 + (2 + 20)] + 4 &\quad \text{associative property}\\
&= [30 + (20 + 2)] + 4 &\quad \text{commutative property}\\
&= [(30 + 20) + 2] + 4 &\quad \text{associative property}\\
&= (30 + 20) + (2 + 4) &\quad \text{associative property}\\
&= 50 + 6 &\quad \text{addition}\\
&= 56 &\quad \text{addition}
\end{aligned}
$$

## Checking the Sum

Several methods are available to test the accuracy of the sum of an addition. The procedures used should be simple enough for the children to understand. Some ways of checking addition are presented below.

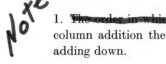

1. ~~The order in which the addends were originally added is reversed~~. If in column addition the sum was found by adding up, the check is made by adding down.

EXAMPLE:

*Addition:*

$$
\begin{array}{r}
6\\
7\\
5\\
9\\
+\ \underline{\phantom{0}}\\
27
\end{array}
$$

When adding up, the order is: $9 + 5 + 7 + 6$.
When adding down, the order is: $6 + 7 + 5 + 9$.
Though different combinations are encountered, the result must be the same.

2. ~~The rule of compensation is used.~~

EXAMPLE:
*Addition:* $25 + 19 = 44$. *Check:* $(25 - 1) + (19 + 1) = 24 + 20 = 44$.

3. Another method of adding is used.

EXAMPLE:
*Addition:* $27 + 24 = 27 + (20 + 4) = (27 + 20) + 4 = 47 + 4 = 51$.
*Check:* $27 + 24 = (20 + 20) + (7 + 4) = 40 + 11 = 51$.

4. One of the two addends is subtracted from the sum and it is determined whether the difference equals the other addend. This check can be made only when there are just two addends.

EXAMPLES:
a) *Addition:* $25 + 12 = 37$.     *Check:* $37 - 12 = 25$, or:
$$37 - 25 = 12.$$

b) *Addition:*
$$\begin{array}{r} 579 \\ 386 \\ +\overline{\phantom{0}965} \end{array}$$
*Check:*
$$\begin{array}{r} 965 \\ 579 \\ -\overline{\phantom{0}386} \end{array}$$
or:
$$\begin{array}{r} 965 \\ 386 \\ -\overline{\phantom{0}579} \end{array}$$

5. Columns consisting of several addends are sometimes divided into smaller groups of addends. Then each group is added and the total of the sums of the groups is determined. This total must equal the original sum.

EXAMPLE:
*Addition:*
$$\begin{array}{r} 14 \\ 25 \\ 19 \\ 36 \\ 28 \\ 30 \\ 18 \\ 45 \\ +\overline{\phantom{0}215} \end{array}$$
*Check:*
$$\begin{array}{r} 14 \\ 25 \\ 19 \\ 36 \\ +\overline{\phantom{0}94} \end{array} + \begin{array}{r} 28 \\ 30 \\ 18 \\ 45 \\ \overline{121} \end{array} + \begin{array}{r} 94 \\ 121 \\ \overline{215} \end{array}$$

6. The Check of Nines. ~~When a whole number has been divided by 9, the remainder is 0, 1, 2, 3, 4, 5, 6, 7, or 8. This remainder is called the excess of nines in that number.~~ In our decimal system, the excess of nines in a given number equals the excess of nines in the sum of the digits.

*Example:* If 763 is divided by 9, the remainder is 7. The sum of the digits of 763 is $7 + 6 + 3 = 16$. If 16 is divided by 9, the remainder is also 7. The equality of the remainders of 763 and of the sum of the digits 7, 6, and 3 can be demonstrated as follows:

$$763 = (7 \times 100) + (6 \times 10) + 3$$
$$= 7 \times (99 + 1) + 6 \times (9 + 1) + 3$$
$$= (7 \times 99) + 7 + (6 \times 9) + 6 + 3$$
$$= (7 \times 99) + (6 \times 9) + 7 + 6 + 3$$

Since both $7 \times 99$ and $6 \times 9$ are multiples of 9, the remainders of 763 and of the sum of 7, 6, and 3 must be equal.

When the accuracy of an addition is tested by using the check of nines, the sum of the digits of each addend is determined. If the sum of the digits is more than 8, the excess of nines is found. The total of the excesses of nines in the addends must equal the excess of nines in the sum of the addition. In the example below, this procedure has been followed.

| Addition: | Sum of the digits: | Excess of nines: |
|---|---|---|
| 4567 | 22 | 4 |
| 1234 | 10 | 1 |
| + 1002 | 3 | + 3 |
| 6803 | 17 | 8 |

Since the excesses of nines in the addends total 8 and the excess of nines in 6803 is also 8, it can be stated that the answer is probably correct. Errors which will not be detected by the check of nines are: (1) An error of 9 or a multiple of 9; (2) A faulty insertion of a zero; (3) An error in the order of the digits.

7. Checking the answer by estimation. The reasonableness of the sum in $149 + 22 = 171$ or in

$$\begin{array}{r} 149 \\ + 22 \\ \hline 171 \end{array}$$

can be determined quickly by adding mentally 150 and 20. In order to develop the ability to approximate answers, the teacher should ask the pupil repeatedly to decide whether an answer makes sense, and should assist him in finding proper techniques of rounding numbers and estimating answers.

## Mental Computation

The approaches described in the previous presentations suggest a meaningful program in addition in which mental computation is emphasized. An examination of these recommended procedures will reveal the following characteristics: (1) New cases in addition are introduced in horizontal form; (2) The structure of the number system is emphasized; (3) Skill is developed in renaming numbers as the sums of their component parts which are more convenient to add than the original numbers; (4) Intelligent estimation to test the reasonableness of an answer is encouraged; and (5) An understanding of number properties and number relationships is developed.

*Note M.C.*

Exercises in mental addition with sums greater than 100 can be patterned after cases previously presented. To assist the teacher in this task, several examples are presented below.

1. $70 + 70 = \square$.

*Think:* How much do I add to 70 to get 100? The answer is 30. Since $70 = 30 + 40$, first add 30 to 70 and then 40 to the obtained sum:

$$70 + 70 = 70 + (30 + 40)$$
$$= (70 + 30) + 40$$
$$= 100 + 40$$
$$= 140$$

2. $75 + 77 = \square$.

a) *Think:* $77 = 70 + 7$. First add 70 to 75 and then 7 to the obtained sum:

$$75 + 77 = 75 + (70 + 7)$$
$$= (75 + 70) + 7$$
$$= 145 + 7$$
$$= 152$$

b) Rename 75 as $70 + 5$ and 77 as $70 + 7$. Add the tens and add the ones, and then find the total of these sums:

$$75 + 77 = (70 + 70) + (5 + 7)$$
$$= 140 + 12$$
$$= 152$$

3. $420 + 170 = \square$.

a) *Think:* $170 = 100 + 70$. First add 100 to 420 and then 70 to the sum:

$$420 + 170 = 420 + (100 + 70)$$
$$= (420 + 100) + 70$$
$$= 520 + 70$$
$$= 590$$

b) Rename 420 as $400 + 20$ and 170 as $100 + 70$. Add the hundreds and add the tens, and then find the total of these sums:

$$420 + 170 = (400 + 100) + (20 + 70)$$
$$= 500 + 90$$
$$= 590$$

4. $97 + 8 = \square$.

*Think:* How much do I add to 97 to get 100? The answer is 3. Since $8 = 3 + 5$, first add 3 to 97 and then 5 to the sum:

$$97 + 8 = 97 + (3 + 5)$$
$$= (97 + 3) + 5$$
$$= 100 + 5$$
$$= 105$$

5. $65 + 98 = \square$.

*Think:* 98 is 2 less than 100. Since $65 + 100 = 165$, $65 + 98 = 163$.

6. $243 + 104 = \square$.

*Think:* $104 = 100 + 4$. First add 100 to 243 and then 4 to the sum:

$$243 + 104 = 243 + (100 + 4)$$
$$= (243 + 100) + 4$$
$$= 343 + 4$$
$$= 347$$

7. $125 + 49 = \square$.

*Think:* 49 is 1 less than 50. Since $125 + 50 = 175$, $125 + 49 = 174$.

8. $2400 + 900 = \square$.

a) $24 + 9 = 33$, so $2400 + 900 = 3300$.

b) *Think:* How much do I add to 2400 to get 3000? The answer is 600. Since $900 = 600 + 300$, first add 600 to 2400 and then 300 to the sum:

$$2400 + 900 = 2400 + (600 + 300)$$
$$= (2400 + 600) + 300$$
$$= 3000 + 300$$
$$= 3300$$

c) *Think:* 900 is 100 less than 1000. Since $2400 + 1000 = 3400$, $2400 + 900 = 3300$.

9. $25 + 13 + 6 + 27 + 35 + 4 = \square$.

In this exercise pairs of addends can be selected which total a multiple of ten:

$$25 + 13 + 6 + 27 + 35 + 4 = (25 + 35) + (13 + 27) + (6 + 4)$$
$$= 60 + 40 + 10$$
$$= 110$$

## SELECTED RESEARCH

Brownell, W. A., *The Development of Children's Number Ideas in the Primary Grades*. Supplementary Educational Monographs, No. 35. Chicago: University of Chicago Press, 1928.

One of the phases of this investigation dealt with the mental processes of pupils as they make the transition from (what is called) concrete number to number as an expression of relations devoid of pronounced sensory elements. The subjects were drawn from second-grade classes which had received instruction in all the simple additive combinations up to $9 + 9$, and from third- and fourth-grade classes which had received instruction in adding three 1-digit numbers in a column. Group tests were administered to measure accuracy and speed separately. Within a week of the group test, the pupils had to work selected examples orally and were questioned regarding methods of calculation used.

Some of Brownell's conclusions follow.

1. Those pupils who revealed a thorough understanding of concrete number made the transition to abstract number and the additive combinations without an undue amount of difficulty.

2. The pupils who had difficulty in making the transition and in learning the addition combinations were those who could not demonstrate thorough understanding of concrete number.

3. Pupils who had difficulty with the addition combinations belonged to one or the other of two types: (a) Pupils who carry over to abstract numbers the immature methods which they use with concrete numbers; and (b) Pupils who see little relation between their previous experience with concrete numbers and their new work with abstract numbers.

4. The problem of teaching addition of three 1-digit numbers rests on the problem of teaching the additive combinations in such a way that the children know them and understand them. The problem of teaching the additive combinations so that they are intelligible to children rests on the problem of developing adequate concepts of number.

# SKILLS TEST

1. Add and check the answer by adding in the reverse direction:

| 22 | 90 | 56 | 83 | 59 |
|----|----|----|----|----|
| 72 | 7  | 26 | 1  | 38 |
| 35 | 40 | 62 | 88 | 5  |
| 70 | 94 | 37 | 17 | 134|

2. Add and check by using the rule of compensation:

   $43 + 29 =$      $73 + 18 =$      $57 + 39 =$      $66 + 19 =$

3. Add and check by subtracting one of the addends from the sum:

| 438 | 850 | 294 | 772 | 481 |
|-----|-----|-----|-----|-----|
| 89  | 333 | 98  | 293 | 185 |

4. Add and check by using the check of nines:

| 8424 | 2749 | 5003 | 6644 | 1243 |
|------|------|------|------|------|
| 1516 | 2994 | 4870 | 2895 | 1111 |
| 3005 | 411  | 2210 | 6739 | 5812 |
| 452  | 7014 | 3563 | 4414 | 3033 |

5. Add and check by using the check of nines:

| $1421.55 | $9112.03 | $145.90 | $1671.75 | $20.57 |
|----------|----------|---------|----------|--------|
| 210.11   | 2510.46  | 138.41  | 1213.15  | 19.19  |
| 12.94    | 2864.11  | 41.00   | 3729.88  | 25.25  |

6. Add by mental computation:

   $25 + 18 =$      $37 + 17 =$      $64 + 28 =$      $55 + 26 =$

   $50 + 34 =$      $48 + 40 =$      $47 + 47 =$      $68 + 24 =$

   $27 + 39 =$      $76 + 16 =$      $35 + 35 =$      $66 + 25 =$

7. Find the answers:

   $5 + {}^-2 =$      $4 + {}^-4 =$      $3 + {}^-6 =$      ${}^-2 + {}^-1 =$

   $8 + {}^-3 =$      $6 + {}^-1 =$      $2 + {}^-9 =$      ${}^-5 + {}^-6 =$

   $6 + {}^-2 =$      $7 + {}^-3 =$      $1 + {}^-8 =$      ${}^-4 + {}^-7 =$

8. Add by mental computation:

   $1.67 + $.25 =$          $2.85 + $1.35 =$          $7.70 + $2.30 =$

   $4.96 + $.07 =$          $9.60 + $1.53 =$          $5.56 + $5.22 =$

   $3.33 + $.78 =$          $7.25 + $3.30 =$          $4.02 + $7.99 =$

# EXERCISES

1. Describe and illustrate how a process in addition, to be selected by you, should be taught.

2. Explain and illustrate three properties of addition.

3. Write all the facts belonging to the "family of seven."

4. Write five mathematical sentences, each expressing an inequality.

5. Enumerate some techniques which should serve to anchor skill in the key addition facts.

6. Prepare an addition table for facts with sums not greater than 6.

7. Give the mathematical justification of the following sentence: $25 + 31 = (20 + 30) + (5 + 1) = 50 + 6 = 56$.

8. A column addition is often added up and checked by adding down. Justify this.

9. Explain the check of nines.

10. Discuss the importance of mental computation in addition.

## For advanced students

11. Criticize the typical placement of addition topics.

12. Write an illustrative lesson on the addition of two 2-digit numbers with regrouping.

13. Report on a piece of research pertaining to addition of whole numbers.

14. As assigned by the instructor of the course, report on one or more of the following articles:

    a) Clendenon, E., "Efficiency in Teaching Basic Facts." *The Arithmetic Teacher*, April, 1959, pp. 144–47.
    b) Flournoy, F., "The Controversy Regarding the Teaching of Higher-Decade Addition." *The Arithmetic Teacher*, October, 1956, pp. 170–73.
    c) Fulkerson, E., "Adding by Tens." *The Arithmetic Teacher*, March, 1963, pp. 139–40.
    d) Oesterle, R. A., "What about Those 'Zero Facts'?" *The Arithmetic Teacher*, March, 1959, pp. 109–11.
    e) Risden, G., "Structuring the Basic Facts." *Education*, January, 1959, pp. 276–79.

## SELECTED REFERENCES

Banks, J. H., *Learning and Teaching Arithmetic*, 2nd Ed. Boston: Allyn and Bacon, Inc., 1964, Chs. IV and V.

Bell, C., C. D. Hammond, and R. B. Herrera, *Fundamentals of Arithmetic for Teachers*. New York: John Wiley & Sons, Inc., 1962, Ch. III.

Buckingham, B. R., *Elementary Arithmetic: Its Meaning and Practice*. Boston: Ginn and Company, 1953, Chs. IV and V.

Dutton, W. H. and L. J. Adams, *Arithmetic for Teachers*. Englewood Cliffs, N.J.: Prentice-Hall, Inc., 1961, Ch. II.

Grossnickle, F. E. and L. J. Brueckner, *Discovering Meanings in Elementary School Mathematics*. New York: Holt, Rinehart & Winston, Inc., 1963, Chs. VI and VII.

Hickerson, J. A., *Guiding Children's Arithmetic Experiences*. Englewood Cliffs, N.J.: Prentice-Hall, Inc., 1952, Ch. VI.

Hollister, G. E. and A. G. Gunderson, *Teaching Arithmetic in Grades I and II*. Boston: D. C. Heath & Company, 1954, Ch. XII.

Howard, C. F. and E. Dumas, *Basic Procedures in Teaching Arithmetic*. Boston: D. C. Heath & Company, 1963, Chs. IV and VII.

Larsen, H. D. and H. G. Ludlow, *Arithmetic for Colleges*. New York: The Macmillan Co., 1963, Ch. III.

Marks, J. L., C. R. Purdy, and L. B. Kinney, *Teaching Arithmetic for Understanding*. New York: McGraw-Hill, Inc., 1958, Ch. VI.

Mueller, F. J., *Arithmetic, Its Structure and Concepts*, 2nd Ed. Englewood Cliffs, N.J.: Prentice-Hall, Inc., 1964, Units VI and VII.

National Council of Teachers of Mathematics, *Topics in Mathematics*. Washington, D.C.: the Council, 1964, Bklt. 2.

Potter, F. F., *The Teaching of Arithmetic*. New York: Philosophical Library, Inc., 1961, Ch. II.

School Mathematics Study Group, *Studies in Mathematics, Vol. IX: A Brief Course in Mathematics for Elementary School Teachers*. Stanford: Leland Stanford Junior University, 1963, Chs. V and VII.

Spitzer, H. F., *The Teaching of Arithmetic*. Boston: Houghton Mifflin Company, 1961, Ch. III.

Swain, R. L., *Understanding Arithmetic*. New York: Holt, Rinehart & Winston, Inc., 1960, Chs. III and IV.

Swenson, E. J., *Teaching Arithmetic to Children*. New York: The Macmillan Co., 1964, Chs. V and VI.

Thorpe, C. B., *Teaching Elementary Arithmetic*. New York: Harper & Row, Publishers, 1962, Ch. XI.

# 11

# SUBTRACTION

DURING THE EARLY ~~stages of mathematics the pupils should already~~ ~~discover that addition and subtraction are inverse operatio~~ns. This is best achieved when these operations are presented concurrently.

In this volume addition and subtraction are considered in separate chapters for purposes of organization. The present chapter is mainly concerned with the teaching of the subtraction of whole numbers and deals in a few paragraphs with subtraction involving negative integers.

## Meaning and Terms

~~Subtraction "undoes" what addition "does" and is called the inverse operation~~ ~~of additi~~on. For example, in $4 + 3 = 7$, 3 has been added to 4 to get 7, whereas in $7 - 3 = 4$, 3 has been subtracted from 7 to get again the original number 4. Thus:

$$4 + 3 = 7,$$

$$\text{and } (4 + 3) - 3 = 4.$$

~~Subtraction can be defined as the operation by which the missing addend~~ ~~is found if the other addend and the sum are kno~~wn. When finding the answer to $5 - 3 = \square$ the question can be asked: What number do I add to 3 to get 5? The given sum ~~(5) is called the~~ *minuend*, the given addend ~~(3) the~~ *subtrahend*, and the ~~missing addend the~~ *difference* or *remainder*. In general, it can be stated that if $a$, $b$, and $c$ represent whole numbers such that $a + b = c$, then $a = c - b$ and $b = c - a$. ~~Subtraction is a binary operation because~~ ~~it is performed on two numbers at a tim~~e.

175

Subtraction can also be thought of in terms of sets and subsets, as is illustrated in the following situations:

a) From set $A$ (containing 5 members) subset $B$ (containing 2 members) is removed, and the number of members in the remainder set $C$ must be determined.

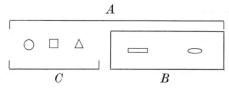

Since $n(A) = 5$ and $n(B) = 2$, $n(C) = 5 - 2 = 3$.

b) Consider set $A$ containing 5 members, and set $B$ containing 3 members. It must be determined how much larger the number of members in $A$ is than in $B$. Thus set $C$—disjoint from $B$—must be found such that the union of $B$ and $C$ can be placed in one-to-one correspondence with $A$. It appears that $C$ must contain 2 members. Thus $n(C) = 2$ and $5 = 3 + 2$, or $5 - 3 = 2$.

## Properties

✔The commutative property does not apply to subtraction of whole numbers.

*Example:* $3 - 2 \neq 2 - 3$.

✔ The associative property does not apply to subtraction of whole numbers.

*Example:* $(8 - 5) - 2 \neq 8 - (5 - 2)$.

✔ The set of whole numbers is not closed with respect to subtraction.

*Example:* In $3 - 5 = \square$, the difference is not a whole number.

Some rules which are used in subtraction, and of which the pupils should acquire functional knowledge, are:

1. The difference between two numbers can be found by renaming both the minuend and the subtrahend as the sum of two numbers, subtracting each part of the subtrahend from a part of the minuend, and adding the obtained differences.

*Example:* $45 - 21 = (40 + 5) - (20 + 1) = (40 - 20) + (5 - 1)$

$$= 20 + 4 = 24.$$

2. The difference between the minuend and the subtrahend remains unchanged if both the minuend and the subtrahend are increased or decreased by the same number. This rule is called the *rule of compensation*, and is applied in the equal-additions method in subtraction and sometimes in mental computation.

*Examples:* $46 - 19 = (46 + 1) - (19 + 1) = 47 - 20 = 27$

$41 - 12 = (41 - 1) - (12 - 1) = 40 - 11 = 29$

3. A number is decreased by the sum of two numbers if that number is decreased first by one of the addends and the obtained difference is decreased by the other addend.

*Example:* $48 - (10 + 9) = (48 - 10) - 9 = 38 - 9 = 29$

4. A number is decreased by the difference between two numbers if the number is increased by the subtrahend and the obtained sum is decreased by the minuend.

*Example:* $56 - (25 - 9) = (56 + 9) - 25 = 65 - 25 = 40$

## Grade Placement of Subtraction Topics

Suggestions for the grade placement and the order of presentation of the key addition and subtraction facts were offered in the preceding chapter. The grade placement of the remaining subtraction topics should follow the same pattern as that which was suggested for the corresponding addition topics.

## The Key Subtraction Facts

In the preceding chapter the 100 key addition facts were presented. Since the operation of subtraction is the inverse of addition, there are 100 key subtraction facts (also called basic subtraction facts). The key addition facts comprise all the possible two-term addition facts which can be formed by using the figures 0 through 9. Thus the key subtraction facts are those obtained when the numbers 0 through 9 are subtracted from 0 through 18, provided that the difference is less than 10. A subtraction fact includes the difference. The key subtraction facts are presented on the following page.

9 + 0 = 9
9 + 1 = 10
9 + 2 = 11
9 + 3 = 12
9 + 4 = 13
9 + 5 = 14
9 + 6 = 15
9 + 7 = 16
9 + 8 = 17
9 + 9 = 18

8 + 0 = 8
8 + 1 = 9
8 + 2 = 10
8 + 3 = 11
8 + 4 = 12
8 + 5 = 13
8 + 6 = 14
8 + 7 = 15
8 + 8 = 16
8 + 9 = 17

7 + 0 = 7
7 + 1 = 8
7 + 2 = 9
7 + 3 = 10
7 + 4 = 11
7 + 5 = 12
7 + 6 = 13
7 + 7 = 14
7 + 8 = 15
7 + 9 = 16

6 + 0 = 6
6 + 1 = 7
6 + 2 = 8
6 + 3 = 9
6 + 4 = 10
6 + 5 = 11
6 + 6 = 12
6 + 7 = 13
6 + 8 = 14
6 + 9 = 15

5 + 0 = 5
5 + 1 = 6
5 + 2 = 7
5 + 3 = 8
5 + 4 = 9
5 + 5 = 10
5 + 6 = 11
5 + 7 = 12
5 + 8 = 13
5 + 9 = 14

4 + 0 = 4
4 + 1 = 5
4 + 2 = 6
4 + 3 = 7
4 + 4 = 8
4 + 5 = 9
4 + 6 = 10
4 + 7 = 11
4 + 8 = 12
4 + 9 = 13

3 + 0 = 3
3 + 1 = 4
3 + 2 = 5
3 + 3 = 6
3 + 4 = 7
3 + 5 = 8
3 + 6 = 9
3 + 7 = 10
3 + 8 = 11
3 + 9 = 12

2 + 0 = 2
2 + 1 = 3
2 + 2 = 4
2 + 3 = 5
2 + 4 = 6
2 + 5 = 7
2 + 6 = 8
2 + 7 = 9
2 + 8 = 10
2 + 9 = 11

1 + 0 = 1
1 + 1 = 2
1 + 2 = 3
1 + 3 = 4
1 + 4 = 5
1 + 5 = 6
1 + 6 = 7
1 + 7 = 8
1 + 8 = 9
1 + 9 = 10

0 + 0 = 0
0 + 1 = 1
0 + 2 = 2
0 + 3 = 3
0 + 4 = 4
0 + 5 = 5
0 + 6 = 6
0 + 7 = 7
0 + 8 = 8
0 + 9 = 9

178

Usually the key subtraction facts are arbitrarily divided into two groups: (1) ~~the so-called "easy" facts, with minuends of 10 or less, and~~ (2) ~~the "hard" facts, the minuends of which are greater than 10.~~

## Reading a Subtraction Fact

A subtraction fact may be read in different ways. For example, $9 - 4 = 5$ can be read as "nine minus four equals five," and "four from nine is five." It is advisable that the pupils in the primary grades become well acquainted with the particular phrase they will use when they advance in mathematics: "nine minus four equals five." It is the teacher's responsibility to attempt to prevent mere verbalism, by ascertaining that the pupils understand the meaning of all phrases and words used.

## Methods of Subtraction

Two methods can be used in finding the answer to a subtraction question—for example, when the difference must be found between 15 and 4:

1. ~~The additive method~~. In determining the answer by the additive method, the question "how much do I add to 4 to get 15?" is asked. This question can be translated into the mathematical sentence $4 + \square = 15$. Thus the missing addend is found.

2. ~~The subtractive method~~. In finding the answer by the subtractive method, the question "how much is 15 minus 4?" is asked. The number sentence is expressed as $15 - 4 = \square$.

Whereas several decades ago the additive method was popular in this country, at present the subtractive method is generally used as the initial method of subtraction. ~~The additive approach has the advantage that its terminology is closely related to that of addition. The subtractive method, however, seems to be easier for elementary-school pupils to understand~~. Therefore it is recommended that, in initial teaching of subtraction, the subtractive method be used, and that the additive method be presented at higher grade levels as a reintroduction of subtraction and as an enrichment activity.

$$\frac{\begin{array}{r} 42 \\ 17 \end{array}}{}$$

In the subtraction question shown above, the digit 7 represents a larger number than the corresponding digit in the minuend. Since there is no whole number that satisfies the equation $2 - 7 = \square$, a technique must be used so that 7 can be subtracted. For the solution of this problem there are various methods available:

1. *The decomposition[1] method*. In this method, 1 ten is regrouped into 10 ones—this process is often incorrectly called "borrowing," the 10 ones are added to the 2 ones, and the difference between the ones and between the tens is determined by one of the two previously described methods:

$$\frac{\begin{array}{r} 3\ 12 \\ \not{4}\ \not{2} \\ 1\ 7 \end{array}}{}$$

a) *The subtractive method*, by which 7 ones are subtracted from 12 ones, and 1 ten from 3 tens;
b) *The additive method*, by which it is determined what number must be added to 7 to get 12 and how many tens must be added to 1 ten to get 3 tens.

2. *The equal-additions method*. In this method, the reasoning is as follows: Since 7 cannot be subtracted from 2, add 10 ones to the 2 ones in the minuend. In order to keep the difference between the minuend and the subtrahend equal, add 1 ten to the 1 ten in the subtrahend. The answer can again be determined by one of the two described methods: (a) the subtractive method, and (b) the additive method.

Of the different methods of subtraction which were presented, the sub-tractive-decomposition method seems to be the most promising. As was stated above, the subtractive approach appears to be easier to understand than the additive method, if it is introduced in concrete situations. Brownell and Moser[2] found that the decomposition method was more successful than the equal-additions method, when taught meaningfully.

---

[1] The verb "decompose" means to separate a substance into its elements.
[2] A resumé of this study is presented at the end of this chapter.

## Types of Subtraction Situations

Three types of subtraction situations can be identified:

1. The "how many left" or "remainder" type.

EXAMPLE:
*Problem:* Bill had 5 marbles. He gave 2 marbles to his friend. How many marbles did Bill have left?
*Number question:* $5 - 2 = \square$.
*Interpretation:* In this subtraction situation it must be determined how many marbles are left after the operation has taken place, and thus the cardinal number of the remainder set must be found. The situation can be easily represented on paper:

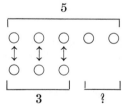

2. The "how many more" or "difference" type.

EXAMPLE:
*Problem:* Tom has 5 marbles and Ray has 3 marbles. How many more marbles does Tom have than Ray?
*Number question:* $5 - 3 = \square$ or $5 = 3 + \square$.
*Interpretation:* It must be determined how many more marbles there are in Tom's set than in Ray's:

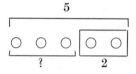

3. The "how many (much) more needed" type.

EXAMPLE:
*Problem:* Ed has 3 marbles. He needs 5 marbles to play a game. How many more marbles does Ed need?
*Number question:* $3 + \square = 5$.
*Interpretation:* One addend and the sum are known and the missing addend must be found. The situation can be represented on paper by drawing 5

marbles, identifying 3 of them, and determining how many are needed to get 5. This is in reality an addition situation.

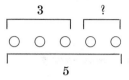

## Introducing the Key Subtraction Facts

Subtraction is the inverse operation of addition, and some of the techniques suggested in Chapter 10 for the teaching of the key addition facts can be adapted and used when the key subtraction facts are introduced. The relation between addition and subtraction can be illustrated when given key subtraction facts are presented together with or shortly after the corresponding key addition facts.

Activities for a meaningful introduction of the key subtraction facts are suggested below. The teacher's selection of techniques should depend upon the background and ability ot the pupils.

1. Concrete materials such as objects, disks, counters, beads, Cuisenaire rods, and Stern blocks are manipulated. Of the group of objects under consideration, a predetermined number of objects is removed and the appropriate number sentence is stated and written.

2. The subtraction fact to be studied is represented on the flannel board or the magnetic board. The corresponding number sentences are presented under the illustration.

3. Cards with pictures, dots, or stars illustrating the number fact are used. The number fact is printed at the bottom of the card. If this sentence is covered, the child, after constructing the fact from the illustration, can check his answer.

4. The pupils draw circles on a line to represent beads on a rod and illustrate a fact in this way. Then the corresponding number sentences are written:

     $5 = 3 + 2$   and   $5 - 2 = 3$

5. Facts are illustrated on the number line:

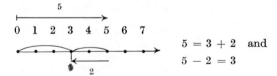

~~By pursuing several such activities and working a great many exercises, the pupils should discover patterns and form generalizations such as the generalization for subtracting 1 from a given number~~.

Before the "hard" subtraction facts are introduced, the teacher should: (1) ascertain that the pupils can find the different component parts of 10; (2) review the principle of place value; and (3) introduce the case in which ones are subtracted from 11 through 19 to get a difference of 10, as in $13 - 3 = 10$. Such skills will assist the pupils when working, for example, the exercise $13 - 7 = \square$ in parts, as follows:

$$13 - 7 = 13 - (3 + 4)$$
$$= (13 - 3) - 4$$
$$= 10 - 4$$
$$= 6$$

## Developing and Anchoring Skills

Gradually the pupils should become so well acquainted with the basic subtraction facts that they readily know the answer to a question when it is presented. In the study for mastery, the facts should be used meaningfully in exercises of various kinds, so that the pupils will see a need for memorizing them. Proper devices should be used for the purpose of developing and anchoring the facts. Because of the great importance of these skills in computation, the final aim should be complete mastery.

Many of the techniques described in Chapter 10 for anchoring the key addition facts can be modified to fit subtraction. Some of these modified techniques, and additional ones, are presented below.

1. Exercises presented in the textbook and workbook and those provided by the teacher, including the following:

a) Finding the relationship between addition and subtraction: Since $3 + 2 = 5, 5 - 2 = \square$.

b) Finding the minuend or the subtrahend:

$$\square - 3 = 6; \qquad 8 - \square = 5.$$

c) Subtracting in parts:

$$16 - 9 = 16 - 6 - \square = \bigcirc.$$

d) Deciding which operation has been performed by supplying the symbol $+$ or $-$:

$$10 \ \square \ 4 = 6; \qquad 7 \ \square \ 2 = 9.$$

e) Subtracting two or more 1-digit numbers.

*Example:* $10 - 3 - 2 = \square$.

When the children find the answer to this number question, they do not see the numeral which names the difference between 10 and 3. If this results in a difficulty, the teacher should encourage the pupils to work several exercises in two steps, as follows: $10 - 3 = 7$, and $7 - 2 = 5$. The number line can also be used to illustrate the process and to allow the pupils to see the numeral which names the difference between the minuend and the first subtrahend:

2. Different presentations of number questions:

a)

| 10 = | | |
|------|---|---|
| 15 | — | $\square$ |
| $\square$ | — | 3 |
| 17 | — | $\square$ |
| $\square$ | — | 7 |

b)

| 16 in all: | |
|---|---|
| $\square$ | 7 |
| $\square$ | 3 |
| $\square$ | 9 |
| $\square$ | 12 |

c)

| Subtract 5: | |
|---|---|
| 16 | $\square$ |
| 9 | $\square$ |
| 12 | $\square$ |
| 7 | $\square$ |

d)

| Just as much: | |
|---|---|
| $11 - 4$ | $9 - \square$ |
| $15 - 7$ | $10 - \square$ |
| $18 - 9$ | $14 - \square$ |
| $11 - 5$ | $9 - \square$ |

e)

| Write the answers. The first one has been done. | | | | | | | |
|---|---|---|---|---|---|---|---|
| | 16 | 8 | 14 | 7 | 15 | 9 | 10 |
| $-7$ | 9 | | | | | | |

3. The construction of a table of the following kind:

| 0 | 1 | 2 | 3 | 4 | 5 | 6 | 7 | 8 | 9 |
|---|---|---|---|---|---|---|---|---|---|
| 9 — 9 | 10 — 9 | 11 — 9 | 12 — 9 | 13 — 9 | 14 — 9 | 15 — 9 | 16 — 9 | 17 — 9 | 18 — 9 |
| 8 — 8 | 9 — 8 | 10 — 8 | 11 — 8 | 12 — 8 etc. | 13 — 8 | 14 — 8 | 15 — 8 | 16 — 8 | 17 — 8 |

4. The use of flashcards in class by small groups of pupils and by individual children. Different sets of flashcards should be used: one set on which the questions and facts are presented horizontally, and another set on which they are presented vertically.

5. Exercises with the subtraction wheel. The addition wheel described in Chapter 10 can be modified for use with the subtraction questions.

6. The completion of number sentences by supplying the symbol $=$, $>$, or $<$ by pupils of at least average ability.

*Example:* $15 - 7 \ \square \ 12 - 5$.

7. Writing and memorizing facts.

## Suggested Sequence for Subtraction Cases

The recommended sequence for the presentation of the cases with minuends not greater than 100 is as follows:

1. The key subtraction facts, interrupted by exercises such as $13 - 3 = \square$, in which ones are subtracted from 11 through 19 to get a difference of 10. Subtraction of two or more 1-digit numbers is undertaken simultaneously and continued after the key facts have been developed.

2. Subtraction of multiples of ten.

   *Example:* $60 - 20 = \square$.

3. Subtraction of a 1-digit number from a 2-digit number resulting in a multiple of ten.

   *Example:* $45 - 5 = \square$.

4. Subtraction of a 1-digit number from a 2-digit number without regrouping.

   *Example:* $28 - 3 = \square$.

5. Subtraction of 10 or a multiple of ten from a 2-digit number.

   *Example:* $45 - 10 = \square$.

6. Subtraction of a 2-digit number from a 2-digit number without regrouping.

   *Example:* 45 − 12 = □.

7. Subtraction of a 1-digit number from a multiple of ten.

   *Example:* 30 − 5 = □.

8. Subtraction of a 1-digit number from a 2-digit number with regrouping.

   *Example:* 35 − 7 = □.

9. Subtraction of a 2-digit number from a 2-digit number with regrouping.

   *Example:* 53 − 16 = □.

The grade placement of subtraction cases with minuends greater than 100 should be based upon a logical sequence. Before the introduction of the case in which a 2-digit number is subtracted from a 2-digit number with regrouping, easy cases with minuends greater than 100 can be presented, as was suggested for the corresponding cases of addition.

*Examples:* 180 − 60 = □; 500 − 300 = □.

In the sections below, suggestions for the teaching of subtraction cases with minuends not greater than 100 are presented. Since subtraction is the inverse operation of addition, the student is also referred to corresponding cases of addition in Chapter 10. Many of the procedures described there can be modified and used for subtraction. For this reason, some of the presentations below have been condensed.

## Subtraction of Multiples of Ten

EXAMPLE:
*Problem:* Dan gave 20 of his 40 baseball cards to his friend. How many cards did Dan have left?
*Number question:* 40 − 20 = □.
*Suggested solutions:*
1. Multiple counting. 20 = 2 tens. Count two tens backward:

$$40 \quad 30 \quad 20.$$

2. Using the tens blocks. The pupil reasons as follows:

$$40 = 4 \text{ tens, and } 20 = 2 \text{ tens.}$$
$$\text{Since } 4 − 2 = 2, 4 \text{ tens} − 2 \text{ tens} = 2 \text{ tens} = 20.$$

3. Using illustrations such as the one shown below.

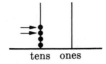

4. Using the hundred board.

5. Using the number line.
   This case is followed by exercises of the following kind:

$$100 - 20 = \square.$$
$$100 - \square = 60.$$
$$\square - 30 = 50.$$

## Subtraction of a 1-digit Number from a 2-digit Number Resulting in a Multiple of Ten

This case is best introduced by reviewing the principle of place value:

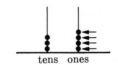

$$34 = \square \text{ tens and } \bigcirc \text{ ones.}$$
$$3 \text{ tens and } 4 \text{ ones} - 4 \text{ ones} = \square \text{ tens.}$$
$$34 - 4 = \square.$$

## Subtraction of a 1-digit Number from a 2-digit Number without Regrouping

EXAMPLE:
*Number question:* $35 - 2 = \square.$
*Solution: Think:* Since $5 - 2 = 3$, $35 - 2 = 33$.

## Subtraction of Ten or a Multiple of Ten from a 2-digit Number

EXAMPLE:
*Number question:* 43 − 10 = □.

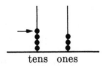

tens  ones

*Solution:* 43 − 10 = 4 tens and 3 ones − 1 ten = 3 tens and 3 ones = **33**.
Or: Since 40 − 10 = 30, 43 − 10 = 33.

## Subtraction of a 2-digit Number from a 2-digit Number without Regrouping

EXAMPLE:
*Number question:* 45 − 12 = □.
*Possible solutions:*
1. Since 12 = 10 + 2, first subtract 10 from 45, and then subtract 2 from the obtained difference:

$$45 - 12 = 45 - (10 + 2)$$
$$= (45 - 10) - 2$$
$$= 35 - 2$$
$$= 33$$

This process can be illustrated on the number line:

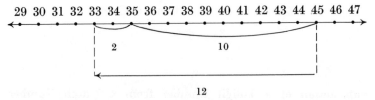

2. The number question is solved by using illustrations or devices such as the counting frame, the hundred board, and the abacus.

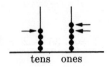

tens  ones

**3.** The answer is found by using the algorism in common use:

$$
\begin{array}{r}
45 \\
-\ 12 \\
\hline
33
\end{array}
$$

## Subtraction of a 1-digit Number from a Multiple of Ten

EXAMPLE:
*Number question:* $30 - 5 = \square$.
*Possible solutions:*
1. The process is illustrated on an abacus:

Step 1

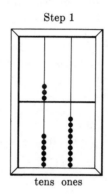

tens  ones

3 tens are isolated.

5 ones must be subtracted.
1 ten is moved down.  Since we have to subtract only 5 ones (and not 1 ten), 5 ones are moved up.

Step 2

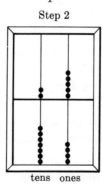

tens   ones

The top part of the abacus now shows 2 tens and 5 ones, or 25.

2. The process can be expressed as follows:
3 tens — 5 ones = 2 tens and 10 ones — 5 ones = 2 tens and 5 ones = 25;
or vertically:

$$30 = 20 + 10$$
$$-\quad 5 = \qquad 5$$
$$\overline{\quad 20 + 5 = 25}$$

3. After the process of regrouping has been clearly
illustrated, the algorism in common use is presented,
as shown at the right. Initially, the pupils are often
allowed to use "crutches."

$$\begin{array}{r} 2\ 10 \\ \cancel{3}\ \cancel{0} \\ -\quad 5 \\ \hline 2\ 5 \end{array}$$

## Subtraction of a 1-digit Number from a 2-digit Number with Regrouping

EXAMPLE:

*Problem:* Ted gave 7 of his 35 foreign postage stamps to his brother. How many stamps did Ted have left?

*Number question:* $35 - 7 = \square$.

*Possible solutions:*

1. First enough is subtracted from 35 to get 30: $35 - 5 = 30$. Since $7 = 5 + 2$, 2 is subtracted from 30: $30 - 2 = 28$. Thus:

$$35 - 7 = 35 - (5 + 2)$$
$$= (35 - 5) - 2$$
$$= 30 - 2$$
$$= 28$$

This process can be illustrated on the number line:

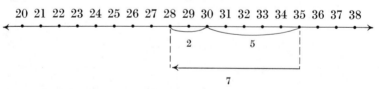

2. The answer is found by using devices such as the abacus, the counting frame, and the hundred board.

3. The teacher creates a situation which is expressed by the sentence $35\cancel{c} - 7\cancel{c} = \square$. Toy money is used and a dime is exchanged for 10 pennies.

4. After the process of regrouping has been illustrated by the use of a device, the number question
is written in vertical arrangement, as shown at the
right, and solved with the help of crutches.

$$\begin{array}{r} 2\ 15 \\ \cancel{3}\ \cancel{5} \\ -\quad 7 \\ \hline 2\ 8 \end{array}$$

## Subtraction of a 2-digit Number from a 2-digit Number with Regrouping

EXAMPLE:

*Problem:* Dick had 42 birthday cards which he wanted to sell. He sold 18 of them. How many cards did Dick have left?

*Number question:* $42 - 18 = \square$.

*Possible solutions:*

1. Since $18 = 10 + 8$, first 10 is subtracted from 42, and then 8 is subtracted from the obtained difference:

$$42 - 18 = 42 - (10 + 8)$$
$$= (42 - 10) - 8$$
$$= 32 - 8$$
$$= 24$$

This process can be illustrated on the number line:

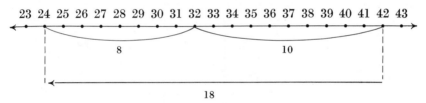

2. The process is illustrated on an abacus:

Step 1

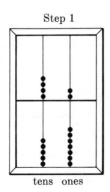

tens  ones

4 tens and 2 ones are isolated.

$18 = 10 + 8$, or 1 ten and 8 ones.

First 8 ones are subtracted.

There are only 2 beads on the top part of the ones rod, thus 1 ten is moved down. Since only 8 ones must be subtracted, 2 ones beads are moved up.

Step 2

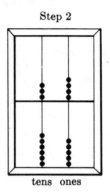

tens   ones

The top part of the abacus shows 3 tens and 4 ones, or 34.

Step 3

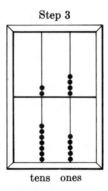

tens   ones

Finally 1 ten must be subtracted (18 = 10 + 8). Thus 1 ten is moved down. The top part of the abacus now shows 2 tens and 4 ones, or 24.

3. Toy money is used. A situation is created in which 1 dime and 8 pennies must be taken away from 4 dimes and 2 pennies. Since this is impossible, 1 dime is exchanged for 10 pennies.

4. The numerals are written in vertical form in expanded notation and renamed as shown before the subtraction is performed:

$$
\begin{array}{r}
42 = 40 + 2 = 30 + 12 \\
- \quad 18 = 10 + 8 = 10 + \phantom{0}8 \\
\hline
20 + \phantom{0}4 = 24
\end{array}
$$

5. The common algorism is presented, as shown at
the right.  Since 8 cannot be subtracted from 2, 42
is renamed 3 tens and 12 ones.  12 ones — 8 ones =
4 ones, and 3 tens — 1 ten = 2 tens.

$$\begin{array}{r} 3\ 12 \\ \not{4}\ \not{2} \\ 1\ 8 \\ \hline - \quad 2\ 4 \end{array}$$

~~Before this method is introduced, the pupils should understand the process of regrouping as described above.~~e.

The student should carefully study the presented sequence of the cases in subtraction.  In each case, either a new step is introduced or two cases which were previously considered separately are combined.  For example, in 45 — 10 = □, one new step is presented; in 45 — 12 □ =, two previously introduced cases are combined:  45 — 10 = □  and  35 — 2 = □.  The author considers this sequence and also the initial presentations of the subtraction questions in horizontal form important for a meaningful development of the subtraction concepts and for a proper development of ability in mental computation.

## Zeros in the Minuend

The presence of a zero in the minuend, as in 407 — 178, may cause difficulty for some pupils.  It is recommended that the "40" in 407 be thought of as 40 tens.  One ten is then exchanged for 10 ones, resulting in 39 tens and 17 ones.  Before this process is suggested, the pupil should be thoroughly acquainted with the process of using a ten to obtain more ones and of using a hundred to obtain more tens.

$$\begin{array}{r} 3\ 9\ 17 \\ \not{4}\ \not{0}\ \not{7} \\ 1\ 7\ 8 \\ \hline - \end{array}$$

*Note*

## Use of the Crutch in Subtraction

In the example shown below, a crutch is used to help the child understand the process of regrouping.  The introduction of this crutch should be preceded by meaningful presentations of the regrouping process.

$$\begin{array}{r} 7\ 11 \\ \not{8}\ \not{1} \\ 1\ 6 \\ \hline - \end{array}$$

Some teachers are hesitant to introduce such a crutch, for fear that the pupil may never abandon the device.  Yet there is some evidence that the dangers of teaching the crutch in subtraction have been greatly overrated. Brownell, Moser, and others[3] found that it facilitated learning in the initial stages. They reported that children abandoned the crutch when a shorter form of solution was taught. Other children had to be encouraged by the teacher to discontinue its use.

~~It is recommended that the teacher introduce the crutch in subtraction, since it helps the pupil move from subtraction without regrouping to subtraction with regrouping. Its use should be discouraged as soon as the pupil is ready for a more mature process.~~

*Note it* ↯

## Subtraction Involving Negative Integers

~~The set of whole numbers is not closed with respect to subtraction.~~ For example, in the set of whole numbers there is no member that satisfies the equation $2 - 3 = \square$. To solve such problems we need the set of integers, which is expressed as $\{\cdots, ^-3, ^-2, ^-1, 0, ^+1, ^+2, ^+3, \cdots\}$. The set of integers is closed with respect to subtraction. This means that for any integers $a$ and $b$ there is an integer $c$ such that $a - b = c$.

Simple cases in subtraction involving negative integers do not seem to be too difficult for the child of average ability. More difficult cases should probably be presented as enrichment exercises.

EXAMPLE 1:
*Number question:* $5 - {^-3} = \square$.
*Solution:* When working the exercise $8 - 5 = \square$, the number must be found which, if added to 5, gives 8 as sum. $8 - 5 = 3$, since $5 + 3 = 8$. Similarly, when determining the answer to $5 - {^-3}$, the number must be found which, if added to $^-3$, gives 5 as sum. The answer can be determined by using the number line.
*Think:* What number do I add to $^-3$ to get 5? First go from $^-3$ to 0, and then from 0 to 5:

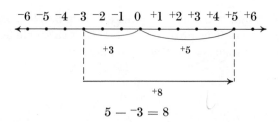

$$5 - {^-3} = 8$$

---

EXAMPLE 2:

*Number question:* $^-7 - ^-3 = \square$.

*Solution:* What number do I add to $^-3$ to get $^-7$? Go from $^-3$ to $^-7$.

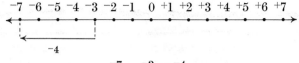

$$^-7 - ^-3 = ^-4$$

EXAMPLE 3:

*Number question:* $5 - ^+7 = \square$.

*Solution:* What number do I add to 7 to get 5? Go from 7 to 5.

$$5 - ^+7 = ^-2$$

EXAMPLE 4:

*Number question:* $^-3 - ^-5 = \square$.

*Solution:* What number do I add to $^-5$ to get $^-3$? Go from $^-5$ to $^-3$.

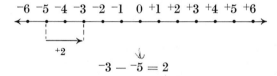

$$^-3 - ^-5 = 2$$

## Miscellaneous Practice Exercises

Teachers who need to supply additional practice exercises in subtraction may find some useful suggestions in the following list:

1. Subtracting mentally numbers called out by the teacher, starting with a given number.

2. Counting backward by equal groups, starting with a given number.

3. Performing various exercises in subtraction by mental computation.

4. Subtracting dollars and cents, both by written and mental computation.

5. Practising the making of change in money situations.

6. Using a different method of subtraction—for example, the equal-additions method.

7. Finding the complement of a number.

## Checking Subtraction

One of the objectives in mathematics instruction is the development of the pupils' skill in checking the correctness of obtained computational results. Thus the teacher should introduce methods of checking subtraction which fit the ability level of the pupils. Some ways of checking subtraction are presented below.

1. The most frequently used check for subtraction is based upon the fact that the operation of subtraction is the inverse of addition. Since the difference plus the subtrahend equals the minuend, it can be determined whether a sentence such as $51 - 13 = 38$ is true or false by adding the difference and the subtrahend: $38 + 13 = 51$. In vertical subtraction the procedure shown below can be followed, so that the numeral which expresses the difference need not be rewritten.

$$-\frac{\begin{array}{r} 547 \\ 159 \end{array}}{388}$$

$$+\frac{\begin{array}{r} 159 \end{array}}{547}$$

A variation of this method is based upon the fact that the minuend minus the difference equals the subtrahend. Thus $51 - 13 = 38$ can be checked by subtracting 38 from 51, which must yield 13 as result.

2. The check of nines in subtraction is based upon the same principles as is the check of nines in addition, and the limitations of the two checks are also the same.

EXAMPLE:

| Subtraction: | Sum of the digits: | Excess of nines: |
|---|---|---|
| 4578 | 24 | 6 |
| − 1784 | 20 | − 2 |
| 2794 | 22 | 4 |

Since the difference between the excesses of nines in the minuend and the subtrahend is equal to the excess of nines in the difference, it may be concluded that the answer is probably correct.

It may happen that the excess of nines in the minuend is smaller than that in the subtrahend. In that case the excess of nines in the minuend is increased by 9.

3. The pupils should become skillful in checking an answer to a subtraction by approximation. The reasonableness of the obtained difference in the example below can be determined quickly by subtracting 300 from 500 by mental computation.

$$
\begin{array}{r}
503 \\
-\ 298 \\
\hline
205
\end{array}
$$

## Mental Computation

In this chapter several mental-computation exercises involving subtraction were presented. To assist the teacher further in the teaching of this important phase, some additional examples follow.

1. $150 - 80 = \square$.
*Think:* How much do I subtract from 150 to get 100? The answer is 50. Since $80 = 50 + 30$, first subtract 50 from 150, and then subtract 30 from the obtained difference:

$$
\begin{aligned}
150 - 80 &= 150 - (50 + 30) \\
&= (150 - 50) - 30 \\
&= 100 - 30 \\
&= 70
\end{aligned}
$$

2. $120 - 73 = \square$.
*Think:* $73 = 70 + 3$. First subtract 70 from 120, and then subtract 3 from the obtained difference:

$$
\begin{aligned}
120 - 73 &= 120 - (70 + 3) \\
&= (120 - 70) - 3 \\
&= 50 - 3 \\
&= 47
\end{aligned}
$$

3. $125 - 60 = \square$.
*Think:* Since $120 - 60 = 60$, $125 - 60 = 65$.

4. $125 - 61 = \square$.
*Think:* $61 = 60 + 1$. First subtract 60 from 125, and then subtract 1 from the obtained difference:

$$
\begin{aligned}
125 - 61 &= 125 - (60 + 1) \\
&= (125 - 60) - 1 \\
&= 65 - 1 \\
&= 64
\end{aligned}
$$

5. $133 - 48 = \square$.

*Think:* $48 = 40 + 8$. First subtract 40 from 133, and then subtract 8 from the obtained difference:

$$133 - 48 = 133 - (40 + 8)$$
$$= (133 - 40) - 8$$
$$= 93 - 8$$
$$= 85$$

6. $1000 - 345 = \square$.

*Think:* $345 = 300 + 40 + 5$. Subtract these numbers consecutively:

$$1000 - 345 = [(1000 - 300) - 40] - 5$$
$$= (700 - 40) - 5$$
$$= 660 - 5$$
$$= 655$$

7. $510 - 130 = \square$.

*Think:* $130 = 100 + 30$. First subtract 100 from 510, and then subtract 30 from the obtained difference:

$$510 - 130 = 510 - (100 + 30)$$
$$= (510 - 100) - 30$$
$$= 410 - 30$$
$$= 380$$

8. $105 - 8 = \square$.

*Think:* First subtract enough from 105 to get 100: $105 - 5 = 100$. Since $8 = 5 + 3$, subtract 3 more: $100 - 3 = 97$.

$$105 - 8 = 105 - (5 + 3)$$
$$= (105 - 5) - 3$$
$$= 100 - 3$$
$$= 97$$

9. $337 - 103 = \square$.

*Think:* $103 = 100 + 3$. First subtract 100 from 337, and then subtract 3 from the obtained difference:

$$337 - 103 = 337 - (100 + 3)$$
$$= (337 - 100) - 3$$
$$= 237 - 3$$
$$= 234$$

10. $425 - 97 = \square$.

*Think:* $97 = 100 - 3$. First subtract 100 from 425, and then add 3 to the obtained difference:

$$425 - 97 = 425 - (100 - 3)$$
$$= (425 - 100) + 3$$
$$= 325 + 3$$
$$= 328$$

11. $177 - 49 = \square$.

*Think:* $49 = 50 - 1$. First subtract 50 from 177, and then add 1 to the obtained difference:

$$177 - 49 = 177 - (50 - 1)$$
$$= (177 - 50) + 1$$
$$= 127 + 1$$
$$= 128$$

12. $3400 - 1600 = \square$.

*Think:* $34 - 16 = 18$, so $3400 - 1600 = 1800$.

## SELECTED RESEARCH

Brownell, W. A., H. E. Moser, and others, *Meaningful versus Mechanical Learning: A Study in Grade III Subtraction.* Duke University Research Studies in Education, No. 8. Durham, N.C.: Duke University Press, 1949.

In this study the results of teaching several methods of subtraction were compared. Approximately 1400 third-graders from 41 classrooms in four school systems were equated in four experimental groups. Half the classes were taught to borrow—regroup—by the decomposition method, and half by the equal-additions method. Each of these two groups was divided again; one part was taught the process meaningfully (rationally), and one mechanically. This resulted in four groups: decomposition—mechanically; decomposition—rationally; equal additions—mechanically, and equal additions—rationally. The study was carried on for a period of 15 school days.

Of the reported results, the following are presented:

1. The meaningfully taught sections were quite consistently superior in performance to the mechanically taught sections.

2. The section to which the decomposition method was taught rationally produced better results than the section to which the equal-additions method was taught rationally.

3. The claim that the extra time needed for meaningful instruction, as compared to mechanical learning, is not lost was substantiated in this study. The record of the section to which the decomposition method was taught rationally shows that the acquired understanding facilitated later learning.

4. The crutch which was used as a device in the teaching of the regrouping process in subtraction facilitated learning.

## SKILLS TEST

*Note*

1. Subtract and check by adding the difference and the subtrahend:

| 456 | 258 | 4045 | 3404 | 25,001 |
|-----|-----|------|------|--------|
| 389 | 107 | 2147 | 1675 | 17,345 |

2. Subtract and check by subtracting the difference from the minuend:

| $707.25 | $90.40 | $1525.04 | $460.00 | $1500.40 |
|---------|--------|----------|---------|----------|
| 348.07 | 78.23 | 600.75 | 351.24 | 227.17 |

3. Subtract and check by applying the check of nines:

| 6065 | 9007 | 5100 | 62,789 | 40,708 |
|------|------|------|--------|--------|
| 3405 | 8888 | 1203 | 31,999 | 27,785 |

4. Find the answers:

$115 - $72.89 = \qquad $109 - $16.32 =

$101 - $13.28 = \qquad $708 - $88.54 =

$37.04 - $.89 = \qquad $1.71 - $.84 =

$11.11 - $.29 = \qquad $3.08 - $.25 =

Find the answers to the following exercises by mental computation.

5.
| $100 - 37 =$ | $1000 - 271 =$ | $800 - 83 =$ | $300 - 161 =$ |
|--------------|----------------|--------------|---------------|
| $100 - 87 =$ | $1000 - 103 =$ | $900 - 31 =$ | $500 - 303 =$ |
| $100 - 13 =$ | $1000 - 648 =$ | $600 - 45 =$ | $700 - 472 =$ |

6.
| $45 - 17 =$ | $65 - 19 =$ | $133 - 70 =$ | $233 - 42 =$ |
|-------------|-------------|--------------|--------------|
| $84 - 15 =$ | $83 - 39 =$ | $158 - 90 =$ | $304 - 13 =$ |
| $92 - 17 =$ | $77 - 49 =$ | $122 - 60 =$ | $427 - 51 =$ |

7.
$4.20 - $1.30 = \qquad $100 - $28 =

$9.10 - $2.20 = \qquad $134 - $42 =

$7.30 - $1.60 = \qquad $116 - $23 =

$1.64 - $.75 = \qquad $102 - $60 =

$1.55 - $.65 = \qquad $103 - $30 =

$1.32 - $.58 = \qquad $101 - $17 =

8. Find the answers:

$3 - {}^-1 =$      ${}^-3 - {}^-2 =$      $7 - {}^+2 =$      ${}^-4 - {}^-6 =$

$6 - {}^-4 =$      ${}^-6 - {}^-3 =$      $9 - {}^+5 =$      ${}^-5 - {}^-9 =$

$8 - {}^-2 =$      ${}^-4 - {}^-3 =$      $8 - {}^+7 =$      ${}^-7 - {}^-8 =$

## EXERCISES

1. Describe how you would teach the case in which a 2-digit number is subtracted from a 2-digit number with regrouping.

2. Illustrate four rules which can be applied in subtraction.

3. Explain and illustrate why subtraction is called the inverse operation of addition.

4. Describe some teaching techniques which can be used to anchor skills in subtraction.

5. Solve the subtraction question $65 - 18 = \square$ by both the additive and the subtractive method.

6. Solve the subtraction question $131 - 74 = \square$ by both the decomposition and the equal-additions method.

7. State and illustrate the rule which is applied when equal amounts are added to the minuend and the subtrahend in the equal-additions method of subtraction.

8. Give examples of the three types of subtraction situations, write the corresponding number questions, and illustrate each situation in a diagram.

9. Illustrate the number sentence $22 - 5 = 17$ on the number line.

10. Find the answer to the exercise $75 - 19 = \square$ by using an abacus.

11. Describe the difficulty which a zero in a minuend may cause a pupil.

12. Find the answer to the exercise $60 - 12 = \square$ by using a device.

13. If possible, study the Cuisenaire rods or the Stern blocks and describe how the device can be used in the teaching of subtraction.

**For advanced students**

14. Prepare an illustrative lesson on the teaching of subtraction involving negative integers.

15. Report on a piece of research pertaining to the subtraction of whole numbers.

16. If, in applying the check of nines in subtraction, the difference between the excesses of nines in the minuend and the subtrahend is equal to the excess of nines in the difference, it is concluded that the answer is "probably" correct. Explain why the word "probably" is included.

17. The sum of two numbers is 15 and their difference is 9. Why does 15 + 9 equal twice the larger number? Why does 15 − 9 equal twice the smaller number?

18. What is your opinion on the use of the crutch as a device in the teaching of the process of regrouping in subtraction?

19. Criticize the contemporary grade placement of subtraction topics.

20. As assigned by the instructor of the course, report on one or more of the following articles:
    a) Bell, C., "Addition, Subtraction, and the Number Base." *The Arithmetic Teacher*, April, 1955, pp. 57–59.
    b) Brownell, W. A. and C. B. Chazal, "The Effects of Premature Drill in Third-Grade Arithmetic." *Journal of Educational Research*, September, 1935, pp. 17–28.
    c) Clark, J. R., "The Use of Crutches in Teaching Arithmetic." *The Arithmetic Teacher*, October, 1954, pp. 6–10.
    d) Gibb, E. G., "Children's Thinking in the Process of Subtraction." *Journal of Experimental Education*, September, 1956, pp. 71–80.
    e) ———, "Take Away Is Not Enough." *The Arithmetic Teacher*, April, 1954, pp. 7–10.
    f) Grossnickle, F. E., "The Effectiveness of Checking Subtraction by Addition." *The Elementary School Journal*, February, 1938, pp. 436–41.
    g) Rheins, G. B. and J. L. Rheins, "A Comparison of Two Methods of Compound Subtraction." *The Arithmetic Teacher*, October, 1955, pp. 63–69.
    h) Weaver, J. F., "Whither Research on Compound Subtraction?" *The Arithmetic Teacher*, February, 1956, pp. 17–20.
    i) Wilburn, D. B., "Methods of Self-instruction for Learning Arithmetic." *Arithmetic 1949*, Supplementary Educational Monographs, No. 70. Chicago: University of Chicago Press, November, 1949, pp. 35–43.

## SELECTED REFERENCES

Banks, J. H., *Learning and Teaching Arithmetic*, 2nd Ed. Boston: Allyn and Bacon, Inc., 1964, Chs. IV and V.
Bell, C., C. D. Hammond, and R. B. Herrera, *Fundamentals of Arithmetic for Teachers*. New York: John Wiley & Sons, Inc., 1962, Ch. V.

Buckingham, B. R., *Elementary Arithmetic: Its Meaning and Practice.* Boston: Ginn and Company, 1953, Chs. IV and VI.

Corle, C. G., *Teaching Mathematics in the Elementary School.* New York: The Ronald Press Company, 1964, Ch. V.

Dutton, W. H. and L. J. Adams, *Arithmetic for Teachers.* Englewood Cliffs, N.J.: Prentice-Hall, Inc., 1961, Ch. III.

Grossnickle, F. E. and L. J. Brueckner, *Discovering Meanings in Elementary School Mathematics.* New York: Holt, Rinehart & Winston, Inc., 1963, Chs. VI and VII.

Howard, C. F. and E. Dumas, *Basic Procedures in Teaching Arithmetic.* Boston: D. C. Heath & Company, 1963, Chs. IV and VII.

Larsen, H. D. and H. G. Ludlow, *Arithmetic for Colleges.* New York: The Macmillan Co., 1963, Ch. IV.

Marks, J. L., C. R. Purdy, and L. B. Kinney, *Teaching Arithmetic for Understanding.* New York: McGraw-Hill, Inc., 1958, Ch. VI.

Mueller, F. J., *Arithmetic, Its Structure and Concepts,* 2nd Ed. Englewood Cliffs, N.J.: Prentice-Hall, Inc., 1964, Units XII and XIII.

National Council of Teachers of Mathematics, *Topics in Mathematics.* Washington, D.C.: the Council, 1964, Bklt. 2.

School Mathematics Study Group, *Studies in Mathematics, Vol. IX: A Brief Course in Mathematics for Elementary School Teachers.* Stanford: Leland Stanford Junior University, 1963, Chs. VI and VII.

Spitzer, H. F., *The Teaching of Arithmetic.* Boston: Houghton Mifflin Company, 1961, Ch. IV.

Swain, R. L., *Understanding Arithmetic.* New York: Holt, Rinehart & Winston, Inc., 1960, Chs. III and IV.

Swenson, E. J., *Teaching Arithmetic to Children.* New York: The Macmillan Co., 1964, Chs. VII and VIII.

Thorpe, C. B., *Teaching Elementary Arithmetic.* New York: Harper & Row, Publishers, 1962, Ch. XII.

# 12

# MULTIPLICATION

WHEN THE CHILD has acquired an understanding of and some skill in the addition and subtraction of equal numbers, he can be introduced to the operations of multiplication and division. This chapter is concerned with the instruction to be given in the multiplication of whole numbers. The teaching of the division of whole numbers will be considered in Chapter 13.

## Meaning and Terms

*Note*

Multiplication is an operation on two numbers resulting in a single number, which is called the *product*. Since only two numbers are involved at a time, the operation is binary in nature. In the number sentence $5 \times 7 = 35$, 7 is the *multiplicand*, 5 is the *multiplier*, and 35 is the *product*. The sentence is usually read "5 times 7 equals 35." Both the multiplicand and the multiplier are called *factors* of the product.

The operation of multiplication may be described as repeated addition of equal addends. For example, the answer to $5 \times 3 = \square$ can be found by adding 3 five times: $3 + 3 + 3 + 3 + 3 = 15$. The addition of these equal groups can be illustrated on the number line:

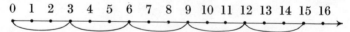

Multiplication may be interpreted as finding the Cartesian product of two sets. If set $A = \{$John, Bill, Tom$\}$ and set $B = \{$Dick, Al$\}$, the elements of the sets can be paired as follows: $\{$(John, Dick), (John, Al), (Bill, Dick), (Bill, Al), (Tom, Dick), (Tom, Al)$\}$. The set made up of all the ordered pairs which can be formed by pairing each element of $A$ with each element of $B$

is called the *Cartesian product* of A and B. The pairings can be placed in an array:

|  | Dick | Al |
|---|---|---|
| John | (John, Dick) | (John, Al) |
| Bill | (Bill, Dick) | (Bill, Al) |
| Tom | (Tom, Dick) | (Tom, Al) |

The product of the cardinal numbers of A and B can be determined by counting the pairings in the array. There are 3 rows of 2 each, or a total of 6 pairings. $3 \times 2 = 6$.

EXAMPLE:

*Problem:* Joan has 3 dolls and 5 dresses for the dolls. How many pairings of dolls and dresses can she make?

*Solution:* The following array expresses the possible number of pairings:

$$
\begin{array}{c|ccccc}
 & \multicolumn{5}{c}{5} \\
\hline
 & * & * & * & * & * \\
3 & * & * & * & * & * \\
 & * & * & * & * & * \\
\end{array}
$$

There are 3 rows of 5 each, or a total of 15. $3 \times 5 = 15$.

## Properties of Multiplication

In Chapter 4 several properties which apply to the multiplication of whole numbers were presented. The student should state what is meant by and give examples of each of these properties: commutation, association, distribution, closure, and the identity element for multiplication.

### Zero in multiplication

The product of any whole number and zero is zero. Thus $4 \times 0 = 0$ and $0 \times 4 = 0$.

## Grade Placement of Multiplication Topics

The grade placement of multiplication topics differs only in minor aspects in the various textbooks. The placement of topics as shown below is typical for the traditional textbooks. In newer programs some of these topics are introduced at lower grade levels. For the author's opinion on the grade placement of topics, the student is referred to Chapter 3.

*Typical Grade Placement of Multiplication Topics*

*Grade I:* 1. Multiple counting.

*Grade II:* 1. Maintenance of skills.

2. Addition of several equal addends.

*Grade III:* 1. Maintenance of skills.

2. Easy multiplication facts.

3. Checking.

4. Estimation of products.

5. Multiplication of 2- and 3-digit numbers by a 1-digit number without regrouping.

6. Vocabulary.

7. Multiplication of money numbers.

*Grade IV:* 1. Maintenance of skills.

2. Mastery of the multiplication facts.

3. Multiplication by 10 and multiples of 10.

4. Multiplication by 1-digit and 2-digit numbers without, and with, regrouping.

5. Extension of the vocabulary.

*Grade V:* 1. Maintenance of skills.

2. Multiplication by powers of ten.

3. Multiplication by 3-digit numbers without, and with, regrouping.

*Grade VI:* 1. Maintenance of skills.

2. Multiplication of multi-digit numbers.

## Foundation Activities for Multiplication

Before the multiplication facts are introduced, the pupils engage in foundation activities designed to prepare them for formal instruction in multiplication. Such direct instruction in multiplication could be undertaken sooner with the average and above-average child than is done in the traditional mathematics program. When the pupil knows that 2 threes equal 6, he can also be taught to interpret the equation $2 \times 3 = 6$.

Foundation experiences for multiplication of whole numbers may include the following:

1. Counting objects by twos, threes, etc.

2. Joining groups of objects, such as 2 balls + 2 balls = □ balls.

3. Adding groups of beads on the counting frame.

4. Multiple rote counting.

5. Manipulating blocks of related sizes, such as Cuisenaire rods, Stern blocks, and the blocks of the fraction board.

6. Interpreting arrays such as 3 groups of 4 elements each.

7. Marking equal intervals on the number line.

8. Finding doubles of numbers.

9. Adding equal addends.

10. Studying examples of arrays such as egg cartons and rows and sheets of trading stamps.

## The Key Multiplication Facts

The key multiplication facts (also called the basic multiplication facts) comprise all the possible two-factor multiplication facts which can be formed by using the figures 0 through 9. There are a total of 100 key multiplication facts, as presented on the following page.

It is suggested that the case in which a number is multiplied by 10 be introduced together with or immediately after the key facts. The rule for multiplying a number by 10 should be developed inductively.

## Introducing the Key Facts

A key fact should be introduced in a meaningful situation. This makes it possible for the child to consider the problem in a concrete setting, in which he can use previously acquired knowledge to arrive at the answer. If the pupil has successfully pursued a meaningful mathematics program in addition, he will be acquainted with exercises such as $3 + 3 = \square$; $2 + 2 + 2 = \square$; $4 + 4 + 4 + 4 = \square$; etc. The interpretations and presentations of the teacher should lead the child toward the standard form of expressing a multiplication question.

$0 \times 0 = 0$  $0 \times 1 = 0$  $0 \times 2 = 0$  $0 \times 3 = 0$  $0 \times 4 = 0$  $0 \times 5 = 0$  $0 \times 6 = 0$  $0 \times 7 = 0$  $0 \times 8 = 0$  $0 \times 9 = 0$

$1 \times 0 = 0$  $1 \times 1 = 1$  $1 \times 2 = 2$  $1 \times 3 = 3$  $1 \times 4 = 4$  $1 \times 5 = 5$  $1 \times 6 = 6$  $1 \times 7 = 7$  $1 \times 8 = 8$  $1 \times 9 = 9$

$2 \times 0 = 0$  $2 \times 1 = 2$  $2 \times 2 = 4$  $2 \times 3 = 6$  $2 \times 4 = 8$  $2 \times 5 = 10$  $2 \times 6 = 12$  $2 \times 7 = 14$  $2 \times 8 = 16$  $2 \times 9 = 18$

$3 \times 0 = 0$  $3 \times 1 = 3$  $3 \times 2 = 6$  $3 \times 3 = 9$  $3 \times 4 = 12$  $3 \times 5 = 15$  $3 \times 6 = 18$  $3 \times 7 = 21$  $3 \times 8 = 24$  $3 \times 9 = 27$

$4 \times 0 = 0$  $4 \times 1 = 4$  $4 \times 2 = 8$  $4 \times 3 = 12$  $4 \times 4 = 16$  $4 \times 5 = 20$  $4 \times 6 = 24$  $4 \times 7 = 28$  $4 \times 8 = 32$  $4 \times 9 = 36$

$5 \times 0 = 0$  $5 \times 1 = 5$  $5 \times 2 = 10$  $5 \times 3 = 15$  $5 \times 4 = 20$  $5 \times 5 = 25$  $5 \times 6 = 30$  $5 \times 7 = 35$  $5 \times 8 = 40$  $5 \times 9 = 45$

$6 \times 0 = 0$  $6 \times 1 = 6$  $6 \times 2 = 12$  $6 \times 3 = 18$  $6 \times 4 = 24$  $6 \times 5 = 30$  $6 \times 6 = 36$  $6 \times 7 = 42$  $6 \times 8 = 48$  $6 \times 9 = 54$

$7 \times 0 = 0$  $7 \times 1 = 7$  $7 \times 2 = 14$  $7 \times 3 = 21$  $7 \times 4 = 28$  $7 \times 5 = 35$  $7 \times 6 = 42$  $7 \times 7 = 49$  $7 \times 8 = 56$  $7 \times 9 = 63$

$8 \times 0 = 0$  $8 \times 1 = 8$  $8 \times 2 = 16$  $8 \times 3 = 24$  $8 \times 4 = 32$  $8 \times 5 = 40$  $8 \times 6 = 48$  $8 \times 7 = 56$  $8 \times 8 = 64$  $8 \times 9 = 72$

$9 \times 0 = 0$  $9 \times 1 = 9$  $9 \times 2 = 18$  $9 \times 3 = 27$  $9 \times 4 = 36$  $9 \times 5 = 45$  $9 \times 6 = 54$  $9 \times 7 = 63$  $9 \times 8 = 72$  $9 \times 9 = 81$

EXAMPLE:

*Problem:* How many pennies equal 3 nickels?

*Solutions:* Several solutions may be presented or suggested by the pupils:

1. The use of toy money: exchanging 3 nickels for pennies and determining the number of pennies.

2. The use of counters or cutouts on the flannel board.

3. Horizontal addition.

4. Vertical addition.

5. The use of the number line.

6. The use of diagrams or arrays.

The teacher guides the class discussion, during which the pupils evaluate and refine suggested procedures. He commends solutions which lead to the correct answer, introduces the standard forms of expressing a multiplication fact as $3 \times 5 = 15$   and

$$\times \frac{\begin{array}{r} 5 \\ 3 \end{array}}{15} ,$$

and suggests that these sentences be read as "three times five equals fifteen." The sentence $3 \times 5 = 15$ is illustrated in an array and on the number line as follows:

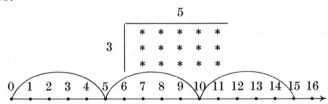

By studying the array and the number line, the pupils are led to discover that $3 \times 5 = 5 \times 3$.

## Developing and Anchoring Skills

After a meaningful introduction of the facts, the children are led to see the need and the usefulness of memorizing the key facts. They must realize that it takes too much time to find the answer by serial addition, or by using the number line, a diagram, or an array to find the answer to a number question.

Various techniques are available for developing and anchoring skill in the key multiplication facts, including the following:

1. Exercises in the pupils' textbook and workbook and those provided by the teacher, such as:

a) Finding a missing factor.
*Examples:* $3 \times \square = 12$; $\square \times 4 = 12$.

b) Expressing one of the factors as the product of two factors.
*Example:* $6 \times 3 = 3 \times \square \times 3$.

c) Expressing a number as the product of two factors.
*Examples:* $10 = \square \times \bigcirc$; $9 = \square \times \square$.

d) Expressing a number as the product of different pairs of factors.
*Example:* $12 = \square \times 2 = 3 \times \bigcirc = 12 \times \triangle$.

e) Applying the commutative property.
*Example:* $4 \times 5 = 5 \times \square$.

2. Different forms of presentation:

a)

| 12 = | | |
|---|---|---|
| 6 | $\times$ | $\square$ |
| $\square$ | $\times$ | 3 |
| 1 | $\times$ | $\square$ |

b)

| Just as much: | |
|---|---|
| $4 \times 4$ | $\square \times \bigcirc$ |
| $6 \times 2$ | $\square \times \bigcirc$ |
| $2 \times 10$ | $\square \times \bigcirc$ |

c)

The total must be 16:

$3 \times \square + 1$
$5 \times \square + 1$
$7 \times \square + 2$

d)

Find the missing numbers:

$4 \times 4 = 3 \times 4 + \square$
$6 \times 2 = 4 \times 2 + \square$
$7 \times 3 = 5 \times 3 + \square$ .

e)

Write the products. The first one has been done.

| | 7 | 9 | 2 | 1 | 5 | 8 | 3 | 6 | 4 |
|---|---|---|---|---|---|---|---|---|---|
| $3 \times$ | 21 | | | | | | | | |

3. The construction of a multiplication table. The numbers named in the top row are to be multiplied by those named in the left column. Some

examples have been given:

| × | 0 | 1 | 2 | 3 | 4 | 5 | 6 | 7 | 8 | 9 | 10 |
|---|---|---|---|---|---|---|---|---|---|---|----|
| 0 | | | | | | | | | | | |
| 1 | | | | | | | | | | | |
| 2 | | | | | 6 | | | | | | |
| 3 | | | | | | 15 | | | | | |
| 4 | | | | | | | | | 32 | | |
| 5 | | | | | | | | | | | |
| 6 | | | | | | | | | | | |
| 7 | | | | | | | | | | | |
| 8 | | | | | | | | | | | |
| 9 | | | | | | | | | | | |
| 10 | | | | | | | | | | | |

4. Reading and writing multiplication facts from illustrations on the number line.

EXAMPLE:

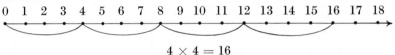

$$4 \times 4 = 16$$

5. Exercises with flashcards on which the questions are presented in horizontal form.

6. Exercises with flashcards on which the questions are presented in vertical form.

7. Writing and memorizing facts.

8. Writing, checking, and memorizing the tables of multiplication.

9. Exercises with the multiplication wheel.
The addition wheel described in Chapter 10 can be modified for use with the multiplication facts.

10. Completing number sentences by supplying the symbol $=$, $>$, or $<$.
*Examples:* $5 \times 3 \;\square\; 2 \times 7$; $6 \times 4 \;\square\; 5 \times 5$; $9 \times 2 \;\square\; 3 \times 6$.

11. Finding or suggesting patterns in the products of the multiplication tables and exploring the reasons for these patterns.

EXAMPLES:
a) Table of 2: the ones digit is always an even number.
b) Table of 3: the sum of the digits is always evenly divisible by 3.

c) Table of 4: there is a regular sequence in the ones digits:

$$4 - 8 - 2 - 6 - 0 - 4 - 8 \text{ -, etc.}$$

d) Table of 5: the ones digit is either a 5 or a 0.

e) Table of 6: there is a regular sequence in the ones digits:

$$6 - 2 - 8 - 4 - 0 - 6 - 2 - 8 \text{ -, etc.}$$

f) Table of 7: each digit occurs once in the ones place:

$$7 - 4 - 1 - 8 - 5 - 2 - 9 - 6 - 3 - 0.$$

g) Table of 8: the ones digits are even numbers which occur in descending order: $8 - 6 - 4 - 2 - 0 - 8 - 6 - 4 - 2 - 0$.

h) Table of 9: (*i*) the sum of the digits is evenly divisible by 9; (*ii*) the ones digits occur in descending order, and the tens digits in ascending order.

12. Verifying statements such as:

The product of two even numbers is always an even number.

The product of two odd numbers is always an odd number.

The product of an even number and an odd number is always an even number.

13. Brief daily reviews of the basic multiplication facts until all the facts have been mastered.

## The Ones Facts and the Zero Facts

The ones facts and the zero facts are best introduced after several other multiplication facts have been presented and understood. The teacher may present questions such as $5 \times 1 = \square$ and $5 \times 0 = \square$ resulting from meaningful situations. Such introductions should be followed by practice exercises.

EXAMPLE 1:

*Problem:* Ron and Tom sold baseball cards for 1¢ each. If they sold 4 cards, how many pennies did they receive?

*Number question:* $4 \times 1 = \square$.

EXAMPLE 2:

*Problem:* In a guessing game a score of 1 was given for each correct guess. Bill got 5 turns and missed each guess. What was Bill's score?

*Number question:* $5 \times 0 = \square$.

The answers to questions such as $1 \times 5 = \square$ and $0 \times 5 = \square$ may be determined by applying the commutative property.

The pupils are finally guided to form these generalizations:

Any number times 1 equals that number.
1 times any number equals that number.
Any number times 0 equals 0.
0 times any number equals 0.

## Multiplying Three 1-digit Numbers

EXAMPLE:
*Problem:* In a set of blocks there are 2 rows of 4 blocks in the bottom layer. If there are 3 layers, how many blocks are there in the set?
*Number question:* $3 \times 2 \times 4 = \square$.
*Solution:* The pupils are guided to discover that any two factors may be multiplied first. This is demonstrated with a set of blocks to which the problem refers. The associative property can also be illustrated on the number line.

## Multiplying with a Power of Ten

EXAMPLE:
*Problem:* If there are 10 rows of 12 chairs each in a room, how many chairs are there in all?
*Number question:* $10 \times 12 = \square$.
*Solution:* The pupils find the answer to this number question by adding 12 ten times. After working several similar exercises, they are guided to discover the rule for multiplying a number by 10 inductively. After the rule has been stated, it is applied deductively.

The answer to a number question such as $12 \times 10 = \square$ can be found by applying the commutative property: $10 \times 12 = 12 \times 10$. The answer is checked by adding 10 twelve times.

When the pupils know how to multiply a number by 10, the development of rules for multiplying a number by other powers of 10 will not cause much difficulty.

## Multiplying a Multiple of Ten and a 1-digit Number

EXAMPLE:
*Problem:* If there are 30 trading stamps on one page of a stamp book, how many stamps are there on 5 pages?

*Number question:* $5 \times 30 = \square$.
*Solution:* Since $5 \times 3$ ones $= 15$ ones, $5 \times 3$ tens $= 15$ tens, or $5 \times 30 = 150$. After several exercises of the same kind have been worked and discussed, the vertical form is presented:

$$\begin{array}{r} 30 \\ \times \phantom{0} 5 \\ \hline 150 \end{array}$$

The answer can also be found by using the following procedure:

$$\begin{aligned} 5 \times 30 &= 5 \times (3 \times 10) \text{ renaming} \\ &= (5 \times 3) \times 10 \text{ associative property} \\ &= 15 \times 10 \text{ multiplication} \\ &= 150 \text{ multiplication} \end{aligned}$$

The number question $30 \times 5 = \square$ can be solved by using the commutative property: $30 \times 5 = 5 \times 30 = 150$. Or the pupils may reason:

$$\begin{aligned} 30 \times 5 &= (10 \times 3) \times 5 \\ &= 10 \times (3 \times 5) \\ &= 10 \times 15 \\ &= 150 \end{aligned}$$

## Multiplying Multiples of Ten

EXAMPLE:
*Problem:* Each of the 20 pupils in Grade IV sold 30 tickets for the school play. How many tickets did they sell in all?
*Number question:* $20 \times 30 = \square$.
*Solution:*

$$\begin{aligned} 20 \times 30 &= (10 \times 2) \times 30 \text{ renaming} \\ &= 10 \times (2 \times 30) \text{ associative property} \\ &= 10 \times 60 \text{ multiplication} \\ &= 600 \text{ multiplication} \end{aligned}$$

After working several similar exercises, the pupils are led to discover that two zeros are annexed to the product of 2 and 3, and reason as follows: Since $2 \times 3 = 6$, $20 \times 30 = 600$. Thus the answer is found by mental computation.

## Multiplying a 2-digit Number by a 1-digit Number without Regrouping

The pupil is prepared for vertical multiplication by pursuing several meaningful steps in horizontal multiplication. He uses previously acquired knowledge and is guided from the horizontal form to the vertical form. The multiplicand in the vertical arrangement is first presented in expanded notation. In the following example these steps are shown.

EXAMPLE:
*Problem:* How many months are there in 3 years?
*Number question:* $3 \times 12 = \square$.
*Solutions:*

a) $3 \times 12 = 3 \times (10 + 2)$ renaming

$= (3 \times 10) + (3 \times 2)$ distributive property

$= 30 + 6$ multiplication

$= 36$ addition

b)
$$
\begin{array}{cc}
12 = & 10 + 2 \\
\times 3 & \times \dfrac{3}{30 + 6} = 36
\end{array}
$$

c)
$$
\begin{array}{l}
12 \\
\times 3 \\
\hline
36
\end{array}
$$
$3 \times 2$ ones $= 6$ ones; write 6 in the ones place;
$3 \times 1$ ten $= 3$ tens; write 3 in the tens place.

## Multiplying a 2-digit Number by a 1-digit Number with Regrouping

EXAMPLE:
*Problem:* How many eggs are there in 7 dozen?
*Number question:* $7 \times 12 = \square$.
*Solutions:*

a) $7 \times 12 = 7 \times (10 + 2)$ renaming

$= (7 \times 10) + (7 \times 2)$ distributive property

$= 70 + 14$ multiplication

$= 84$ addition

b)      $12 = \quad 10 + 2$

$\times \dfrac{7}{\phantom{-}} \quad \times \dfrac{7}{70 + 14} = 84$

c) A useful device for illustrating the process of regrouping is the counting frame which has 10 rows of 10 beads each. Seven groups of 10 beads each and 7 groups of 2 beads each are isolated on the frame, and the 7 groups of 2 beads each are regrouped to form one group of 10 beads and one group of 4 beads.

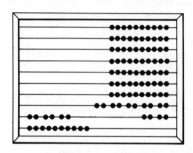

After regrouping, it is evident that $7 \times 12$ results in 8 tens and 4 ones, or 84.

d) The standard algorism is used.

The child is guided to think as follows:

$\begin{array}{r} 12 \\ \times \dfrac{7}{84} \end{array}$    $7 \times 2$ ones $= 14$ ones; write 4 in the ones place and remember 1 ten; $7 \times 1$ ten $= 7$ tens; 7 tens $+$ 1 ten $=$ 8 tens; write 8 in the tens place.

## Multiplying a Multi-digit Number by a 1-digit Number

EXAMPLE 1:

*Problem:* The teacher has 2 boxes of pencils. If there are 144 pencils in each box, how many pencils are there in all?

*Number question:* $2 \times 144 = \square$.

*Solutions:*

a) $2 \times 144 = 2 \times (100 + 40 + 4)$ renaming

$\qquad = (2 \times 100) + (2 \times 40) + (2 \times 4)$ distributive property

$\qquad = 200 + 80 + 8$ multiplication

$\qquad = 288$ addition

b)     1 hundred,  4 tens, 4 ones                              144
$\times$ $\underline{\hspace{3.5cm} 2}$         Thus:          $\times$ $\underline{\hspace{0.3cm} 2}$
       2 hundreds, 8 tens, 8 ones                             200    $(2 \times 100)$
                                                               80    $(2 \times 40)$
                                                                8    $(2 \times 4)$
                                                          $\overline{\hspace{0.8cm}}$
                                                              288

c) If first the ones are multiplied, then the tens, and finally the hundreds, the multiplication is written as follows:

         144                    144
$\times$ $\underline{\hspace{0.3cm} 2}$                 $\times$ $\underline{\hspace{0.3cm} 2}$
           8         or as:       8     (ones)
          80                      8     (tens)
         200                      2     (hundreds)
       $\overline{\hspace{0.8cm}}$             $\overline{\hspace{0.8cm}}$
         288                    288

d) From the preceding presentation the standard          144
algorism is derived.                              $\times$ $\underline{\hspace{0.3cm} 2}$
The child is guided to think as follows:                 288
$2 \times 4$ ones = 8 ones;  write 8 in the ones place;
$2 \times 4$ tens = 8 tens;  write 8 in the tens place;
$2 \times 1$ hundred = 2 hundreds;  write 2 in the
hundreds place.

EXAMPLE 2:

*Problem:*  Tom has 8 scrapbooks filled with pictures.  If there are 192 pictures in each book, how many pictures does Tom have in all?
*Number question:*  $8 \times 192 = \square$.

a) $8 \times 192 = 8 \times (100 + 90 + 2)$ renaming

$\qquad = (8 \times 100) + (8 \times 90) + (8 \times 2)$ distributive property

$\qquad = 800 + 720 + 16$ multiplication

$\qquad = 1536$ addition

b)                              192
                        $\times$ $\underline{\hspace{0.4cm} 8}$
        $8 \times \ \ \ 2 =$          16
        $8 \times \ \ 90 =$          720
        $8 \times 100 =$            800
                          $\overline{\hspace{1cm}}$
                                  1536

c) With the help of the previous presentations and
the interpretations of the teacher, the standard
algorism is developed.

$$\begin{array}{r} 192 \\ \times\ \ 8 \\ \hline 1536 \end{array}$$

$8 \times 2$ ones $= 16$ ones; write 6 in the ones place and
remember 1 ten;
$8 \times 9$ tens $= 72$ tens; $72$ tens $+ 1$ ten $= 73$ tens;
write 3 in the tens place and remember 7 hundreds;
$8 \times 1$ hundred $= 8$ hundreds; 8 hundreds $+ 7$
hundreds $= 15$ hundreds; write 5 in the hundreds
place and 1 in the thousands place.

EXAMPLE 3:
*Problem:* Lois bought two books for \$2.08 each. How much did she pay for
the two books?
*Number question:* $2 \times \$2.08 = \square$.
*Solutions:*
a) Horizontal form:

$$2 \times \$2.08 = 2 \times (\$2 + \$.08)$$
$$= (2 \times \$2) + (2 \times \$.08)$$
$$= \$4 + \$.16$$
$$= \$4.16$$

b) Vertical form:

$$\begin{array}{r} \$2.08 \\ \times\ \ 2 \\ \hline \$4.16 \end{array}$$    This is the standard algorism. The fact that
$2 \times 0 = 0$ should be stressed.

## Multiplying Two 2-digit Numbers

EXAMPLE 1:
*Problem:* How many eggs are there in 20 dozen?
*Number question:* $20 \times 12 = \square$.
*Solutions:*

$$\text{a) } 20 \times 12 = (10 \times 2) \times 12$$
$$= 10 \times (2 \times 12)$$
$$= 10 \times 24$$
$$= 240$$

b) $12 = 10 + 2$

$$\times \frac{20}{\quad} \qquad \times \frac{20}{200 + 40} = 240$$

c)

$$20 \times 2 = \times \frac{\begin{array}{r} 12 \\ 20 \end{array}}{40}$$

$$20 \times 10 = \frac{200}{240}$$

d) When using the short form of multiplication, the pupil learns to reason as follows: If 12 is multiplied by 2, the product is 24. If 12 is multiplied by 20, a zero is annexed to 24, making the product 240. Thus 12 can be multiplied by 20 by first writing the zero, and then writing the product of 12 and 2 to the left of the zero.

$$\times \frac{\begin{array}{r} 12 \\ 20 \end{array}}{240}$$

EXAMPLE 2:

*Problem:* One day a farmer sold 13 dozen eggs. How many eggs did he sell that day?

*Number question:* $13 \times 12 = \square$.

*Solutions:*

a) $13 \times 12 = (10 + 3) \times 12$

$\qquad = (10 \times 12) + (3 \times 12)$

$\qquad = 120 + 36$

$\qquad = 156$

b) The horizontal presentation of the multiplication can be expressed vertically. The product of 3 and 12 can be written as the first partial product:

$$\times \frac{\begin{array}{r} 12 \\ 13 \end{array}}{36}$$
$$\frac{120}{156}$$

c) When multiplying vertically, the steps can be recorded as follows:

$$\times \frac{\begin{array}{r} 12 \\ 13 \end{array}}{\phantom{0}}$$

$3 \times 2$ ones = $\quad$ 6

$3 \times 1$ ten = $\quad$ 30

$1$ ten $\times 2 =$ $\quad$ 20

$1$ ten $\times 1$ ten = $\frac{100}{156}$

d) In the final step the standard algorism is developed:

$$\begin{array}{r} 12 \\ 13 \\ \times\overline{\phantom{0}36} \\ 12 \\ \hline 156 \end{array}$$

The teacher explains that the zero in 120 is usually omitted, since the places which the digits occupy indicate their positional value.

EXAMPLE 3:

*Problem:* A grocer bought 36 boxes of apples. If there were 48 apples in each box, how many apples did he buy?

*Number question:* $36 \times 48 = \square$.

*Solutions:*

a) First the horizontal form of solution is developed. (Many pupils may have to find the answers to partial products by vertical multiplication and may have to add the partial products in a column.)

$$\begin{aligned} 36 \times 48 &= (30 + 6) \times 48 \\ &= (30 \times 48) + (6 \times 48) \\ &= 1440 + 288 \\ &= 1728 \end{aligned}$$

b) The partial products found by the first method of solution are written vertically:

$$\begin{array}{rr} & 48 \\ & \times\overline{\phantom{0}36} \\ 6 \times 48 = & 288 \\ 30 \times 48 = & 1440 \\ \hline & 1728 \end{array}$$

c) The standard algorism is developed. The pupil is guided to reason as follows:

6 × 8 = 48; write down the 8 ones and remember the 4 tens;

6 × 4 tens = 24 tens; 24 tens + 4 tens = 28 tens; write 8 in the tens place and 2 in the hundreds place;

3 tens × 8 = 24 tens; write 4 in the tens place and remember 2 hundreds;

3 tens × 4 tens = 12 hundreds; 12 hundreds + 2 hundreds = 14 hundreds; write 4 in the hundreds place and 1 in the thousands place.

Finally the partial products are added.

$$\begin{array}{r} 48 \\ 36 \\ \times\overline{\phantom{0}288} \\ 144 \\ \hline 1728 \end{array}$$

## Multiplying Two Multi-digit Numbers

EXAMPLE 1:
*Problem:* Multiply 337 by 242.
*Number question:* $242 \times 337 = \square$.
*Solutions:*
a) The multiplication is worked horizontally:

$$
\begin{aligned}
242 \times 337 &= (200 + 40 + 2) \times 337 \\
&= (200 \times 337) + (40 \times 337) + (2 \times 337) \\
&= 67{,}400 + 13{,}480 + 674 \\
&= 81{,}554
\end{aligned}
$$

b) The horizontal form of solution is written vertically:

|  | 337 |  |  | 337 |
|---|---:|---|---|---:|
|  | $\times$ 242 |  |  | $\times$ 242 |
| $200 \times 337 =$ | 67400 | or | $2 \times 337 =$ | 674 |
| $40 \times 337 =$ | 13480 |  | $40 \times 337 =$ | 13480 |
| $2 \times 337 =$ | 674 |  | $200 \times 337 =$ | 67400 |
|  | 81,554 |  |  | 81,554 |

c) The algorism in common use is developed, as in the immediately preceding example.

$$
\begin{array}{r}
337 \\
\times\, 242 \\
\hline
674 \\
1348 \\
674 \\
\hline
81{,}554
\end{array}
$$

EXAMPLE 2:
*Problem:* Multiply 406 by 307.
*Number question:* $307 \times 406 = \square$.
*Solutions:*
a) The difficulty which presents itself in this example is the zero in the multiplier. The pupil must realize that $307 = 300 + 7$, and that 406 is multiplied by 7 and by 300:

$$
\begin{aligned}
307 \times 406 &= (300 + 7) \times 406 \\
&= (300 \times 406) + (7 \times 406) \\
&= 121{,}800 + 2842 \\
&= 124{,}642
\end{aligned}
$$

b) The solution in a) is written as follows:

$$300 \times 406 = \begin{array}{r} 406 \\ \times\,307 \\ \hline 121800 \end{array}$$
$$7 \times 406 = \quad\;\; 2842$$
$$\hline$$
$$124{,}642$$

or

$$7 \times 406 = \begin{array}{r} 406 \\ \times\,307 \\ \hline 2842 \end{array}$$
$$300 \times 406 = \;121800$$
$$\hline$$
$$124{,}642$$

c) The standard algorism is developed. The pupil should understand by now that the second partial product shown represents hundreds and that the two zeros in that partial product are usually not written.

$$\begin{array}{r} 406 \\ \times\,307 \\ \hline 2842 \\ 1218\;\; \\ \hline 124{,}642 \end{array}$$

## Checking the Product

Various methods can be applied to check the product of a multiplication. The method selected will depend upon the mathematical maturity of the pupils.

1. *Dividing the product by one of the factors.*
When the product of a multiplication is divided by one of the factors, the quotient must equal the other factor.
*Example:* $5 \times 13 = 65$, and $65 \div 13 = 5$, or $65 \div 5 = 13$.

2. *Multiplying the factors in reversed order.*
*Example:* The sentence $17 \times 38 = 646$ can be checked by finding the answer to $38 \times 17 = \square$.

3. *Applying the rule of compensation.*
*Example:* The mathematical sentence $24 \times 25 = 600$ can be checked by dividing one factor and multiplying the other factor by the same number:

$$24 \times 25 = 12 \times 50 = 6 \times 100 = 600.$$

4. *Writing the steps in horizontal form.*
*Example:* The mathematical sentence $15 \times 22 = 330$ can be checked by multiplying 22 first by 10, and then by 5, and adding the products:

$$15 \times 22 = (10 + 5) \times 22$$
$$= (10 \times 22) + (5 \times 22)$$
$$= 220 + 110$$
$$= 330$$

5. *Approximating.*

When an exact answer is not required, but an approximate answer is sufficient, the numbers can be rounded, and then multiplied by mental computation.

*Example:* The reasonableness of the answer in the mathematical sentence $38 \times 61 = 2318$ can be checked by multiplying 60 by 40. Since $60 \times 40 = 2400$, 2318 appears to be a reasonable answer for $38 \times 61 = \square$.

6. *Applying the check of nines.*

In the upper grades, pupils of at least average ability can learn to check the product of a multiplication by applying the check of nines. The excesses of nines in each of the two factors are multiplied, and the excess of nines in this product must equal the excess of nines in the product of the original multiplication.

*Example:*

|  |  |  |
|---|---|---|
| 125 | Excess of nines in the multiplicand: | 8 |
| 17 | Excess of nines in the multiplier: | 8 |
| 875 | Product of 8 and 8: | $\times \overline{64}$ |
| 125 |  |  |
| 2125 | Excess of nines in 64: 1 | |
|  | Excess of nines in 2125: 1 | |

Since the excesses of nines in 64 and 2125 are equal, it may be stated that the answer is probably correct.

The limitations of the check of nines have been presented in the chapter on addition.

## Mental Computation

In the preceding paragraphs the importance of mental computation in the introduction of a new multiplication case has been illustrated. For the benefit of the teacher who is not yet sufficiently familiar with techniques used in mental computation, the following summary is presented.

1. $10 \times 16 = \square$.

A number is multiplied by 10 by annexing a zero to the numeral that stands for the number. Thus $10 \times 16 = 160$.

2. $100 \times 175 = \square$.

A number is multiplied by 100 by annexing two zeros to the numeral that stands for the number. Thus $100 \times 175 = 17,500$.

3. $1000 \times 28 = \square$.

A number is multiplied by 1000 by annexing three zeros to the numeral that stands for the number. Thus $1000 \times 28 = 28,000$.

4. $6 \times 12 = \square$.
*Think:*

$$6 \times 12 = 6 \times (10 + 2)$$
$$= (6 \times 10) + (6 \times 2)$$
$$= 60 + 12$$
$$= 72$$

5. $9 \times 12 = \square$.
*Think:*

$$9 \times 12 = (10 - 1) \times 12$$
$$= (10 \times 12) - (1 \times 12)$$
$$= 120 - 12$$
$$= 108$$

6. $7 \times 125 = \square$.
*Think:*

$$7 \times 125 = 7 \times (100 + 20 + 5)$$
$$= (7 \times 100) + (7 \times 20) + (7 \times 5)$$
$$= 700 + 140 + 35$$
$$= 875$$

7. $20 \times 36 = \square$.
*Think:*

$$20 \times 36 = (2 \times 10) \times 36$$
$$= 2 \times (10 \times 36)$$
$$= 2 \times 360$$
$$= 720$$

Or: Since $2 \times 36 = 72,\ 20 \times 36 = 720$.

8. $99 \times 45 = \square$.
*Think:*

$$99 \times 45 = (100 - 1) \times 45$$
$$= (100 \times 45) - (1 \times 45)$$
$$= 4500 - 45$$
$$= 4455$$

9. $101 \times 45 = \square$.
*Think:*

$$101 \times 45 = (100 + 1) \times 45$$
$$= (100 \times 45) + (1 \times 45)$$
$$= 4500 + 45$$
$$= 4545$$

Find the product of 101 and other 2-digit numbers. Note the repetition of the digits. This occurs only when the multiplicand is a 2-digit number.

10. $1001 \times 143 = \square$.
*Think:*

$$
\begin{aligned}
1001 \times 143 &= (1000 + 1) \times 143 \\
&= (1000 \times 143) + (1 \times 143) \\
&= 143{,}000 + 143 \\
&= 143{,}143
\end{aligned}
$$

Find the product of 1001 and other 3-digit numbers. Note the repetition of the digits. This occurs only when the multiplicand is a 3-digit number.

11. $15 \times 42 = \square$.
*Think:* $15 = 10 + 5$ and $5 = \frac{1}{2} \times 10$.

$$
\begin{aligned}
15 \times 42 &= (10 + 5) \times 42 \\
&= (10 \times 42) + (5 \times 42) \\
&= 420 + (\tfrac{1}{2} \times 420) \\
&= 420 + 210 \\
&= 630
\end{aligned}
$$

12. $12 \times 42 = \square$.
*Think:*

$$
\begin{aligned}
12 \times 42 &= (10 + 2) \times 42 \\
&= (10 \times 42) + (2 \times 42) \\
&= 420 + 84 \\
&= 504
\end{aligned}
$$

13. $4 \times 17 \times 25 = \square$.
*Think:* Since the product of 4 and 25 is 100, these numbers are multiplied first:

$$
\begin{aligned}
(4 \times 17) \times 25 &= (17 \times 4) \times 25 \\
&= 17 \times (4 \times 25) \\
&= 17 \times 100 \\
&= 1700
\end{aligned}
$$

14. $40 \times 3000 = \square$.
*Think:* Since $4 \times 3 = 12$, $40 \times 3000 = 120{,}000$.

15. $24 \times 25 = \square$.
*Think:* The product of a multiplication remains unchanged if one of the factors is divided by a number provided that the other factor is multiplied by the same number. Thus $24 \times 25 = 12 \times 50 = 6 \times 100 = 600$.

# SELECTED RESEARCH

Brownell, W. A. and Carper, D. V., *Learning the Multiplication Combinations*. Durham, N.C.: Duke University Press, 1943, Chs. III and IV.

The primary purpose of the study was to determine how children learn the basic multiplication combinations.

The sample consisted of 593 pupils in grades III to V of four schools.

Two techniques were used: group testing and interviewing. The group tests were intended to yield two measures: rate of work and accuracy of answers. During the individual interviews it was attempted to determine the terms in which children think about the combinations. Group tests and interviews were conducted in December in grades 4B and 5B, and in May in grades 3A, 4A, and 5A. The group test consisted of the 81 basic multiplication combinations, excluding the zero combinations. Thus the highest possible score was 81. From these scores the accuracy of the answers was determined. Each pupil underscored the combination he was working at intervals of 30 seconds, as announced by the examiner. The rate of work was determined from these marks. During the interview 15 combinations, generally the more difficult ones, were presented to the pupils; the examiner determined the numerical answer supplied, the thought process applied, and the actual words the child used when describing the process. The children's procedures were classified into these categories:

> *Meaningful habituation:* the correct answer was confidently given with every evidence of understanding;
> *Rote memory:* the correct answer was confidently given with no evidence of understanding;
> *Guessing;*
> *Solution:* the child derived the answer by starting with a familiar situation. ..., *as in:* $3 \times 4 = (2 \times 4) + 4$;
> *Counting;*
> *Reversal:* $3 \times 6 = \square$. Since $6 \times 3 = 18, 3 \times 6 = 18$;
> *Tables:* the child recited the tables to arrive at the answer;
> *Visualization:* the child reproduced groups of objects to arrive at the answer;
> *No attempt;*
> *Indeterminate:* the child supplied the answer to a combination, but the examiner could not ascertain how he got it;
> *Miscellaneous.*

The findings concerning the rate of work and the accuracy of the answers suggested that, in the sample tested, the basic multiplication combinations had been mastered by the end of grade 4A. However, the interview data showed that mastery was not attained in grade 4A, but that pupils at that grade level were still using processes short of meaningful habituation. Even at the end of grade 5A too many pupils—more than 10%—still obtained the answers by immature processes.

The investigator suggested that children do not rapidly come to mature thought processes, and hence to true mastery of the multiplication combinations, but that they move through a series of stages from immature to mature processes. Some children move fast, and even seem to skip a stage. Others move slowly, and seem to stop at some intermediate stage.

## SKILLS TEST

1. Multiply and check each answer by dividing the product by one of the factors.

   | | | | |
   |---|---|---|---|
   | $33 \times 75 =$ | $66 \times 93 =$ | $22 \times 64 =$ | $39 \times 49 =$ |
   | $20 \times 64 =$ | $47 \times 51 =$ | $80 \times 93 =$ | $65 \times 75 =$ |

2. Multiply and check each answer by multiplying the factors in reversed order.

   | | | | |
   |---|---|---|---|
   | $13 \times 175 =$ | $96 \times 671 =$ | $87 \times 103 =$ | $23 \times 177 =$ |
   | $32 \times 105 =$ | $25 \times 525 =$ | $80 \times 705 =$ | $54 \times 652 =$ |

3. Multiply and check each answer by applying the rule of compensation.

   | | | | |
   |---|---|---|---|
   | $12 \times 25 =$ | $50 \times 44 =$ | $125 \times 64 =$ | $76 \times 50 =$ |
   | $74 \times 50 =$ | $25 \times 88 =$ | $250 \times 56 =$ | $52 \times 25 =$ |

4. Multiply and check each answer by applying the check of nines.

   | | | | |
   |---|---|---|---|
   | $157 \times 346 =$ | $779 \times 304 =$ | $1654 \times 9480 =$ | $6510 \times 4444 =$ |
   | $902 \times 257 =$ | $205 \times 106 =$ | $7002 \times 9540 =$ | $2509 \times 1009 =$ |

Find the answers to the following exercises by mental computation.

5. | | | | |
   |---|---|---|---|
   | $10 \times 57 =$ | $100 \times 946 =$ | $20 \times 600 =$ | $900 \times 20 =$ |
   | $10 \times 71 =$ | $100 \times 205 =$ | $70 \times 90 =$ | $40 \times 600 =$ |

6. | | | | |
   |---|---|---|---|
   | $3 \times 13 =$ | $8 \times 26 =$ | $3 \times 68 =$ | $8 \times 74 =$ |
   | $8 \times 25 =$ | $5 \times 73 =$ | $4 \times 93 =$ | $6 \times 16 =$ |

7. | | | | |
   |---|---|---|---|
   | $9 \times 44 =$ | $99 \times 27 =$ | $11 \times 72 =$ | $101 \times 15 =$ |
   | $9 \times 79 =$ | $99 \times 38 =$ | $11 \times 63 =$ | $101 \times 34 =$ |

8. | | | | |
   |---|---|---|---|
   | $1001 \times 341 =$ | $15 \times 26 =$ | $12 \times 33 =$ | $13 \times 12 =$ |
   | $1001 \times 191 =$ | $15 \times 36 =$ | $13 \times 21 =$ | $14 \times 32 =$ |

9. $105 \times 13 =$    $20 \times 15 =$    $6 \times 104 =$    $3 \times 115 =$
   $103 \times 12 =$    $30 \times 42 =$    $7 \times 203 =$    $8 \times 121 =$

10. $4 \times 6 \times 25 =$    $2 \times 14 \times 50 =$    $10 \times 75 \times 10 =$
   $8 \times 9 \times 125 =$    $2 \times 37 \times 5 =$    $5 \times 45 \times 20 =$

# EXERCISES

1. Explain and illustrate different interpretations of multiplication.

2. State what is meant by and illustrate the commutative and the associative properties of multiplication.

3. Describe several foundation activities for multiplication.

4. Describe various activities designed to anchor the key multiplication facts.

5. Write an illustrative lesson dealing with the case in which a number is multiplied by 10.

6. Explain and illustrate the distributive property of multiplication with respect to addition.

7. Describe the steps you would take when introducing the multiplication case in which a 3-digit number is multiplied by a 1-digit number.

8. Write and justify the steps taken when the number question $30 \times 23 = \square$ is solved by horizontal multiplication.

9. Show the steps you would take when introducing the multiplication case in which a 2-digit number is multiplied by a 2-digit number.

10. Describe various methods which can be used to check the product of a multiplication.

**For advanced students**

11. Explain the check of nines used to check an answer to a multiplication.

12. Report on an important piece of research pertaining to the multiplication of whole numbers.

13. As assigned by the instructor of the course, report on one or more of the following articles:
    a) Gibney, T. C., "Multiplication for the Slow Learner." *The Arithmetic Teacher*, February, 1962, pp. 74–76.

b) Grossnickle, F. E., "Discovering the Multiplication Facts." *The Arithmetic Teacher*, October, 1959, pp. 195–98 and 208.

c) Hannon, H., "A New Look at the Basic Principles of Multiplication with Whole Numbers." *The Arithmetic Teacher*, November, 1960, pp. 357–61.

d) Hickerson, J. A., "Why 'Indent' in Multiplication?" *The Arithmetic Teacher*, December, 1956, pp. 236–41.

e) Stern, C., "New Experiments with Multiplication." *The Arithmetic Teacher*, December, 1960, pp. 381–88.

f) Ulrich, L. E., Sr., "Casting Out Nines." *The Arithmetic Teacher*, October, 1955, pp. 77–79.

g) Volpel, M. C., "The Hundred-Board." *The Arithmetic Teacher*, December, 1959, pp. 295–301.

# SELECTED REFERENCES

Banks, J. H., *Learning and Teaching Arithmetic*, 2nd Ed. Boston: Allyn and Bacon, Inc., 1964, Chs. VI and VII.

Bell, C., C. D. Hammond, and R. B. Herrera, *Fundamentals of Arithmetic for Teachers*. New York: John Wiley & Sons, Inc., 1962, Ch. IV.

Buckingham, B. R., *Elementary Arithmetic: Its Meaning and Practice*. Boston: Ginn and Company, 1953, Chs. IV and VII.

Corle, C. G., *Teaching Mathematics in the Elementary School*. New York: The Ronald Press Company, 1964, Ch. VI.

Dutton, W. H. and L. J. Adams, *Arithmetic for Teachers*. Englewood Cliffs, N.J.: Prentice-Hall, Inc., 1961, Ch. IV.

Grossnickle, F. E. and L. J. Brueckner, *Discovering Meanings in Elementary School Mathematics*. New York: Holt, Rinehart & Winston, Inc., 1963, Chs. VIII and IX.

Howard, C. F. and E. Dumas, *Basic Procedures in Teaching Arithmetic*. Boston: D. C. Heath & Company, 1963, Ch. VIII.

Larsen, H. D. and H. G. Ludlow, *Arithmetic for Colleges*. New York: The Macmillan Co., 1963, Ch. V.

Marks, J. L., C. R. Purdy, and L. B. Kinney, *Teaching Arithmetic for Understanding*. New York: McGraw-Hill, Inc., 1958, Ch. VII.

Mueller, F. J., *Arithmetic: Its Structure and Concepts*, 2nd Ed. Englewood Cliffs, N.J.: Prentice-Hall, Inc., 1964, Units VIII and IX.

National Council of Teachers of Mathematics, *Topics in Mathematics*. Washington, D.C.: the Council, 1964, Bklts. 2 and 4.

School Mathematics Study Group, *Studies in Mathematics, Vol. IX: A Brief Course in Mathematics for Elementary School Teachers*. Stanford: Leland Stanford Junior University, 1963, Chs. VIII and X.

Spitzer, H. F., *The Teaching of Arithmetic*. Boston: Houghton Mifflin Company, 1961, Ch. V.

Swenson, E. J., *Teaching Arithmetic to Children*. New York: The Macmillan Co., 1964, Chs. IX and X.

Taylor, E. H. and C. N. Mills, *Arithmetic for Teacher-training Classes*. New York: Holt, Rinehart & Winston, Inc., 1955, Ch. V.

Thorpe, C. B., *Teaching Elementary Arithmetic*. New York: Harper & Row, Publishers, 1962, Ch. XIII.

Ward, M. and C. E. Hardgrove, *Modern Elementary Mathematics*. Reading, Mass.: Addison-Wesley Publishing Company, Inc., 1964, Chs. VI and VII.

# 13

---

# DIVISION

---

MULTIPLICATION AND DIVISION are inverse operations. It is anticipated that the teaching and studying of these operations concurrently will contribute toward a better understanding of the necessary concepts. The present chapter considers the teaching of the division of whole numbers.

## Meaning and Terms

Division "undoes" what multiplication "does," and is called the inverse operation of multiplication. For example, in $2 \times 3 = 6$, 3 has been multiplied by 2 to get 6, whereas in $6 \div 2 = 3$, 6 has been divided by 2 to get again the original number 3. Thus:

$$2 \times 3 = 6,$$

and
$$(2 \times 3) \div 2 = 3.$$

When finding the answer to $15 \div 5 = \square$ the question can be asked: By what number do I multiply 5 to get 15? The operation of division is thus used to find the missing factor in a multiplication situation when one of the two factors and the product are known. It is binary in nature because only two numbers are involved at a time.

*Example:* If $n \times 4 = 12$, then $n = 12 \div 4 = 3$. This situation is illustrated in the following array:

$$
\begin{array}{c}
\phantom{n}\ \ 4 \\
n\ \left|\begin{array}{cccc}
* & * & * & * \\
* & * & * & * \\
* & * & * & *
\end{array}\right.
\end{array}
$$

There are 12 elements in the array.

231

Division may be illustrated by subtracting successively equal groups. For example, the answer to $25 \div 5 = \square$ can be found by subtracting 5 successively: $25 - 5 = 20$ (1), $20 - 5 = 15$ (2), $15 - 5 = 10$ (3), $10 - 5 = 5$ (4), $5 - 5 = 0$ (5). Thus 5 fives equal 25, and $25 \div 5 = 5$.

There are several ways to indicate division. For example, $12 \div 4$; $4)\overline{12}$; and $\frac{12}{4}$ each indicate division.

The *dividend* is divided by the *divisor* to obtain the *quotient*. At present the divisor is often called the *known factor* and the quotient the *missing factor* of the *product*.

## Properties

The commutative property does not apply to the division of whole numbers.

*Example:* $12 \div 4 \neq 4 \div 12$.

The associative property does not apply to the division of whole numbers.

*Example:* $(24 \div 4) \div 2 \neq 24 \div (4 \div 2)$.

The set of whole numbers is not closed under division. For example, in $15 \div 2$, the quotient is not a whole number.

The distributive property of division with respect to addition was presented in Chapter 4. This property is used extensively in mental computation.

*Compensation in division:* In a division the dividend and the divisor can both be multiplied or divided by the same number (the number not being zero), without affecting the quotient.

*Examples:* $12 \div 6 = 24 \div 12$; $12 \div 6 = 4 \div 2$.

This property is often used in mental computation.

*Examples:* $625 \div 25 = 1250 \div 50 = 2500 \div 100 = 25$.
$$72 \div 18 = 36 \div 9 = 4.$$

## Zero in Division

1. $0 \div 2 = \square$.

Zero can be used as a dividend. Since the operation of division is the inverse of multiplication, zero divided by any number (the number not being zero) is equal to zero. $0 \div 2 = 0$, since $0 \times 2 = 0$.

2. $0 \div 0 = \square$.

Any number multiplied by zero yields zero as the product. Hence, $0 \div 0$ cannot be uniquely defined.

3. $2 \div 0 = \square$.

Since any number multiplied by zero yields zero as the product, $2 \div 0$ is undefined.

## Two Division Situations  — *Know*

The multiplication situation $3 \times 4$ apples $= 12$ apples can be inversed to two different division questions:

1. If 12 apples are put into boxes so that each box holds four apples, how many boxes are filled?  *Know*

2. If 12 apples are divided into three equal groups, how many apples will there be in each group?  *find  size of  the  share*

In the first situation the number of equal groups must be found. This kind of division is called *measurement division*.

In the second situation the size of the share must be determined. This kind of division is called *partition division*.

The two situations are described below for the benefit of the teacher. There does not seem to be much need for the pupil to learn to make the distinction.

### Measurement division

In measurement division it must be determined how many groups of a given size are contained in the dividend. The question is, thus, how many times the one equals the other.

EXAMPLE:
We have 12 children working on committees. There are 4 children on each committee. How many committees are there?
*Number sentence:* $12 \div 4 = 3$.
There are 3 committees.

This division situation is shown graphically as follows:

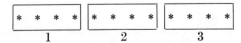

The number line can also be used to illustrate the problem:

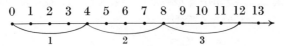

Since it must be determined how many groups of 4 children can be taken from a group of 12 children, the answer can also be found by serial subtraction:

$$12 - 4 = 8 \ (1) \qquad 8 - 4 = 4 \ (2) \qquad 4 - 4 = 0 \ (3)$$

Because of the ease with which a measurement situation can be diagramed, it is recommended that measurement division be introduced to the pupils before partition division is undertaken.

**Partition division**

In partition division the number of groups is known and the size of the share must be determined.

EXAMPLE:
Twelve apples are equally divided among 3 boys. How many apples does each boy get?
*Number sentence:* $12 \div 3 = 4$.
Each boy gets 4 apples.

This situation is not as easy to show graphically as is the measurement situation:

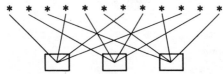

The partition situation can be changed into a measurement situation by dividing the 12 apples into groups of 3 apples each. In each group of 3 apples there is 1 apple for each boy. Each boy gets as many apples as there are groups of 3 apples. This process can be illustrated on the number line:

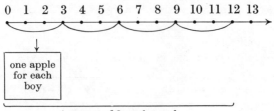

# Grade Placement of Division Topics

The grade placement of division topics differs only in minor aspects in the various textbooks.

The placement of topics as shown below is typical for the traditional arithmetic program. In some of the newer programs, many of these topics are introduced at earlier grade levels. This trend is to be encouraged.

*Typical Grade Placement of Division Topics*

*Grade I:* 1. Separation of a collection of objects into equal groups.
2. Multiple counting.

*Grade II:* 1. Maintenance of skills.
2. Expression of a number as the sum of two or more equal numbers
3. Division situations such as: How many fours equal 8?

*Grade III:* 1. Maintenance of skills.
2. Easy division facts in measurement situations.
3. Easy division facts in partition situations.
4. Vocabulary.
5. Finding a unit-fractional part of a number.

*Grade IV:* 1. Maintenance of skills.
2. Extension of the vocabulary.
3. Mastery of all the division facts.
4. One-digit and two-digit divisors and multi-digit dividends.
5. Remainders.
6. Zero in the quotient.
7. Estimation of quotients.

*Grade V:* 1. Maintenance of skills.
2. Two-digit and three-digit divisors.
3. Two-digit and three-digit quotients.

*Grade VI:* 1. Maintenance of skills.
2. Multi-digit divisors.

# Foundation Activities for Division

The key division facts—presented elsewhere in this chapter—are usually not introduced in the primary grades. However, in these grades foundation experiences can prepare children for direct and thoroughly planned instruction in division.

The introduction of easy division facts could probably be undertaken sooner than is the practice now. If children can answer the question "How many fours equal eight?" and can understand the meaning of the division symbol, it seems logical to present the division question $8 \div 4 = \square$.

Foundation experiences for division of whole numbers include the following activities:

1. *Counting objects by twos, threes, etc.*
   Although counting objects by twos, threes, etc. is first of all a preparation for multiplication, these exercises can also be considered foundation activities for division.

2. *Working with blocks.*
   Manipulating blocks of related sizes such as those of the fraction board, the Cuisenaire rods, or the Stern blocks is a recommended foundation activity for division. Through this activity children will begin to see that the size of a certain block is one half the size of another; that four selected blocks, when put together, equal the length of another block; etc.

3. *Separating a collection of objects into smaller groups.*
   *Example:* Draw a line around a group of four stars. Make as many groups of four as you can.

   ```
   *   *   *   *   *   *   *   *   *   *
   *   *   *   *   *   *   *   *   *   *
   ```

4. *Multiple counting.*
   Depending on the pupils' level in arithmetic, counting by twos, threes, etc. without referring to objects is undertaken to develop the children's skill in determining answers to questions such as: How many twos equal eight? The number line is a useful device in developing this skill.

   *Example:* Count by twos to 10. Show the steps on the number line.

   0   1   2   3   4   5   6   7   8   9   10

5. *Doubles, etc.*
   Exercises such as $6 = \square + \square$ and $9 = \square + \square + \square$ develop skill in renaming a number. The number line is used here also:

   0   1   2   3   4   5   6
   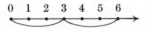

6. *Serial subtraction.*
   With serial subtraction the question is: How many twos can I subtract from 8?

7. *Teaching the concepts of "part" and "whole" and their relationship.*

8. *Teaching the concept of one half.*

## The Key Division Facts

The key division facts (also called the basic division facts) are the inverse of the basic multiplication facts. Since there are no facts in which a number is divided by zero, there are only 90 basic division facts. These facts are presented on page 238.

## Introducing the Key Facts

The children should understand that the operation of division is the inverse of multiplication, or that division "undoes" what multiplication "does." It is therefore recommended that the key division facts be introduced together with, or soon after, the presentation of the corresponding multiplication facts. When the pupils know that two fours equal eight, the teacher should guide them to see that eight divided by two equals four. Then the multiplication and division sentences are written and compared, and the necessary vocabulary is introduced.

In introducing the first basic division facts, meaningful situations must be used. An exercise such as $8 \div 2 = \square$ deals with abstract numbers, but a word problem resulting in this number question gives the child something concrete to think about.

*Example:* Ann pastes 8 pictures in her scrapbook. She puts only 2 pictures on a page. How many pages does Ann fill?

Several ways of solving this problem are available:

1. The most meaningful way is actually to use 8 pictures and put 2 on a page until all 8 are used. The child finds out that 4 groups of 2 pictures each are contained in 8 pictures. Following this, counters such as disks or beads on a counting frame may be used, to give the pupil practice in separating the collection into groups of two each and counting the groups.

2. The situation can be shown in a diagram:

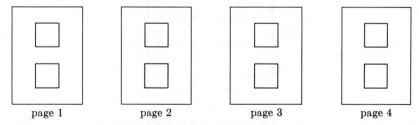

|      page 1      |      page 2      |      page 3      |      page 4      |

In order to put 8 pictures in the scrapbook, 4 pages are needed if 2 pictures are put on one page.

| | | | |
|---|---|---|---|
| 0 × 9 = 0 | 0 × 8 = 0 | 0 × 7 = 0 | 0 × 6 = 0 |
| 1 × 9 = 9 | 1 × 8 = 8 | 1 × 7 = 7 | 1 × 6 = 6 |
| 2 × 9 = 18 | 2 × 8 = 16 | 2 × 7 = 14 | 2 × 6 = 12 |
| 3 × 9 = 27 | 3 × 8 = 24 | 3 × 7 = 21 | 3 × 6 = 18 |
| 4 × 9 = 36 | 4 × 8 = 32 | 4 × 7 = 28 | 4 × 6 = 24 |
| 5 × 9 = 45 | 5 × 8 = 40 | 5 × 7 = 35 | 5 × 6 = 30 |
| 6 × 9 = 54 | 6 × 8 = 48 | 6 × 7 = 42 | 6 × 6 = 36 |
| 7 × 9 = 63 | 7 × 8 = 56 | 7 × 7 = 49 | 7 × 6 = 42 |
| 8 × 9 = 72 | 8 × 8 = 64 | 8 × 7 = 56 | 8 × 6 = 48 |
| 9 × 9 = 81 | 9 × 8 = 72 | 9 × 7 = 63 | 9 × 6 = 54 |

| | | | | |
|---|---|---|---|---|
| 0 × 5 = 0 | 0 × 4 = 0 | 0 × 3 = 0 | 0 × 2 = 0 | 0 × 1 = 0 |
| 1 × 5 = 5 | 1 × 4 = 4 | 1 × 3 = 3 | 1 × 2 = 2 | 1 × 1 = 1 |
| 2 × 5 = 10 | 2 × 4 = 8 | 2 × 3 = 6 | 2 × 2 = 4 | 2 × 1 = 2 |
| 3 × 5 = 15 | 3 × 4 = 12 | 3 × 3 = 9 | 3 × 2 = 6 | 3 × 1 = 3 |
| 4 × 5 = 20 | 4 × 4 = 16 | 4 × 3 = 12 | 4 × 2 = 8 | 4 × 1 = 4 |
| 5 × 5 = 25 | 5 × 4 = 20 | 5 × 3 = 15 | 5 × 2 = 10 | 5 × 1 = 5 |
| 6 × 5 = 30 | 6 × 4 = 24 | 6 × 3 = 18 | 6 × 2 = 12 | 6 × 1 = 6 |
| 7 × 5 = 35 | 7 × 4 = 28 | 7 × 3 = 21 | 7 × 2 = 14 | 7 × 1 = 7 |
| 8 × 5 = 40 | 8 × 4 = 32 | 8 × 3 = 24 | 8 × 2 = 16 | 8 × 1 = 8 |
| 9 × 5 = 45 | 9 × 4 = 36 | 9 × 3 = 27 | 9 × 2 = 18 | 9 × 1 = 9 |

3. The question is asked: How many times can we take 2 from 8? $8 - 2 = 6$ (1), $6 - 2 = 4$ (2), $4 - 2 = 2$ (3), $2 - 2 = 0$ (4). We can take 4 twos from 8.

4. The problem can be solved by using the number line:

$$0 \quad 1 \quad 2 \quad 3 \quad 4 \quad 5 \quad 6 \quad 7 \quad 8 \quad 9 \quad 10 \quad 11$$

I can rename 8 as 4 twos.

5. The answer can be found by relating the division situation to the corresponding multiplication situation: since 4 twos equal 8, 4 groups of 2 each are contained in 8. The relation can be shown in an array, as presented at the right.

$$
2 \,\Big| \begin{array}{cccc} & & 4 & \\ * & * & * & * \\ * & * & * & * \end{array}
$$

After the division process has been developed meaningfully by ways such as those presented above, the division symbolism is introduced and arithmetic symbols are substituted for language symbols. The division sentence $8 \div 2 = 4$ is then presented, and the new vocabulary is stressed in the teaching that follows.

When the process of division is understood by the pupils and several word problems have been solved, the presentation of exercises of the following kind is recommended:

$$4 \times 3 = \square; \quad 12 = \square \times 3; \quad 12 \div 3 = \square; \quad 12 \div \square = 4;$$

$$\text{Since } 3 \times 4 = 12, \; 12 \div 4 = \square.$$

Partition division is introduced only after several measurement divisions have been discussed and are understood by the children.

*Example:* Twelve marbles are divided among 3 boys. How many marbles does each boy receive?

The most meaningful way to solve this problem is to have 12 marbles actually divided among 3 boys, each boy receiving 1 marble at a time until all the 12 marbles have been divided. Then a diagram is made, illustrating what has been done.

The teacher can also show that 3 marbles are needed if each boy will receive 1 marble, and he can then ask the question: "How many times can we take 3 marbles from 12 marbles?" When the partition situation has thus been changed to a measurement division, the number line can be used easily and serial subtraction can be employed.

$$\frac{4}{3)\overline{12}}$$

When the form $3)\overline{12}$ is presented, it is stressed that 4 means 4 ones, and that the numeral 4 is written above the 2 in 12, which also represents ones.

## Developing and Anchoring Skills

It is not sufficient that pupils have an understanding of the division process and know how to find the answer to a division question. After an understanding of the basic division facts has been acquired, the children must practice in order to master the facts and anchor the skills. The final goal is that the children know instantly the answer to a basic division question when it is presented. When teachers are satisfied with understanding only, the skills will not be fixed well enough; this means that, at higher grade levels teachers will have to do too much review work in the basic facts.

Several techniques can be employed by the resourceful teacher to assure mastery of the basic facts. Following are some examples of techniques and devices which can be used. Several of these have been explained in previous chapters.

1. Flashcards, including those on which the question is presented in horizontal form.
2. The division wheel, which is a modification of the addition wheel.
3. The electric board.
4. The construction of a division table which is a modification of the multiplication table.
5. Division card games.
6. The supplying of missing factors.
7. The writing, checking, and memorizing of the tables of facts.
8. Graphical illustrations on the number line.
9. Brief daily reviews of the facts.

The multiplication board may be used as a division board, since division is the inverse operation of multiplication.

## Division with a Remainder

Division with remainders must be introduced in word problems, since the answer to the problem depends on the situation. For example, the division question $10 \div 3 = \square$ has different answers, depending on the situation it represents:

1. Ten inches of ribbon are divided into 3 equal parts. How long is each part?

The number sentence is $10 \div 3 = 3\frac{1}{3}$. Each part is $3\frac{1}{3}''$.

2. Jim has 10¢. He buys chocolate bars for 3¢ a piece. How many bars can Jim buy, and how many pennies does he have left?

The number sentence is $10 \div 3 = 3$, remainder 1. Jim can buy 3 bars, and has 1¢ left. Thus $10 \div 3 = 3$ r. 1.

3. If the price of 3 apples is 10¢, how much does 1 apple cost? Since we cannot pay $3\frac{1}{3}$¢, the grocer will charge 4¢. Hence, the answer is 4¢.

4. How much interest does a bank pay on $5.00 at 2% per year, in 4 months? The bank pays on this amount, in 1 year, $2 \times \$.05 = \$.10$, or 10¢. In 4 months the interest is $\frac{1}{3}$ of 10¢. Since $10 \div 3 = 3\frac{1}{3}$, the bank pays 3¢.

## Dividing by a 1-digit Divisor

Division of a multi-digit dividend by a 1-digit divisor is introduced in cases in which there is no regrouping and no remainder.

*Example:* Four boys divided 48 baseball cards equally among themselves. How many cards did each boy get?

*Number question:* $4\overline{)48}$, or $48 \div 4 = \square$.

At this stage the pupils know already that 4 tens divided by 4 equals 1 ten, or that 40 divided by 4 equals 10. They also know the fact $8 \div 4 = 2$. Hence:

$$48 \div 4 = (40 + 8) \div 4$$
$$= (40 \div 4) + (8 \div 4)$$
$$= 10 + 2$$
$$= 12$$

*distributive property*

After the problem has been worked with reference to objects, the common method of division is developed. The following steps are discussed:

1. How many fours equal 40? 10 fours equal 40. The 1 (for 1 ten) is written in the tens column, above the 4 in 48. 10 fours are subtracted from 48.

$$\begin{array}{r} 1 \\ 4\overline{)48} \\ \underline{40} \\ 8 \end{array}$$

2. How many fours equal 8? 2 fours equal 8. The numeral 2 is written above the 8 in 48, and 8 is subtracted from the partial dividend 8.

$$
\begin{array}{r}
12 \\
4{\overline{\smash{)}48}} \\
40 \\
\hline
8 \\
8 \\
\hline
0
\end{array}
$$

3. The teacher emphasizes again that $48 = 40 + 8$, and that first 40 and then 8 has been divided by 4, resulting in $10 + 2 = 12$.

4. The answer may be checked by multiplying the quotient and the divisor: $4 \times 12 = 48$. Through proper guide questions, the pupils are again led to conclude that the operation of division is the inverse of multiplication, or that division "undoes" what multiplication "does."

5. In the class discussion it is pointed out that, usually, the zero in 40 is not written, but understood, and that the division is written as shown at the right.

$$
\begin{array}{r}
12 \\
4{\overline{\smash{)}48}} \\
4 \\
\hline
8 \\
8 \\
\hline
0
\end{array}
$$

A more difficult case to be presented is a division such as $91 \div 7 = \square$. Through the use of devices such as beads, children should understand that 70 and 21 are divided by 7, and that the two quotients are added. This is an excellent preparation for mental computation.

When divisions with 3-digit quotients are introduced, special attention should be paid to those exercises which call for a zero in the quotient. These exercises are very difficult for some children. The reason is that, after bringing down a figure from the dividend, the divisor is larger than the partial dividend then under consideration. It is recommended that an exercise such as $525 \div 5 = \square$ be first worked horizontally as follows:

$$
\begin{aligned}
525 \div 5 &= (500 + 25) \div 5 \\
&= (500 \div 5) + (25 \div 5) \\
&= 100 + 5 \\
&= 105
\end{aligned}
$$

and that the pupils find out why there is a zero in the quotient.

## Various Algorisms

A different procedure for performing division is the subtractive method, which has been applied in the example at the right. Pupils estimate the number of times the divisor can be taken from the dividend or from the partial dividend. After a sufficient amount of practice, they will become more accurate in their estimations and, consequently, the form will be shortened.

```
4 | 172
  |  40 | 10
  | ----
  | 132
  |  40 | 10
  | ----
  |  92
  |  40 | 10
  | ----
  |  52
  |  40 | 10
  | ----
  |  12
  |  12 |  3
  | ----  ----
  |   0   43
```

The length of the procedure is often said to be a disadvantage, but it should be realized that pupils learn to shorten the process as their proficiency increases. Some teachers introduce this form as initial work in division, then change to the conventional form after the process is well understood.

The subtractive method of division can likewise be introduced at higher grade levels, as an enrichment activity or as a reintroduction of division.

Another expanded form of division is shown at the right. The value of each digit in the quotient is shown. This method should be introduced in initial work in long division and used extensively later, when more difficult cases of division by mental computation are taught. An example of such a mental computation exercise follows.

$$
\begin{array}{r}
3 \\
40 \overline{)43} \\
4 \overline{)172} \\
160 \\
\hline
12 \\
12 \\
\hline
0
\end{array}
$$

$$172 \div 4 = (160 + 12) \div 4$$
$$= (160 \div 4) + (12 \div 4)$$
$$= 40 + 3$$
$$= 43$$

When both the horizontal and vertical forms of division are used, the pupil will have a better opportunity to understand the process.

## Dividing by 2- and 3-digit Divisors

Division with 2-digit divisors is introduced in problems in which divisors and dividends are multiples of ten. These situations should be related to multiplication: Since $4 \times 20 = 80$, $80 \div 20 = 4$. Then the long form is written

and discussed. The pupils should try to answer the question why, in $20\overline{)80}$,
$$\begin{array}{r} 4 \\ 20\overline{)80} \\ \underline{80} \\ 0 \end{array}$$
the quotient is 4. The leading questions are: "How many twos are there in 8?" "So, how many 20's are there in 80?" "What number times 20 equals 80?"

Other examples, such as $150 \div 30 = \square$, follow, and the pupils are led to discover that the quotient can be found by asking: "How many threes are there in 15?" which leads to: "How many 3 tens are there in 15 tens?," or "How many 30's are there in 150?"

After these cases have been mastered, division exercises resulting in remainders are presented, such as $183 \div 30 = \square$, and soon those with a 2-digit quotient, such as $630 \div 30 = \square$, can be introduced.

Three-digit divisors do not present much more difficulty when the estimated quotient figure is the true quotient figure, as in $800 \div 200$. The difficulties appear when the estimated quotient figure is not the true quotient figure.

## Estimating a Quotient Figure

In exercises such as $28\overline{)140}$, various methods for estimating the quotient can be used:

1. *The one-rule, round-down method.* The pupil rounds 28 to 20, and decides that there are 7 twos in 14, but $7 \times 28 = 196$, so he tries $6 \times 28$. $6 \times 28 = 168$, and 168 is still too large to be subtracted from 140. After trying $5 \times 28$, the pupil decides that 5 is the true quotient. He has tried three times and has erred twice. It should be noticed that, when working the exercise $140 \div 21 = \square$ by this method, there will be two trials and one error.

2. *The one-rule, round-up method.* The pupil rounds 28 to 30, and decides that there are 4 threes in 14. Since $4 \times 28 = 112$, he tries $5 \times 28$, and finds 5 to be the true quotient. The pupil has tried twice and erred once. When

working the exercise 140 ÷ 21 by this method, he will try three times and err twice.

3. *The two-rule method:*
a) *Round down* when the ones figure is 1, 2, 3, or 4;
b) *Round up* when the ones figure is 5, 6, 7, 8, or 9.

*Note*
*#*

After working some division exercises, the reader will discover that the two-rule method eliminates work for the pupil, since the estimated quotient figure is more often the true quotient figure than it is with the one-rule methods.

Although the two-rule method results in fewer corrections of the estimated quotient figure, it should be realized that the pupils have to decide whether the first digit in the divisor should be rounded up or down and that, during the process of determining the true quotient figure, the estimated quotient may have to be either increased or decreased. This places an extra burden on the pupil. For this reason and for others presented below (which make the round-up method inferior to the round-down method), the author does not recommend the use of the two-rule method in initial teaching of this case.

Of the two one-rule methods, the one-rule, round-down method seems to be the better. Pupils are accustomed to working with the given divisor when they start division with 2-digit divisors. Moreover, the one-rule, round-down method better paves the way for the mature method of estimating the quotient by inspection. When 156 must be divided by 26, the mature pupil should see 156 as 120 + 36. He will work with 20's, and not with 30's.

The one-rule, round-up method has still another disadvantage. Pupils who have not yet had much experience in dividing by a 2-digit divisor do not always identify a case in which the estimated quotient must be increased. As a result, they may work an exercise in the manner shown below.

$$\begin{array}{r} 41 \\ 28\overline{)140} \\ 112 \\ \hline 28 \\ 28 \\ \hline 0 \end{array}$$

4. As pupils become more mature in mathematics, they should *estimate the quotient figure by inspection.* They should use their knowledge of the number system and rename the divisor and the dividend as sums of tens and ones (when the divisor is a 2-digit number), then decide upon a reasonable estimate and check it. These pupils will make use of the distributive property for multiplication with respect to addition.

*Example:* $272 \div 34 = \square$. The quotient must be less than 10, since $10 \times 34 = 340$. If the pupil estimates the quotient to be 7, he will think $7 \times 34 = (7 \times 30) + (7 \times 4) = 210 + 28 = 238$. Then he will try 8 as quotient: $8 \times 34 = (8 \times 30) + (8 \times 4) = 240 + 32 = 272$.

## Checking the Quotient

Various methods can be applied for checking the quotient. The method selected will depend upon the mathematical maturity of the pupil.

1. *Application of the relation between the terms.* This check is based upon the fact that the product of the quotient and the divisor plus the remainder equals the dividend.
*Examples:* $35 \div 7 = 5$, and $5 \times 7 = 35$;

$$36 \div 7 = 5, \text{ remainder } 1, \text{ and } 5 \times 7 + 1 = 36;$$

$$1325 \div 49 = 27, \text{ remainder } 2, \text{ and } 27 \times 49 + 2 = 1325.$$

2. *Approximation.* When an exact answer is not required, but an approximate answer is sufficient, the dividend and the divisor may be rounded and an approximate answer can sometimes be found easily by mental computation.
*Example:* The reasonableness of the quotient in $1323 \div 49 = 27$ can be checked by dividing 1300 by 50.

3. *The check of nines.* In the upper grades, pupils of at least average ability can learn to check a quotient by applying the check of nines. The excess of nines is determined in the quotient, the divisor, and the remainder. The excesses of nines in the divisor and the quotient are multiplied, and to this product the excess of nines in the remainder (if any) is added. This sum (or the excess of nines in this sum) must equal the excess of nines in the dividend.

*Example:*

| | | |
|---|---|---|
| 23 | Excess of nines in the quotient: | 5 |
| 434)9988 | Excess of nines in the divisor: | $\times \, 2$ |
| 868 | Product: | 10 |
| 1308 | Excess of nines in the remainder: | 6 |
| 1302 | Total: | $+ \, \overline{16}$, or 7 |
| 6 | Excess of nines in the dividend: | 7 |

The limitations of the check of nines have already been presented in Chapter 10.

## Short and Long Division

In long division the complete process of division is shown, as in the example below:

$$
\begin{array}{r}
9 \\
5\overline{)47} \\
45 \\
\hline
2
\end{array}
$$

In short division the computation is left out, as in $\quad 5\overline{)47}^{\,9\frac{2}{5}}$

There is a need for both the long and the short forms of division. As stated previously, an ideal way to introduce the basic division facts is to show the relation between a division fact and the corresponding multiplication fact. For example, since $5 \times 2 = 10$, $10 \div 2 = 5$. This is the short form of division, which is introduced as one of the first steps. The same division fact is then shown in the long form, *e.g.*

$$
\begin{array}{r}
5 \\
2\overline{)10} \\
10 \\
\hline
0
\end{array}
$$

or $10 \div 2 = 5$, in order to prepare the pupils for more difficult division

$$
\begin{array}{r}
10 \\
\hline
0
\end{array}
$$

problems.

Thorpe writes:

"When pupils have mastered the division facts and have learned the simple algorism, $3\overline{)6}^{\,2}$, as meaning how many 3's in 6, they are using short division, not long division, as in $3\overline{)6}^{\,2}_{\,6}$. A logical next step is $3\overline{)60}$. This implies how many 3's in 6 tens, or how many 3's in 60, and the answer is 20, shown as $3\overline{)60}^{\,20}$. This is still short division form."[1]

It seems logical to recommend that pupils do as much short division as their ability allows, provided that it is done meaningfully. Pupils should be taught how to rename numbers mentally, then divide each part, and add the quotients. This leads to the neglected area of mental computation.

---

[1] Thorpe, C. B., *Teaching Elementary Arithmetic* (New York: Harper & Row, Publishers, 1962), p. 152.

## Mental Computation in Division

The teaching of mental computation in division according to a well-defined, sequential plan should result in a better understanding of the number properties and in proficiency in mentally computing simple division problems.

*Examples:*

1.
$$42 \div 3 = (30 + 12) \div 3$$
$$= (30 \div 3) + (12 \div 3)$$
$$= 10 + 4$$
$$= 14$$

In this example, 30 is selected as one of the addends, since it equals $10 \times 3$.

2.
$$84 \div 4 = (80 + 4) \div 4$$
$$= (80 \div 4) + (4 \div 4)$$
$$= 20 + 1$$
$$= 21$$

Since $80 = 20 \times 4$, this number is selected as one of the addends of the sum that renames 84.

3.
$$468 \div 9 = (450 + 18) \div 9$$
$$= (450 \div 9) + (18 \div 9)$$
$$= 50 + 2$$
$$= 52$$

It is clear why 450, equalling $50 \times 9$, is selected as one of the addends.

4.
$$396 \div 4 = (400 - 4) \div 4$$
$$= (400 \div 4) - (4 \div 4)$$
$$= 100 - 1$$
$$= 99$$

396 is written as $400 - 4$, since it is easy to divide first 400 by 4, then 4 by 4, and to subtract the quotients.

Through inductive teaching, the pupils should be led to discover the rules for dividing a number by 10, 100, etc.

Inductively, the rule of compensation should be found by using simple exercises. Then the rule is applied in more difficult situations.

*Example:*     $650 \div 25 = 1300 \div 50 = 2600 \div 100 = 26.$

## SELECTED RESEARCH

Grossnickle, F. E., "An Experiment with Two Methods of Estimation in the Quotient." *Elementary School Journal*, May, 1937, pp. 668–77. Copyright 1937 by The University of Chicago.

Grossnickle conducted a study in which the results of teaching two methods of estimating the quotient were compared: (1) the apparent method (the one-rule, round-down method); (2) the increase-by-one method (the two-rule method). The two methods were taught to sample groups of fourth-grade pupils, one sample consisting of 216, and the other of 233 pupils. The experiment lasted 76 days.

The results of the final test indicated that the pupils using the apparent method scored slightly higher than the other group, but in most cases the differences were too small to be statistically significant.

Van Engen, H. and E. G. Gibb, *General Mental Functions Associated with Division.* Educational Service Studies, No. 2. Cedar Falls, Iowa: Iowa State Teachers College, 1956.

The purpose of the study was to compare the results of teaching division by the conventional method with those of teaching division by the subtractive method. The sample consisted of 12 fourth-grade classes randomly selected from all self-contained fourth-grade classes in Des Moines, Iowa, and Sioux City, Iowa.

The conclusions were summarized as follows:

1. Children taught the conventional method of division will no doubt attain greater achievement in solving kinds of problems taught than will the children taught the subtractive method. However, the subtractive methods group worked with problems where the number of digits both in the divisor and in the dividend increased. Only the dividend increased in number of digits in problems included in the conventional instructional program.

2. The subtractive method of division can be expected to be more effective in enabling children to transfer familiar experiences to unfamiliar situations where the general context still remains the same.

3. Children taught the subtractive method can be expected to have a better understanding of the idea of division. For them the processing does not appear to be a matter of using a series of steps such as divide, multiply subtract, compare, etc., as was true of the children using the conventional method.

4. There is no reason to expect real differences between the contributions of the mental functions of the two methods to retention of skill and understanding that may be achieved. This seems to be more closely tied up with teaching procedure, regardless of method of division.

5. Partitive and measurement situations are different for the two groups insofar as the ability to comprehend the situation is concerned. At the end of the fourth-year arithmetic program one would expect to find that the idea of quotitive division is easier for those taught the subtractive method, and that the idea of partitive division is easier for the conventional method group.

6. Children of low intellectual ability can be expected to have less difficulty understanding the process of division if they use the subtractive method rather than the conventional method.

7. Apparently method differences in the processing of division problems make little difference in the high intellectual groups—that is, other than what might be expected between the two methods groups when variables of intelligence and arithmetic achievement are controlled.

## SKILLS TEST

1. Divide and check by multiplying the quotient and the divisor:

   $806 \div 62 =$     $2044 \div 28 =$     $5069 \div 137 =$     $26{,}832 \div 258 =$

   $495 \div 11 =$     $1932 \div 23 =$     $6032 \div 104 =$     $84{,}436 \div 404 =$

2. Divide and check by using the check of nines:

   $4{,}560{,}792 \div 3714 =$     $11{,}111{,}100 \div 2002 =$     $1{,}720{,}546 \div 263 =$

3. Find the answers by mental computation:

   $4 \div 2 =$     $40 \div 20 =$     $4000 \div 2000 =$     $40{,}000 \div 2000 =$

   $40 \div 2 =$     $400 \div 200 =$     $4000 \div 2 =$     $40{,}000 \div 20{,}000 =$

   $400 \div 2 =$     $400 \div 20 =$     $4000 \div 20 =$     $4000 \div 200 =$

4. Find the answers by mental computation:

   $91 \div 7 =$     $256 \div 4 =$     $440 \div 2 =$     $420 \div 3 =$

   $75 \div 5 =$     $399 \div 7 =$     $440 \div 20 =$     $960 \div 8 =$

5. Find the answers by mental computation:

   $392 \div 4 =$     $291 \div 3 =$     $594 \div 6 =$     $490 \div 5 =$

6. Use the rule of compensation to find the answers:

   $108 \div 18 =$     $48 \div 12 =$     $350 \div 25 =$     $1250 \div 250 =$

   $84 \div 14 =$     $144 \div 24 =$     $1600 \div 50 =$     $650 \div 25 =$

7. Determine whether the quotients are correct by using the check: quotient $\times$ divisor $+$ remainder $=$ dividend:

   $197 \div 15 = 13 \text{ r. } 2$     $845 \div 25 = 33 \text{ r. } 10$     $26{,}134 \div 125 = 209 \text{ r. } 9$

# EXERCISES

1. Explain and illustrate the difference between measurement division and partition division.

2. Give examples of two properties of division.

3. Explain why a zero in a quotient may be difficult for pupils who are beginning their study of division.

4. Describe some activities for the primary grades which are designed to develop the concept of division.

5. Should pupils memorize the basic division facts? Defend your answer.

6. Describe and illustrate how you would introduce division with a remainder.

7. Explain and illustrate the difference between the subtractive method and the traditional method of division.

8. Describe a device that can be used by pupils in the study for mastery of the division facts.

## For advanced students

9. Criticize the typical grade placement of division topics.

10. Describe the different methods for estimating a quotient figure. What is, in your opinion, the best method? Why?

11. Describe the check of nines in division.

12. Report on a piece of research pertaining to division of whole numbers.

13. Write an illustrative lesson on the division of a 3-digit number by a 2-digit number, in which the first estimated quotient figure is not the true quotient figure.

14. As assigned by the instructor of the course, report on one or more of the following articles:
    a) Capps, L. R., "Making Division Meaningful and Logical." *The Arithmetic Teacher*, April, 1962, pp. 198–202.
    b) Christofferson, H. C., "Meanings in Division." *The Arithmetic Teacher*, February, 1957, pp. 21–23.
    c) Hartung, M. L., "Estimating the Quotient in Division, a Critical Analysis of Research." *The Arithmetic Teacher*, April, 1957, pp. 100–11.
    d) Hilaire, P. A., "Let's Take a Look at Division." *The Arithmetic Teacher*, May, 1961, pp. 220–25.

e) Wood, B. Adams, "A Method in Division of Whole Numbers." *The Arithmetic Teacher*, April, 1958, pp. 145–48.
f) Zweng, M. J., "Division Problems and the Concept of Rate." *The Arithmetic Teacher*, December, 1964, pp. 547–56.

## SELECTED REFERENCES

Banks, J. H., *Learning and Teaching Arithmetic*, 2nd Ed. Boston: Allyn and Bacon, Inc., 1964, Chs. VI and VII.

Bell, C., C. D. Hammond, and R. B. Herrera, *Fundamentals of Arithmetic for Teachers*. New York: John Wiley & Sons, Inc., 1962, Ch. VI.

Buckingham, B. R., *Elementary Arithmetic: Its Meaning and Practice*. Boston: Ginn and Company, 1953, Chs. IV and VIII.

Corle, C. G., *Teaching Mathematics in the Elementary School*. New York: The Ronald Press Company, 1964, Ch. VII.

Dutton, W. H. and L. J. Adams, *Arithmetic for Teachers*. Englewood Cliffs, N.J.: Prentice-Hall, Inc., 1961, Ch. V.

Grossnickle, F. E. and L. J. Brueckner, *Discovering Meanings in Elementary School Mathematics*. New York: Holt, Rinehart & Winston, Inc., 1963, Chs. VIII and IX.

Hickerson, J. A., *Guiding Children's Arithmetic Experiences*. Englewood Cliffs, N.J.: Prentice-Hall, Inc., 1952, Ch. IX.

Howard, C. F. and E. Dumas, *Basic Procedures in Teaching Arithmetic*. Boston: D. C. Heath & Company, 1963, Ch. VIII.

Larsen, H. D. and H. G. Ludlow, *Arithmetic for Colleges*, 3rd Ed. New York: The Macmillan Co., 1963, Ch. VI.

Marks, J. L., C. R. Purdy, and L. B. Kinney, *Teaching Arithmetic for Understanding*. New York: McGraw-Hill, Inc., 1958, Ch. VII.

Mueller, F. J., *Arithmetic: Its Structure and Concepts*, 2nd Ed. Englewood Cliffs, N.J.: Prentice-Hall, Inc., 1964, Units XIV and XV.

National Council of Teachers of Mathematics, *Topics in Mathematics*. Washington, D.C.: the Council, 1964, Bklts. 2 and 4.

School Mathematics Study Group, *Studies in Mathematics, Vol. IX: A Brief Course in Mathematics for Elementary School Teachers*. Stanford: Leland Stanford Junior University, 1963, Chs. IX and XI.

Spitzer, H. F., *The Teaching of Arithmetic*. Boston: Houghton Mifflin Company, 1961, Ch. VI.

Thorpe, C. B., *Teaching Elementary Arithmetic*. New York: Harper & Row, Publishers, 1962, Ch. XIV.

# 14

---

# FRACTIONS

---

IN THE SET of integers there is no element that can replace $n$ in the equation $1 \div 2 = n$ and make the statement true. Moreover, if we have only the integers to work with, the result of a measurement must be expressed by a measure that is an integer, while greater accuracy is often required. Thus the need for an extension of the number system which comprises the set of integers is evident. This extended number system is called the *rational number system.*

## Meaning and Terms

A *rational number* is a number that can be expressed as the quotient of an integer and a non-zero integer. It should be understood that integers are included in the set of rational numbers $\left(5 = \dfrac{5}{1}, \, {}^{-}3 = \dfrac{{}^{-}3}{1}\right)$.

The subset of the rational numbers consisting of 0 and the positive rational numbers we shall call the *fractional numbers*. In this chapter fractional numbers are expressed as *fractions* which take the form $\dfrac{a}{b}$, in which $a$ stands for a whole number and $b$ for a natural number. These fractions are also called *common fractions*.

The fraction $\frac{1}{2}$ can replace $n$ in the equation $1 \div 2 = n$ and make the statement true. The sentence $1 \div 2 = \frac{1}{2}$ expresses that a unit is divided into congruent subunits (subunits which have the same measure), each of which equals $\frac{1}{2}$ of the original unit. In general, if a unit is divided into $n$ congruent subunits, the measure of each subunit is $\dfrac{1}{n}$ of the original unit.

On the number line shown below, the same point is named by the fractions $\frac{1}{2}$, $\frac{2}{4}$, and $\frac{4}{8}$. Since these fractions are associated with the same point on the line, they are different expressions for the same idea. These fractions are called *equivalent fractions*. A test for equivalent fractions $\frac{a}{b}$ and $\frac{c}{d}$ is whether or not $a \times d = b \times c$. Thus $\frac{1}{2} = \frac{2}{4}$, since $1 \times 4 = 2 \times 2$, and $\frac{2}{4} = \frac{4}{8}$, since $2 \times 8 = 4 \times 4$. The simplest name—sometimes called the standard form—for the fractional number here under consideration is $\frac{1}{2}$. In this fraction the lowest possible terms are used.

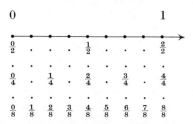

Many more fractions—each representing the same point on the line, and thus the same fractional number—could be written, for example, under the point on the line identified by $\frac{1}{2}$, $\frac{2}{4}$, and $\frac{4}{8}$. Indeed, an infinite number of fractions represents that same point on the line, and therefore the same fractional number.

Fractions may represent four different situations:

1. A fraction may express one or more equal parts of a whole.
   *Examples:* The trip took $\frac{1}{2}$ hour. We ate $\frac{3}{4}$ cake.

2. A fraction may express one of the equal parts of a group of units.
   *Example:* When 5 boys divide 2 apples equally, each boy will get $\frac{2}{5}$ apple.

3. A fraction may indicate the division of a whole number by a natural number.
   *Example:* $\frac{3}{4} = 3 \div 4$.

4. A fraction may express a ratio.
   *Example:* Bill spelled 3 of the 20 words in his spelling test incorrectly. The ratio of the number of words spelled incorrectly to the total number of words in the test was 3 to 20, or $\frac{3}{20}$.

In a fraction such as $\frac{2}{3}$, 2 represents the *numerator*, and 3 the *denominator*. The denominator is the "namer" of the number of congruent subunits into which the original unit or group is divided. The word denominator is derived from the Latin word *nom*, which means "name." The numerator of a fraction is the "numberer" or the "counter" of the subunits expressed by the denominator. For example, the fraction $\frac{2}{3}$ indicates that the original unit has been divided into three subunits and that two of these subunits are considered. The denominator and the numerator are called the *terms* of the fraction.

A *mixed fraction* contains a numeral naming a whole number and a fraction. *Examples:*
$1\frac{1}{2}$; $3\frac{1}{4}$; $5\frac{3}{4}$. The mixed fraction $1\frac{1}{2}$ is a name for $1 + \frac{1}{2}$.

A *proper fraction* represents a number which is less than 1. *Examples:*
$\frac{7}{8}$; $\frac{3}{4}$; $\frac{12}{15}$.

An *improper fraction* represents a number which is equal to or greater than 1. *Examples:* $\frac{5}{5}$; $\frac{7}{5}$; $\frac{12}{8}$.

A *unit fraction* has 1 as its numerator. *Examples:* $\frac{1}{2}$; $\frac{1}{4}$; $\frac{1}{12}$.

A *multipart fraction* has a numerator which is greater than 1. *Examples:*
$\frac{2}{3}$; $\frac{4}{5}$; $\frac{7}{3}$.

*Like fractions* or *similar fractions* have the same denominator. *Examples:*
$\frac{3}{4}$ and $\frac{1}{4}$; $\frac{1}{9}$ and $\frac{8}{9}$; $\frac{3}{5}$ and $\frac{2}{5}$.

*Unlike fractions* or *dissimilar fractions* have different denominators.
*Examples:* $\frac{3}{4}$ and $\frac{3}{5}$; $\frac{1}{3}$ and $\frac{1}{2}$; $\frac{4}{7}$ and $\frac{2}{9}$.

Two numbers are said to be *reciprocals* or *multiplicative inverses* if their product is 1. *Examples:* The reciprocal of $\frac{2}{3}$ is $\frac{3}{2}$, since $\frac{2}{3} \times \frac{3}{2} = 1$. The reciprocal of $\frac{5}{6}$ is $\frac{6}{5}$, since $\frac{5}{6} \times \frac{6}{5} = 1$.

## Some Important Properties of Fractional Numbers

*Commutative property of addition and multiplication.*
*Examples:* $\frac{1}{2} + \frac{1}{4} = \frac{1}{4} + \frac{1}{2}$
$\qquad\quad\ \frac{1}{2} \times \frac{1}{4} = \frac{1}{4} \times \frac{1}{2}$

*Associative property of addition and multiplication.*
*Examples:* $(\frac{1}{2} + \frac{1}{4}) + \frac{1}{3} = \frac{1}{2} + (\frac{1}{4} + \frac{1}{3})$
$\qquad\quad\ (\frac{1}{2} \times \frac{1}{4}) \times \frac{1}{3} = \frac{1}{2} \times (\frac{1}{4} \times \frac{1}{3})$

*Distributive property of multiplication and division with respect to addition.*
*Examples:* $\frac{2}{3} \times (\frac{6}{11} + \frac{3}{11}) = (\frac{2}{3} \times \frac{6}{11}) + (\frac{2}{3} \times \frac{3}{11}) = \frac{4}{11} + \frac{2}{11} = \frac{6}{11}$
$\qquad\quad\ (\frac{1}{9} + \frac{1}{12}) \div \frac{1}{3} = (\frac{1}{9} \div \frac{1}{3}) + (\frac{1}{12} \div \frac{1}{3}) = \frac{1}{3} + \frac{1}{4} = \frac{7}{12}$

*Closure property of addition, multiplication, and division—excepting division by zero.*
*Examples:* $\frac{1}{5} + \frac{2}{5} = \frac{3}{5}$
$\qquad\quad\ \frac{1}{5} \times \frac{2}{5} = \frac{2}{25}$
$\qquad\quad\ \frac{1}{5} \div \frac{2}{3} = \frac{3}{10}$

*Identity element for addition:* A fractional number remains unchanged if 0 is added to it. (*Note:* $0 = \frac{0}{1} = \frac{0}{2} = \frac{0}{3}$, etc.)
*Example:* $\frac{3}{4} + 0 = \frac{3}{4}$

*Identity element for multiplication:* A fractional number remains unchanged if it is multiplied by 1. (*Note:* $1 = \frac{1}{1} = \frac{2}{2} = \frac{3}{3}$, etc.)
*Example:* $1 \times \frac{3}{4} = \frac{3}{4}$

*Reciprocal property:* The product of a fractional number and its reciprocal is 1. This property is also called the *multiplicative inverse property*.
*Example:* $\frac{5}{8} \times \frac{8}{5} = 1$

## Rules

The following rules should be noted:

1. Multiplying both terms of a fraction by the same natural number does not change the value of the fraction.

   *Example:* $\frac{1}{2} = \dfrac{2 \times 1}{2 \times 2} = \frac{2}{4}$.

   If $\frac{1}{2}$ is written as $\frac{2}{4}$, it has been renamed or changed to higher terms, but its value has not changed. $\frac{1}{2}$ and $\frac{2}{4}$ are equivalent fractions and are only different names for the same fractional number.

2. Dividing both terms of a fraction by the same natural number does not change the value of the fraction.

   *Example:* $\frac{3}{9} = \dfrac{3 \div 3}{9 \div 3} = \frac{1}{3}$.

   If $\frac{3}{9}$ is written as $\frac{1}{3}$, it has been renamed or changed to its lowest terms, but its value has not changed. $\frac{3}{9}$ and $\frac{1}{3}$ are different names for the same fractional number.

3. Multiplying the numerator of a fraction by a natural number multiplies the value of the fraction by that number.
   *Example:* Multiplying the numerator of the fraction $\frac{2}{5}$ by 2 results in the number expressed by the fraction $\frac{4}{5}$, the value of which fraction is twice as large as the value of the original fraction $\frac{2}{5}$.

4. Multiplying the denominator of a fraction by a natural number divides the value of the fraction by that number.
   *Examples:* Multiplying the denominator of the fraction $\frac{3}{4}$ by 2 results in the number expressed by the fraction $\frac{3}{8}$, the value of which fraction is half as large as that of the original fraction $\frac{3}{4}$.

5. Dividing the numerator of a fraction by a natural number divides the value of the fraction by that number.
   *Example:* Dividing the numerator of the fraction $\frac{4}{5}$ by 2 results in the number expressed by the fraction $\frac{2}{5}$, the value of which fraction is half as large as that of the original fraction $\frac{4}{5}$.

6. Dividing the denominator of a fraction by a natural number multiplies the value of the fraction by that number.
   *Example:* Dividing the denominator of the fraction $\frac{3}{8}$ by 2 results in the number expressed by the fraction $\frac{3}{4}$, the value of which fraction is twice as large as that of the original fraction $\frac{3}{8}$.

## Grade Placement of Fraction Topics

*Kindergarten:* 1. Foundation experiences.

*Grades I and II:* 1. Functional use of frequently used fractions.

    2. Finding a part of a whole in a concrete situation.

    3. Finding a part of a small group of objects.

*Grade III:* 1. Maintaining skills.

    2. Finding a part of a whole and of a group, using smaller fractions and larger groups.

*Grade IV:* 1. Maintaining skills.

    2. Introducing the meaning of multipart fractions and mixed fractions.

    3. Comparing values of fractions.

    4. Introducing equivalent fractions.

    5. Adding and subtracting with like fractions.

*Grade V:* 1. Maintaining skills.

    2. Introducing the concept of common denominators.

    3. Adding and subtracting with unlike fractions.

    4. Relating fractions to decimals.

*Grade VI:* 1. Maintaining skills.

    2. Multiplying with fractions.

    3. Dividing with fractions.

    4. Relating fractions to per cents.

## Foundation Activities

When entering school, many children have already acquired some ideas of fractional parts. They may have used expressions such as "half a glass of milk," half an apple," and "half an hour." The teacher needs to provide a rich environment in which such concepts are extended, other concepts are built, and the needed vocabulary and symbols are introduced.

For kindergarten pupils cooperative activities are recommended. If, for example, a cake is baked under the direction of the teacher, the children use fractional parts as they try to read the recipe, weigh and measure the ingredients, decide that the baking time is half an hour, and finally cut the cake into parts. In such activities learning takes place best.

Suggested foundation activities for the primary grades are:

1. Folding, tearing, or cutting a sheet of paper into two or more parts.

2. Dividing a group such as six blocks into two equivalent groups.

3. Comparing parts of circular and rectangular cutouts and answering questions of the following kind:
   a) How many halves equal one whole?
   b) Which is larger, $\frac{1}{2}$ or $\frac{1}{4}$?
   c) How many fourths equal one half?

4. Measuring the length of an object by using a foot ruler graduated in half inches.

5. Measuring different amounts of various materials by using measuring cups, measuring spoons, cartons of various sizes, and other common containers.

6. Manipulating rods of different lengths in free and directed activities.

7. Weighing objects on scales. Labeled bags filled with sand and weighing 1 pound, $\frac{1}{2}$ pound, $\frac{1}{4}$ pound, etc. can be used as weights.

In grade III the use of unit fractions as a part of a whole and as a part of a group is extended to include smaller fractions. When the pupils have acquired the concept of division, they are introduced to exercises such as $\frac{1}{4}$ of 20; they should be able to interpret $\frac{1}{4}$ of 20 as $20 \div 4$.

## Different Fractions Expressing the Same Fractional Number

Prerequisites for performing operations involving fractional numbers are a knowledge of multipart fractions and the understanding that the same fractional number may be named by an endless number of fractions. Specific instruction in changing a fraction to another, equivalent fraction is essential.

### Whole numbers and improper fractions

Circular disks, divided into halves, fourths, eighths, etc., illustrate the equivalence of 1, $\frac{2}{2}$, $\frac{4}{4}$, $\frac{8}{8}$, etc.:

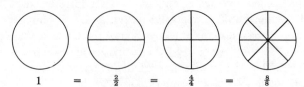

$$1 \quad = \quad \frac{2}{2} \quad = \quad \frac{4}{4} \quad = \quad \frac{8}{8}$$

This can also be shown on the number line:

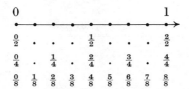

$$\frac{0}{2} \qquad \frac{1}{2} \qquad \frac{2}{2}$$

$$\frac{0}{4} \quad \frac{1}{4} \quad \frac{2}{4} \quad \frac{3}{4} \quad \frac{4}{4}$$

$$\frac{0}{8} \quad \frac{1}{8} \quad \frac{2}{8} \quad \frac{3}{8} \quad \frac{4}{8} \quad \frac{5}{8} \quad \frac{6}{8} \quad \frac{7}{8} \quad \frac{8}{8}$$

Other useful aids for teaching equivalent fractions are the fraction charts. Three different charts are recommended. The first one illustrates one whole, two halves, four fourths, etc. On the second one, the unit has been divided into thirds, sixths, and twelfths. The third one represents one whole, two halves, three thirds, etc.

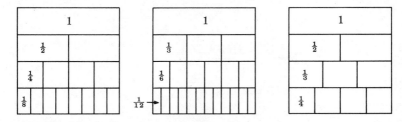

The study of these charts is followed by working related exercises and by meaningful manipulation of the fraction board, which resembles the fraction chart but which has movable pieces fitting in grooves.

## Mixed fractions and improper fractions

Mixed fractions are easily illustrated with circular cutouts. The pupil will have no trouble identifying $1\frac{1}{2}$ circles. When the whole circle is replaced by two halves, it is shown that $1\frac{1}{2} = \frac{3}{2}$:

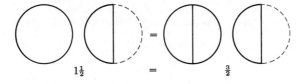

$$1\frac{1}{2} \qquad = \qquad \frac{3}{2}$$

Similarly:

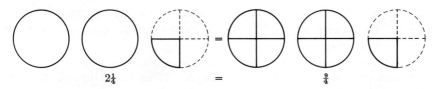

$$2\frac{1}{4} \qquad = \qquad \frac{9}{4}$$

These presentations are followed by illustrations of equivalent fractions on the number line:

The teacher may supply the pupils with a sheet on which number lines like the foregoing are provided. With the initial help of these number lines, the children change mixed fractions to improper fractions, and vice versa. For example,

$$2\tfrac{1}{4} = \frac{4}{4} + \frac{4}{4} + \frac{1}{4} = \frac{4+4+1}{4} = \frac{9}{4}, \text{ or}$$

$$2\tfrac{1}{4} = \frac{(2 \times 4) + 1}{4} = \frac{9}{4}, \text{ and}$$

$$\frac{9}{4} = 9 \div 4 = 2\tfrac{1}{4}.$$

### Changing a fraction to one with higher or lower terms

Cutouts, diagrams, and number lines are also useful to illustrate that the same fractional number can be expressed by different fractions:

The children interpret such presentations and are guided to write:

$$\tfrac{1}{2} = \tfrac{2}{4} \text{ and } \tfrac{2}{4} = \tfrac{1}{2},$$

$$\tfrac{1}{2} = \tfrac{4}{8} \text{ and } \tfrac{4}{8} = \tfrac{1}{2},$$

$$\tfrac{1}{4} = \tfrac{2}{8} \text{ and } \tfrac{2}{8} = \tfrac{1}{4}.$$

At this stage the pupils should practise with the rules which state that the terms of a fraction can be multiplied or divided by the same number without changing the value.

To change $\tfrac{6}{12}$ to its lowest terms, it is determined by inspection that 6 is the largest number by which both 6 and 12 can be evenly divided, and that the terms of the fraction must therefore be divided by that number:

$$\frac{6}{12} = \frac{6 \div 6}{12 \div 6} = \frac{1}{2}.$$

The fraction $\frac{1}{3}$ is changed to sixths by writing the number question $\frac{1}{3} = \frac{\square}{6}$ or $\frac{1}{3} = \frac{n}{6}$ and thinking: Since the denominator of $\frac{1}{3}$ is multiplied by 2 to get 6, the numerator must also be multiplied by 2:

$$\frac{1}{3} = \frac{2 \times 1}{2 \times 3} = \frac{2}{6}.$$

## Addition with Fractions

In addition with fractions four main types are distinguished:

1. Fractions with like denominators;

2. Fractions with unlike denominators, the smallest common denominator of which is one of the given denominators;

3. Fractions with unlike denominators, the smallest common denominator of which is the product of the given denominators;

4. Fractions with unlike denominators, the smallest common denominator of which is larger than one of the given denominators but smaller than the product of the given denominators.

Illustrations of possible methods of solution of selected cases follow.

EXAMPLE 1:

*Problem:* One week Ted spent $\frac{1}{3}$ of his allowance on supplies and $\frac{1}{3}$ on stamps for his collection. What part of his allowance did Ted spend on supplies and stamps together?

*Number question:* $\frac{1}{3} + \frac{1}{3} = \square$.

*Solutions:*

1. The exercise is illustrated on the flannel board or on the magnetic board:

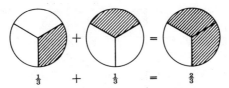

2. The process is shown on the number line:

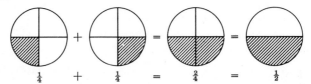

$$\frac{1}{3} + \frac{1}{3} = \frac{1+1}{3} = \frac{2}{3}$$

3. The pupils reason: 1 third + 1 third = 2 thirds, so $\frac{1}{3} + \frac{1}{3} = \frac{2}{3}$. Ted spent $\frac{2}{3}$ of this allowance on supplies and stamps together.

EXAMPLE 2:
*Problem:* Add $\frac{1}{4} + \frac{1}{4}$.
*Number question:* $\frac{1}{4} + \frac{1}{4} = \square$.
*Solutions:*
1. Cutouts:

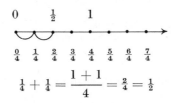

2. Number line:

$$\frac{1}{4} + \frac{1}{4} = \frac{1+1}{4} = \frac{2}{4} = \frac{1}{2}$$

3. The pupils reason: 1 fourth + 1 fourth = 2 fourths, so $\frac{1}{4} + \frac{1}{4} = \frac{2}{4} = \frac{1}{2}$.

EXAMPLE 3:
*Problem:* Add $\frac{3}{4}$ and $\frac{1}{4}$.
*Number question:* $\frac{3}{4} + \frac{1}{4} = \square$.
*Solutions:*
1. Cutouts:

2. Number line:

$$\frac{3}{4} + \frac{1}{4} = \frac{3 + 1}{4} = \frac{4}{4} = 1$$

3. The pupils reason: 3 fourths + 1 fourth = 4 fourths, so $\frac{3}{4} + \frac{1}{4} = \frac{4}{4} = 1$.

EXAMPLE 4:
*Problem:* Add $2\frac{3}{4} + 1\frac{3}{4}$.
*Number question:* $2\frac{3}{4} + 1\frac{3}{4} = \square$.
*Solutions:*

1. Cutouts:

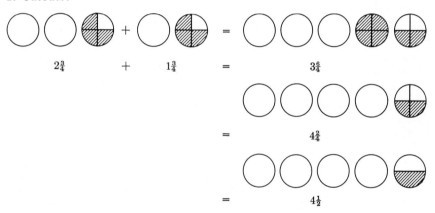

$$2\frac{3}{4} \quad + \quad 1\frac{3}{4} \quad = \quad 3\frac{6}{4}$$

$$= \quad 4\frac{2}{4}$$

$$= \quad 4\frac{1}{2}$$

2. Number line:

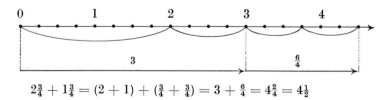

$$2\frac{3}{4} + 1\frac{3}{4} = (2 + 1) + \left(\frac{3}{4} + \frac{3}{4}\right) = 3 + \frac{6}{4} = 4\frac{2}{4} = 4\frac{1}{2}$$

3. Vertical form of solution:

$$
\begin{array}{l}
2\frac{3}{4} \\
1\frac{3}{4} \\
+ \text{---} \\
4\frac{2}{4} = 4\frac{1}{2}
\end{array}
$$

*Think:* $\frac{3}{4} + \frac{3}{4} = \frac{6}{4} = 1\frac{2}{4}$
Write the $\frac{2}{4}$ and remember the 1.

$1 + 1 + 2 = 4$. Write the 4. Express $4\frac{2}{4}$ in its simplest form.

EXAMPLE 5:

*Problem:* Add $\frac{1}{2}$ and $\frac{1}{4}$.

*Number question:* $\frac{1}{2} + \frac{1}{4} = \square$.

*Note:* From previous work, the pupils know that the numerators of like fractions are added to find the sum of the fractions. Thus, the fractions $\frac{1}{2}$ and $\frac{1}{4}$ must first be expressed as a pair of like fractions.

*Solutions:*

1. Cutouts:

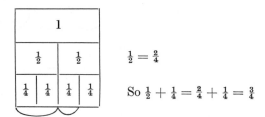

2. Fraction board:

$$\frac{1}{2} = \frac{2}{4}$$

So $\frac{1}{2} + \frac{1}{4} = \frac{2}{4} + \frac{1}{4} = \frac{3}{4}$

3. Number line:

$$\frac{1}{2} + \frac{1}{4} = \frac{3}{4}$$

EXAMPLE 6:

*Problem:* Add $\frac{1}{2}$ and $\frac{1}{3}$.

*Number question:* $\frac{1}{2} + \frac{1}{3} = \square$.

*Solutions:*

1. The larger denominator of $\frac{1}{2}$ and $\frac{1}{3}$ is not a common denominator of the two fractions. By studying a fraction chart, the pupils decide that the

smallest common denominator of the fractions is 6:

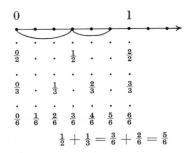

$$\tfrac{1}{2} = \tfrac{3}{6} \qquad\qquad \tfrac{1}{3} = \tfrac{2}{6}$$

Then the fractions are added:

$$\tfrac{1}{2} + \tfrac{1}{3} = \tfrac{3}{6} + \tfrac{2}{6} = \tfrac{5}{6} \quad \text{or} \quad \begin{aligned} \tfrac{1}{2} &= \tfrac{3}{6}\\ +\tfrac{1}{3} &= \tfrac{2}{6}\\ \hline &\phantom{=}\tfrac{5}{6} \end{aligned}$$

2. Number line:

$$\begin{array}{c} 0 \qquad\qquad\qquad 1 \\[4pt] \tfrac{0}{2} \quad\cdot\quad \tfrac{1}{2} \quad\cdot\quad \tfrac{2}{2} \\[4pt] \tfrac{0}{3} \quad \tfrac{1}{3} \quad \tfrac{2}{3} \quad \tfrac{3}{3} \\[4pt] \tfrac{0}{6}\ \tfrac{1}{6}\ \tfrac{2}{6}\ \tfrac{3}{6}\ \tfrac{4}{6}\ \tfrac{5}{6}\ \tfrac{6}{6} \end{array}$$

$$\tfrac{1}{2} + \tfrac{1}{3} = \tfrac{3}{6} + \tfrac{2}{6} = \tfrac{5}{6}$$

EXAMPLE 7:

*Problem:* Add $\tfrac{3}{4}$ and $\tfrac{5}{6}$.

*Number question:* $\tfrac{3}{4} + \tfrac{5}{6} = \square$.

*Solution:* To find the smallest common denominator of the given fractions, the pupils are guided during a class discussion to follow this procedure:

1. Determine whether the larger denominator (6) is a common denominator of the fractions under consideration. The larger denominator cannot be evenly divided by 4, and is therefore not a common denominator.

2. Multiply the larger denominator (6) by 2: $2 \times 6 = 12$. Twelve can be evenly divided by both 4 and 6, so 12 is the smallest common denominator. (If 12 were not a multiple of the given denominators, the next step would be to multiply 6 by 3, etc.)

Thus:

$$\tfrac{3}{4} + \tfrac{5}{6} = \tfrac{9}{12} + \tfrac{10}{12} = \tfrac{19}{12} = 1\tfrac{7}{12}$$

Or:

$$\begin{aligned} \tfrac{3}{4} &= \tfrac{9}{12}\\ +\tfrac{5}{6} &= \tfrac{10}{12}\\ \hline &\phantom{=}\tfrac{19}{12} = 1\tfrac{7}{12} \end{aligned}$$

EXAMPLE 8:

*Problem:* Add $1\frac{3}{4}$, $2\frac{1}{6}$, $3\frac{9}{15}$, and $1\frac{4}{25}$.

*Number question:* $1\frac{3}{4} + 2\frac{1}{6} + 3\frac{9}{15} + 1\frac{4}{25} = \square$.

*Solution:* The technique for finding the smallest common denominator, as described in Example 7 above, is too cumbersome to use when solving a problem such as the one under consideration. Therefore, the pupils find the least common multiple (L.C.M) of the denominators, as described in Chapter 5. Since 300 is the L.C.M. of 4, 6, 15, and 25, and is thus the smallest common denominator of the fractions, each fraction is expressed with a denominator of 300 and the sum of the addends is found:

$$1\frac{3}{4} = 1\frac{225}{300}$$
$$2\frac{1}{6} = 2\frac{50}{300}$$
$$3\frac{9}{15} = 3\frac{180}{300}$$
$$1\frac{4}{25} = 1\frac{48}{300}$$
$$\overline{\phantom{xxxx} 7\frac{503}{300} = 8\frac{203}{300}}$$

## Subtraction with Fractions

In subtraction with fractions, the different types are introduced in order of difficulty. In general, the same guidelines as those presented for addition with fractions can be followed. The student is urged to outline the types of subtraction problems in order of difficulty, and to determine whether this sequence is in agreement with the order of presentation in some of the widely-used pupils' textbooks.

Illustrations of possible solutions of selected cases follow.

EXAMPLE 1:

*Problem:* Subtract $\frac{1}{4}$ from $\frac{1}{2}$.

*Number question:* $\frac{1}{2} - \frac{1}{4} = \square$.

*Solutions:*

1. Fraction chart:

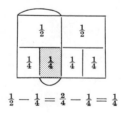

$$\frac{1}{2} - \frac{1}{4} = \frac{2}{4} - \frac{1}{4} = \frac{1}{4}$$

2. Cutouts:

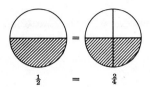

$$\tfrac{1}{2} \quad = \quad \tfrac{2}{4}$$

How much is left if one fourth is subtracted from two fourths?

$$\tfrac{1}{2} - \tfrac{1}{4} = \tfrac{2}{4} - \tfrac{1}{4} = \frac{2-1}{4} = \tfrac{1}{4}$$

3. Number line:

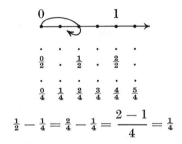

$$\tfrac{1}{2} - \tfrac{1}{4} = \tfrac{2}{4} - \tfrac{1}{4} = \frac{2-1}{4} = \tfrac{1}{4}$$

EXAMPLE 2:

*Problem:* Subtract $\tfrac{1}{4}$ from $\tfrac{3}{5}$.

*Number question:* $\tfrac{3}{5} - \tfrac{1}{4} = \square$.

*Solution: Think:* The smallest number into which 4 and 5 can be evenly divided is 20. Thus 20 is the smallest common denominator of the fractions $\tfrac{3}{5}$ and $\tfrac{1}{4}$. The fractions are therefore changed to fractions with a denominator of 20:

$$\tfrac{3}{5} - \tfrac{1}{4} = \tfrac{12}{20} - \tfrac{5}{20} = \tfrac{7}{20} \qquad \text{Or:} \qquad \begin{aligned} \tfrac{3}{5} &= \tfrac{12}{20} \\ - \tfrac{1}{4} &= \tfrac{5}{20} \\ \hline &\phantom{=}\tfrac{7}{20} \end{aligned}$$

EXAMPLE 3:

*Problem:* Subtract $1\tfrac{3}{4}$ from $3\tfrac{1}{6}$.

*Number question:* $3\tfrac{1}{6} - 1\tfrac{3}{4} = \square$.

*Solution: Think:* The smallest number into which both 4 and 6 can be evenly divided is 12. Thus twelve is the smallest common denominator of the fractions $\tfrac{1}{6}$ and $\tfrac{3}{4}$. The fractions are therefore changed to fractions with a denominator of 12: $3\tfrac{1}{6} - 1\tfrac{3}{4} = 3\tfrac{2}{12} - 1\tfrac{9}{12}$. Since $\tfrac{9}{12}$ cannot be subtracted from $\tfrac{2}{12}$, one whole in the minuend is changed to $\tfrac{12}{12}$ and added to $\tfrac{2}{12}$. Then the fractions are subtracted.

$$3\tfrac{2}{12} - 1\tfrac{9}{12} = 2\tfrac{14}{12} - 1\tfrac{9}{12} = 1\tfrac{5}{12} \qquad \text{Or:} \qquad \begin{aligned} 3\tfrac{1}{6} &= 3\tfrac{2}{12} = 2\tfrac{14}{12} \\ - 1\tfrac{3}{4} &= 1\tfrac{9}{12} = 1\tfrac{9}{12} \\ \hline & \phantom{=1\tfrac{9}{12}=} 1\tfrac{5}{12} \end{aligned}$$

## Multiplication with Fractions

In the following presentation of multiplication with fractions, six main types will be considered:

Type I:      $5 \times \frac{2}{3} = \square$
Type II:     $\frac{3}{4} \times 12 = \square$
Type III:    $\frac{1}{3} \times \frac{1}{4} = \square$
Type IV:     $3 \times 1\frac{3}{5} = \square$
Type V:      $2\frac{1}{3} \times 9 = \square$
Type VI:     $1\frac{1}{2} \times 1\frac{1}{4} = \square$

Illustrations of possible methods of solution are presented below.

### Type I

EXAMPLE 1:
*Problem:* The space between lines on a sheet of ruled paper is $\frac{1}{4}$ inch. What is the total width of 3 spaces?
*Number question:* $3 \times \frac{1}{4} = \square$.
*Solution:* The answer to $3 \times \frac{1}{4} = \square$ can be found by adding $\frac{1}{4}$ three times:

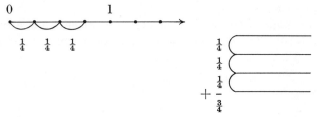

The illustrations indicate that $3 \times \frac{1}{4} = \frac{1}{4} + \frac{1}{4} + \frac{1}{4} = \frac{3}{4}$.

This can also be expressed as $3 \times \frac{1}{4} = \dfrac{3 \times 1}{4} = \frac{3}{4}$.

The total width of 3 spaces is $\frac{3}{4}$ inch.

After working several similar exercises, the pupils are guided to formulate the rule: Multiplying the numerator of a fraction by a number multiplies the value of the fraction by that number.

EXAMPLE 2:
*Problem:* The space between lines on ruled paper is $\frac{1}{4}$ inch. What is the total width of 6 spaces?
*Number question:* $6 \times \frac{1}{4} = \square$.

*Solution:* The answer to $6 \times \frac{1}{4}$ can be found by adding $\frac{1}{4}$ six times. The answer is then written in its simplest form.

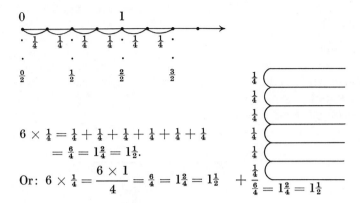

$$6 \times \tfrac{1}{4} = \tfrac{1}{4} + \tfrac{1}{4} + \tfrac{1}{4} + \tfrac{1}{4} + \tfrac{1}{4} + \tfrac{1}{4}$$
$$= \tfrac{6}{4} = 1\tfrac{2}{4} = 1\tfrac{1}{2}.$$

Or: $6 \times \tfrac{1}{4} = \dfrac{6 \times 1}{4} = \tfrac{6}{4} = 1\tfrac{2}{4} = 1\tfrac{1}{2}$

The total width of 6 spaces is $1\frac{1}{2}$ inches.

## Type II

EXAMPLE 1:

*Problem:* Ann and Linda had sold 9 magazine subscriptions. Ann had sold $\frac{2}{3}$ of them and Linda the remainder. How many subscriptions had Ann sold?

*Number question:* $\frac{2}{3} \times 9 = \square$.

*Solution:* When this case is presented, the pupils have already worked such exercises as $\frac{1}{2}$ of $6 = 6 \div 2 = 3$, and $\frac{1}{3}$ of $9 = 9 \div 3 = 3$. Since $\frac{2}{3} \times 9$ means 2 out of the 3 equal parts of 9, the product is $2 \times (9 \div 3) = 2 \times 3 = 6$.

Ann had sold 6 subscriptions.

*Assignment:* The student should find an alternate method of solution in which the commutative property is used.

EXAMPLE 2:

*Problem:* If it costs 5¢ to use an electric iron for one hour, how much does it cost to use it for $\frac{3}{4}$ hour?

*Number question:* $\frac{3}{4} \times 5 = \square$.

*Solution:* Since 5 cannot be evenly divided by 4, another procedure is followed when finding the answer to this number question: $\frac{3}{4} \times 5$ means 3 of the 4 equal parts of 5. Thus $\frac{3}{4} \times 5 = 3 \times \frac{5}{4}$ or $\dfrac{3 \times 5}{4} = \tfrac{15}{4} = 3\tfrac{3}{4}$.

It costs $3\frac{3}{4}$¢ to use the electric iron for $\frac{3}{4}$ hour.

*Assignment:* The student should find an alternate method of solution in which the commutative property is used.

## Type III

EXAMPLE 1:

*Problem:* Mrs. Black bought $\frac{1}{2}$ pound of cheese. She used one half of the amount she bought for a recipe. What fractional part of a pound did Mrs. Black use?

*Number question:* $\frac{1}{2} \times \frac{1}{2} = \square$.

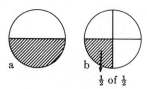

$\frac{1}{2}$ of $\frac{1}{2}$

*Solution:* In illustration (a) $\frac{1}{2}$ of the circle has been shaded. In illustration (b) a vertical line divides the circle into fourths. One half of the shaded part of circle (a) equals one fourth of the whole circle. Thus $\frac{1}{2}$ of $\frac{1}{2} = \frac{1}{4}$, or $\frac{1}{2} \times \frac{1}{2} = \frac{1}{4}$.

Mrs. Black used $\frac{1}{4}$ pound of cheese.

It should be observed that the number of equal parts (1) has not changed, but that the size of the parts has become half as large:

$$\frac{1}{2} \times \frac{1}{2} = \frac{1 \times 1}{2 \times 2} = \frac{1}{4}$$

The number of parts remains the same, since the numerator is multiplied by 1.

The size of the parts becomes half as large, since the denominator is multiplied by 2.

It is important that the pupils understand that multiplying by a number that is less than 1 results in a product which is smaller than the multiplicand.

EXAMPLE 2:

*Problem:* Mr. Farmer has $\frac{3}{4}$ acre of land. He uses $\frac{2}{3}$ of it for a vegetable garden. What fractional part of an acre is Mr. Farmer's vegetable garden?

*Number question:* $\frac{2}{3} \times \frac{3}{4} = \square$.

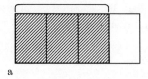

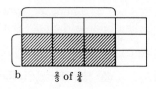

a                                                b        $\frac{2}{3}$ of $\frac{3}{4}$

*Solution:* In diagram (a) $\frac{3}{4}$ of the unit is shaded. In diagram (b) the unit has been divided by horizontal lines into three equal parts, resulting in 12 small rectangles. Three fourths of the unit equals 9 small rectangles, and $\frac{2}{3} \times 9$ small rectangles = 6 small rectangles or $\frac{6}{12}$ of the unit. Thus $\frac{2}{3}$ of $\frac{3}{4} = \frac{6}{12} = \frac{1}{2}$.

Mr. Farmer's vegetable garden is $\frac{6}{12}$ acre, or $\frac{1}{2}$ acre.

After working several similar exercises, the pupils are guided to formulate the rule for this case: Multiply the numerators and multiply the denominators and, if necessary, write the answer in its simplest form. This leads to the common algorism: $\frac{2}{3} \times \frac{3}{4} = \dfrac{2 \times 3}{3 \times 4} = \frac{6}{12} = \frac{1}{2}$.

## Type IV

EXAMPLE:

*Problem:* Jane wanted to make 6 earrings for a craft project. Each ring would take $2\frac{3}{4}$ inches of copper metal strip. How many inches of copper metal strip did Jane have to buy?

*Number question:* $6 \times 2\frac{3}{4} = \square$.

*Solutions:*

1. Number line:

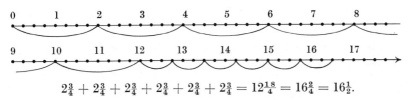

$$2\tfrac{3}{4} + 2\tfrac{3}{4} + 2\tfrac{3}{4} + 2\tfrac{3}{4} + 2\tfrac{3}{4} + 2\tfrac{3}{4} = 12\tfrac{18}{4} = 16\tfrac{2}{4} = 16\tfrac{1}{2}.$$

2. Horizontal form:

*Think:* $2\frac{3}{4} = 2 + \frac{3}{4}$. Thus:

$$6 \times 2\tfrac{3}{4} = 6 \times (2 + \tfrac{3}{4}) = (6 \times 2) + (6 \times \tfrac{3}{4}) = 12 + \tfrac{18}{4} = 16\tfrac{2}{4} = 16\tfrac{1}{2}.$$

3. Vertical form:

$$\begin{array}{r} 2\frac{3}{4} \\ \times\, 6 \\ \hline 12\frac{18}{4} = 16\frac{2}{4} = 16\frac{1}{2} \end{array}$$

4. Using improper fractions:

$$6 \times 2\tfrac{3}{4} = 6 \times \tfrac{11}{4} = \tfrac{6}{1} \times \tfrac{11}{4} = \dfrac{6 \times 11}{1 \times 4} = \tfrac{66}{4} = 16\tfrac{2}{4} = 16\tfrac{1}{2}.$$

Jane had to buy $16\frac{1}{2}$ inches of copper metal strip.

## Type V

EXAMPLE:

*Problem:* Dave made a hike of $1\frac{1}{2}$ hours. He walked an average of 4 miles per hour. How many miles did Dave walk?

*Number question:* $1\frac{1}{2} \times 4 = \square$.

*Solutions:*

1. Horizontal form:

*Think:* $1\frac{1}{2} = 1 + \frac{1}{2}$. Thus:

$$1\frac{1}{2} \times 4 = (1 + \tfrac{1}{2}) \times 4 = (1 \times 4) + (\tfrac{1}{2} \times 4) = 4 + 2 = 6.$$

2. Using improper fractions:

$$1\frac{1}{2} \times 4 = \tfrac{3}{2} \times \tfrac{4}{1} = \frac{3 \times 4}{2 \times 1} = \tfrac{12}{2} = 6.$$

3. Using the commutative property:

*Think:* $1\frac{1}{2} \times 4 = 4 \times 1\frac{1}{2}$ (by the commutative property). Thus:

$$1\frac{1}{2} \times 4 = 4 \times 1\frac{1}{2} = 4 \times (1 + \tfrac{1}{2}) = (4 \times 1) + (4 \times \tfrac{1}{2}) = 4 + 2 = 6.$$

Dave walked 6 miles.

## Type VI

EXAMPLE:

*Problem:* Ronald made a hike of $3\frac{1}{2}$ hours. He averaged $3\frac{1}{4}$ miles per hour. How many miles did Ronald hike?

*Number question:* $3\frac{1}{2} \times 3\frac{1}{4} = \square$.

*Solution:* *Think:* $3\frac{1}{2} = \tfrac{7}{2}$ and $3\frac{1}{4} = \tfrac{13}{4}$. Thus:

$$3\frac{1}{2} \times 3\frac{1}{4} = \tfrac{7}{2} \times \tfrac{13}{4} = \frac{7 \times 13}{2 \times 4} = \tfrac{91}{8} = 11\tfrac{3}{8}.$$

Ronald hiked $11\frac{3}{8}$ miles.

## Dividing before multiplying

When multiplying with fractions, the process can sometimes be shortened by dividing out factors common to both a numerator and a denominator of the fractions before multiplying.

EXAMPLES:

$$\tfrac{4}{7} \times \tfrac{1}{8} = \frac{4 \times 1}{7 \times 8} = \frac{\overset{1}{\cancel{4}} \times 1}{7 \times \underset{1}{\cancel{4}} \times 2} = \tfrac{1}{14} \qquad \frac{\overset{1}{\cancel{3}}}{\underset{1}{\cancel{3}}} \times \frac{\overset{1}{\cancel{5}}}{\underset{4}{\cancel{12}}} = \tfrac{1}{4} \qquad \frac{1}{\underset{1}{\cancel{4}}} \times \frac{\overset{2}{\cancel{8}}}{\underset{3}{\cancel{9}}} \times \frac{\overset{1}{\cancel{3}}}{5} = \tfrac{2}{15}$$

This process is often called *cancellation*. Since this term is misleading, it is better to use the expression "dividing before multiplying."

## Division with Fractions

In division with fractions, six main types will be considered:

Type I:     $2 \div \frac{1}{4} = \square$
Type II:    $\frac{1}{4} \div 2 = \square$
Type III:   $\frac{1}{2} \div \frac{1}{3} = \square$
Type IV:   $18 \div 2\frac{1}{2} = \square$
Type V:    $7\frac{2}{3} \div 2 = \square$
Type VI:   $3\frac{1}{2} \div 1\frac{1}{2} = \square$

Illustrations of possible methods of solution follow.

### Type I

EXAMPLE 1:
*Problem:* Two acres of land are divided into building lots of $\frac{1}{2}$ acre each. How many lots can be sold?
*Number question:* $2 \div \frac{1}{2} = \square$.
*Solutions:* In this situation, a measurement type of division is involved. For such a problem various methods of solution are available:
1. Serial subtraction:

The pupils determine by serial subtraction how many times $\frac{1}{2}$ can be subtracted from 2. The serial subtraction is shown at the right. Since four $\frac{1}{2}$'s equal 2, $2 \div \frac{1}{2} = 4$.

Four lots can be sold.

$$
\begin{array}{r}
2 \\
-\ \frac{1}{2}\ (1) \\
\hline
1\frac{1}{2} \\
-\ \frac{1}{2}\ (2) \\
\hline
1 \\
-\ \frac{1}{2}\ (3) \\
\hline
\frac{1}{2} \\
-\ \frac{1}{2}\ (4) \\
\hline
0
\end{array}
$$

2. Diagrams:

| $\frac{1}{2}$ | $\frac{1}{2}$ |
|---|---|
| $\frac{1}{2}$ | $\frac{1}{2}$ |

The diagrams illustrate that 2 halves equal 1 whole. Thus, 4 halves equal 2 wholes.
$2 \div \frac{1}{2} = 4$

3. Number line:

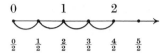

By counting the spaces it is determined that 4 halves equal 2.

4. Common denominator method:

$$2 \div \tfrac{1}{2} = \tfrac{4}{2} \div \tfrac{1}{2} = \frac{4 \div 1}{2 \div 2} = \tfrac{4}{1} = 4$$

2 is changed to an improper fraction with the same denominator as the fraction $\tfrac{1}{2}$. Since the quotient of the denominators is 1, the answer to the division question is the quotient of the numerators ($4 \div 1 = 4$).

5. Inversion method:

When the inversion method is used, the dividend is multiplied by the reciprocal of the divisor. The pupils should therefore first learn to find the reciprocal of a number. (The term "reciprocal" was introduced previously in this chapter.)

For a meaningful development of the inversion method, the number line can be used. In order to solve the number question under consideration, halves are marked on the line and the mathematical sentence stating that $2 \div \tfrac{1}{2}$ equals 2 times 2 halves is written:

$$2 \div \tfrac{1}{2} = 2 \times 2 = 4$$

The teacher points out that 2 can be written as $\tfrac{2}{1}$ and asks whether the following sentence is true:

$$2 \div \tfrac{1}{2} = \tfrac{2}{1} \times \tfrac{2}{1} = \frac{2 \times 2}{1 \times 1} = \tfrac{4}{1} = 4$$

Several other exercises are then presented, including those which have multipart fractions as divisors, as in the following example.

EXAMPLE 2:

*Problem:* Three acres of land were divided into building lots of $\tfrac{3}{4}$ acre each. How many building lots could be sold?

*Number question:* $3 \div \tfrac{3}{4} = \square$.

*Solutions:* The answer to this number question can be found in ways similar to those used in the immediately preceding example. The inversion method is developed below.

The number line or a diagram can be used to show how many fourths are contained in 3:

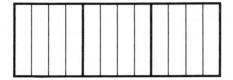

Twelve fourths equal 3.

Thus: $3 \div \frac{1}{4} = \frac{3}{1} \times \frac{4}{1} = \dfrac{3 \times 4}{1 \times 1} = \frac{12}{1} = 12$.

What happens to the number of parts if the 3 acres are not divided into parts of $\frac{1}{4}$ acre, but into parts of $\frac{3}{4}$ acre each? Since the *size* of the parts becomes three times as large, the *number* of parts becomes three times as small. Instead of 12 lots, there are now only 4 lots available. Thus:

$$3 \div \frac{3}{4} = \dfrac{3 \times 4}{3} = \frac{12}{3} = 4$$

⌐‑‑‑‑‑‑‑‑‑‑‑‑‑‑‑‑‑‑‑‑‑‑‑‑‑The number of parts becomes 3 times as small.

This sentence can be written as:

$$3 \div \frac{3}{4} = \frac{3}{1} \times \frac{4}{3} = \dfrac{3 \times 4}{1 \times 3} = \frac{12}{3} = 4$$

A great deal of class discussion and much practice should precede the rule: When dividing by a number expressed as a fraction, multiply the dividend by the reciprocal of the divisor.

Though probably only the brightest pupils will understand the rationale of the inversion method, the teacher should put forth efforts to present the process clearly, and certainly he himself should be able to explain the method.

The inversion method is often justified as follows:

$3 \div \frac{3}{4} = \dfrac{3}{\frac{3}{4}}$ — The division is expressed in a different way.

$= \dfrac{3 \times \frac{4}{3}}{\frac{3}{4} \times \frac{4}{3}}$ — Multiplying the dividend and the divisor of a division by the same number does not change the quotient.

$= \dfrac{3 \times \frac{4}{3}}{1}$ — $\frac{3}{4} \times \frac{4}{3} = 1$

$= 3 \times \frac{4}{3}$ — If the divisor is 1, the quotient is equal to the dividend.

## Type II

EXAMPLE:

*Problem:* If $\frac{1}{2}$ pound of cheese is equally divided between two boys, what fraction of a pound does each boy get?

*Number question:* $\frac{1}{2} \div 2 = \square$.
*Solutions:*
1. Diagram:

$\frac{1}{2} \div 2 = \frac{1}{4}$

2. Number line:

$$\frac{1}{2} \div 2 = \frac{1}{4}$$

3. Common denominator method:

$$\frac{1}{2} \div 2 = \frac{1}{2} \div \frac{4}{2} = \frac{1 \div 4}{2 \div 2} = \frac{\frac{1}{4}}{1} = \frac{1}{4}$$

4. Inversion method:

$$\frac{1}{2} \div 2 = \frac{1}{2} \div \frac{2}{1} = \frac{1}{2} \times \frac{1}{2} = \frac{1 \times 1}{2 \times 2} = \frac{1}{4}$$

Each boy gets $\frac{1}{4}$ pound of cheese.

## Type III

EXAMPLE:
*Problem:* A contractor has to pave a road of $\frac{1}{2}$ mile. He can pave $\frac{1}{4}$ mile per day. How many days will it take him to pave the road?
*Number question:* $\frac{1}{2} \div \frac{1}{4} = \square$.
*Solutions:*
1. Common denominator method:

$$\frac{1}{2} \div \frac{1}{4} = \frac{2}{4} \div \frac{1}{4} = \frac{2 \div 1}{4 \div 4} = \frac{2}{1} = 2$$

2. Inversion method:

$$\frac{1}{2} \div \frac{1}{4} = \frac{1}{2} \times \frac{4}{1} = \frac{1 \times \overset{2}{\cancel{4}}}{\underset{1}{\cancel{2}} \times 1} = \frac{2}{1} = 2$$

It will take the contractor 2 days to pave the road.
*Remark:* It is recommended that the pupils use the inversion method as the regular method for working division exercises involving fractions. The common denominator method or, if applicable, other methods of solution should be used from time to time to check the correctness of an answer.

## Type IV

EXAMPLE:

*Problem:* Ray took a hike of 14 miles. He walked an average of $3\frac{1}{2}$ miles per hour. How long did the hike take?

*Number question:* $14 \div 3\frac{1}{2} = \square.$

*Solution:* $14 \div 3\frac{1}{2} = \frac{14}{1} \div \frac{7}{2} = \frac{\overset{2}{\cancel{14}}}{1} \times \frac{2}{\underset{1}{\cancel{7}}} = \frac{2 \times 2}{1 \times 1} = \frac{4}{1} = 4$

The hike took 4 hours.

*Check:* $14 \div 3\frac{1}{2} = \frac{28}{2} \div \frac{7}{2} = \frac{28 \div 7}{2 \div 2} = \frac{4}{1} = 4$

## Type V

EXAMPLE:

*Problem:* $5\frac{3}{4}$ yards of ribbon are divided into two equal parts. How long is each part?

*Number question:* $5\frac{3}{4} \div 2 = \square.$

*Solution:* $5\frac{3}{4} \div 2 = \frac{23}{4} \div \frac{2}{1} = \frac{23}{4} \times \frac{1}{2} = \frac{23 \times 1}{4 \times 2} = \frac{23}{8} = 2\frac{7}{8}$

Each part is $2\frac{7}{8}$ yards.

*Check:* $5\frac{3}{4} \div 2 = \frac{23}{4} \div \frac{8}{4} = \frac{23 \div 8}{4 \div 4} = \frac{\frac{23}{8}}{1} = \frac{23}{8} = 2\frac{7}{8}$

## Type VI

EXAMPLE:

*Problem:* Rex walked $12\frac{1}{4}$ miles. He averaged $3\frac{1}{2}$ miles per hour. How long did it take him to walk the $12\frac{1}{4}$ miles?

*Number question:* $12\frac{1}{4} \div 3\frac{1}{2} = \square.$

*Solution:* $12\frac{1}{4} \div 3\frac{1}{2} = \frac{49}{4} \div \frac{7}{2} = \frac{\overset{7}{\cancel{49}}}{\underset{2}{\cancel{4}}} \times \frac{\overset{1}{\cancel{2}}}{\underset{1}{\cancel{7}}} = \frac{7 \times 1}{2 \times 1} = \frac{7}{2} = 3\frac{1}{2}$

It took Rex $3\frac{1}{2}$ hours to walk $12\frac{1}{4}$ miles.

*Check:* $12\frac{1}{4} \div 3\frac{1}{2} = \frac{49}{4} \div \frac{7}{2} = \frac{49}{4} \div \frac{14}{4} = \frac{49 \div 14}{4 \div 4} = \frac{\frac{49}{14}}{1}$

$$= \frac{49}{14} = 3\frac{7}{14} = 3\frac{1}{2}$$

## SELECTED RESEARCH

Howard, C. F., "Three Methods of Teaching Arithmetic." *California Journal of Educational Research*, January, 1950, pp. 25–29.

The investigator attempted to determine whether the teaching of addition with common fractions by different methods resulted in significantly different achievement.

The sample consisted of 15 fifth and sixth grades, divided into three groups—A, B, and C, to which addition with common fractions was taught by the following three different plans of procedure.

The teachers of group A showed the pupils the processes of addition with fractions without the use of visual aids. Much practice in computation was provided.

With group B considerable time was spent in presenting each new step, and manipulative materials were used. The practice work consisted of verbal problems, but there was no practice in mere computation.

The method used for group C was a combination of the methods used for groups A and B. Each step was introduced meaningfully, visual aids were used, and practice in computation was provided.

After 16 weeks of instruction, there was no significant difference in achievement among the groups. When the same tests were administered again to the same pupils after the summer vacation, group C scored significantly higher than the other two groups.

Capps, L. R., "Division of Fractions." *The Arithmetic Teacher*, January, 1962, pp. 10–16.

This study was concerned with the difficulties which manifest themselves in multiplication with fractions as a result of teaching division with fractions by the common denominator method.

The sample consisted of 20 sixth-grade classes. The instructional period lasted three weeks. A pretest, a posttest, and a test three weeks after the close of the instructional period were administered.

The following findings were reported:

1. With reference to the ability to multiply with fractions immediately after instruction, the inversion method of teaching division with fractions yielded significantly better results than did the common denominator method.

2. With reference to the ability to multiply with fractions three weeks after the close of the instructional period, the groups showed significant differences in favor of the inversion method.

3. During the three-week retention period without review of fraction processes, the common denominator group gained significantly in the ability to multiply with fractions. In the same period, the inversion group showed no significant change.

The investigator concluded that many facets of the two methods need further investigation before either can be condemned or commended.

## SKILLS TEST

1. $12\frac{5}{8} + 7\frac{2}{3} =$   $19\frac{1}{2} + 16\frac{3}{5} =$   $24\frac{5}{6} + 5\frac{3}{4} =$   $3\frac{1}{5} + 2\frac{9}{10} =$

2. $10\frac{1}{7} - 3\frac{1}{2} =$   $20\frac{1}{4} - 5\frac{4}{5} =$   $60\frac{1}{3} - 4\frac{1}{2} =$   $9\frac{3}{5} - \frac{7}{8} =$

3. $\frac{1}{3}$ of $21 =$   $\frac{1}{5}$ of $55 =$   $\frac{1}{8}$ of $104 =$   $\frac{1}{4}$ of $72 =$

4. $\frac{2}{3}$ of $12 =$   $\frac{3}{8}$ of $24 =$   $\frac{5}{7}$ of $77 =$   $\frac{3}{10}$ of $120 =$

5. $\frac{3}{5} = \frac{\square}{20}$   $\frac{5}{9} = \frac{\square}{27}$   $\frac{2}{3} = \frac{\square}{21}$   $\frac{7}{8} = \frac{\square}{56}$

6. $\frac{5}{6} = \frac{15}{\square}$   $\frac{2}{3} = \frac{20}{\square}$   $\frac{7}{8} = \frac{77}{\square}$   $\frac{4}{5} = \frac{48}{\square}$

7. $5 \times 1\frac{2}{5} =$   $9 \times 3\frac{3}{4} =$   $4\frac{1}{2} \times 6\frac{1}{3} =$   $\frac{3}{7} \times \frac{7}{12} =$

8. 16 is $\frac{4}{5}$ of _____   35 is $\frac{7}{8}$ of _____

9. Find the reciprocal of :

 $5$   $\frac{1}{4}$   $\frac{5}{6}$   $\frac{8}{5}$

10. Find the answers by using the common denominator method.

 $6 \div 1\frac{1}{2} =$   $12\frac{1}{2} \div 1\frac{1}{4} =$   $4\frac{1}{5} \div 3\frac{1}{2} =$   $\frac{7}{10} \div \frac{2}{5} =$

11. Find the answers by using the inversion method.

 $8 \div 1\frac{3}{5} =$   $2\frac{2}{5} \div \frac{3}{10} =$   $3\frac{1}{3} \div 1\frac{8}{9} =$   $1\frac{1}{5} \div \frac{3}{10} =$

12. $(2\frac{1}{2} \times 1\frac{2}{5}) + (1\frac{3}{4} \div 3\frac{1}{2}) =$   $(3\frac{1}{5} \times 2\frac{1}{2}) - (\frac{3}{4} \div \frac{1}{2}) =$

## EXERCISES

1. Distinguish between "fractional numbers" and "fractions."

2. Give an example in which a fraction expresses a ratio.

3. Give an example of:
   a) a mixed fraction
   b) a multipart fraction
   c) an improper fraction
   d) a unit fraction
   e) a proper fraction
   f) a pair of equivalent fractions

4. Name and give examples of several properties of fractional numbers.

5. List some activities which a first-grade teacher may select for the purpose of developing the concept of fractional numbers.

6. Suggest two possible methods of solution for the number question $1\frac{3}{5} \div 2\frac{1}{2} = \square$.

7. Explain and illustrate how you would teach children to find the lowest common denominator of the fractions $\frac{5}{6}$ and $\frac{4}{9}$.

8. Find the L.C.M. of the denominators of the fractions $\frac{1}{6}$, $\frac{5}{8}$, $\frac{2}{15}$, and $\frac{7}{20}$.

9. Write an illustrative lesson dealing with the case in which a whole number is multiplied by a fractional number.

10. Justify the inversion method.

## For advanced students

11. Report on a piece of research on the teaching of fractions.

12. As assigned by the instructor of the course, report on one or more of the following articles:
    a) Bray, C. J., "To Invert or Not to Invert." *The Arithmetic Teacher*, May, 1963, pp. 274–76.
    b) Chabe, A. M., "Rationalizing 'Inverting and Multiplying.'" *The Arithmetic Teacher*, May, 1963, pp. 272–73.
    c) Christofferson, H. C., "Division by a Fraction Made Meaningful." *The Mathematics Teacher*, January, 1948, pp. 32–35.
    d) Hannon, H., "'Sets' Aid in Adding Fractions." *The Arithmetic Teacher*, February, 1959, pp. 35–38.
    e) ———, "Why Invert the Divisor?" *The Arithmetic Teacher*, December, 1957, pp. 262–65.
    f) Hoffman, H. W., "Meaning for Multiplication of Fractions." *The Arithmetic Teacher*, March, 1958, pp. 89–90.
    g) Kolesnik, T. S., "The Division of Common Fractions." *The Arithmetic Teacher*, March, 1960, pp. 133–34.
    h) Van Engen, H., "Rate Pairs, Fractions, and Rational Numbers." *The Arithmetic Teacher*, December, 1960, pp. 389–99.

## SELECTED REFERENCES

Banks, J. H., *Learning and Teaching Arithmetic*, 2nd Ed. Boston: Allyn and Bacon, Inc., 1964, Chs. VIII and IX.

Bell, C., C. D. Hammond, and R. B. Herrera, *Fundamentals of Arithmetic for Teachers*. New York: John Wiley & Sons, Inc., 1962, Chs. IX and X.

Brumfield, C. F. *et al.*, *Principles of Arithmetic*. Reading, Mass.: Addison-Wesley Publishing Company, Inc., 1963, Chs. X and XI.

Buckingham, B. R., *Elementary Arithmetic: Its Meaning and Practice*. Boston: Ginn and Company, 1953, Chs. I and IX.

Dutton, W. H. and L. J. Adams, *Arithmetic for Teachers*. Englewood Cliffs, N.J.: Prentice-Hall, Inc., 1961, Chs. VIII and IX.

Grossnickle, F. E. and L. J. Brueckner, *Discovering Meanings in Elementary School Mathematics*. New York: Holt, Rinehart & Winston, Inc., 1963, Chs. X and XI.

Heddens, J. W., *Today's Mathematics*. Chicago: Science Research Associates, Inc., 1964, Units XIII–XV.

Howard, C. F. and E. Dumas, *Basic Procedures in Teaching Arithmetic*. Boston: D. C. Heath & Company, 1963, Chs. V and IX.

Larsen, H. D. and H. G. Ludlow, *Arithmetic for Colleges*. New York: The Macmillan Co., 1963, Ch. VII.

Marks, J. L., C. R. Purdy, and L. B. Kinney, *Teaching Arithmetic for Understanding*. New York: McGraw-Hill, Inc., 1958, Ch. VIII.

Mueller, F. J., *Arithmetic: Its Structure and Concepts*, 2nd Ed. Englewood Cliffs, N.J.: Prentice-Hall, Inc., 1964, Units XVII–XX.

National Council of Teachers of Mathematics, *Topics in Mathematics*. Washington, D.C.: the Council, 1964, Bklt. 6.

School Mathematics Study Group, *Studies in Mathematics, Vol. IX: A Brief Course in Mathematics for Elementary School Teachers*. Stanford: Leland Stanford Junior University, 1963, Chs. XVIII–XXII.

Spitzer, H. F., *The Teaching of Arithmetic*. Boston: Houghton Mifflin Company, 1961, Ch. VII.

Thorpe, C. B., *Teaching Elementary Arithmetic*. New York: Harper & Row, Publishers, 1962, Ch. XVI.

Ward, M. and C. E. Hardgrove, *Modern Elementary Mathematics*. Reading, Mass.: Addison-Wesley Publishing Company, Inc., 1964, Ch. IX.

# 15

---

# DECIMALS

---

IN THE PRECEDING chapter common fractions were presented as a form in which fractional numbers can be expressed. In this chapter another form of expressing such numbers will be considered, namely *decimals*, also called *decimal fractions*.

The use of decimals instead of common fractions leads to considerable facility in the computation and comparison of fractional numbers, since the understood denominator of decimals is a power of ten. For example, it is easier to add or compare .75 and .72 than $\frac{3}{4}$ and $\frac{18}{25}$.

Decimals are widely used in daily life, and almost exclusively in scientific and technical work. The elementary-school pupil should therefore develop an understanding of and a reasonable skill in working with decimals.

## Meaning, Terms, and Notation

The fractions $\frac{4}{10}$, $\frac{16}{100}$, and $\frac{125}{1000}$ can be rewritten as *decimals* in this way: .4, .16, and .125. Thus in decimals the principle of positional value is extended to places to the right of the ones, which are identified by the decimal point. Numerals such as .3 and .78 are sometimes called *pure decimals*. Examples of *mixed decimals* are 1.6 and 12.43.

### Terminating and repeating decimals

Some fractions can be expressed as terminating decimals, others as repeating decimals. The denominators of fractions such as $\frac{2}{5}$, $\frac{7}{10}$, and $\frac{9}{50}$ have only those prime factors that are prime factors of 10 (2 and 5). When the division indicated by such a fraction is performed, the process terminates, and the result is called a *terminating decimal*.

Examples:

$$
\begin{array}{ccc}
\text{a)} \quad \dfrac{.4}{5)\overline{2.0}} & \text{b)} \quad \dfrac{.35}{20)\overline{7.00}} & \text{c)} \quad \dfrac{.18}{50)\overline{9.00}} \\
\end{array}
$$

a)
```
      .4
  5)2.0
    2 0
  ------
       0
```
b)
```
      .35
 20)7.00
    6 0
  ------
    1 00
    1 00
  ------
       0
```
c)
```
      .18
 50)9.00
    5 0
  ------
    4 00
    4 00
  ------
       0
```

$$\tfrac{2}{5} = .4 \qquad \tfrac{7}{20} = .35 \qquad \tfrac{9}{50} = .18$$

If the division indicated by fractions such as $\tfrac{1}{9}$ and $\tfrac{1}{6}$ (the denominators of which have prime factors other than 2 and 5) is performed, the process does not terminate, but a repeating pattern is observed in the quotient. The result is called a *repeating decimal*.

Examples:

a)
```
       .111 ...
  9)1.000 ...
    9
  ----
    10
     9
  ----
    10
     9
  ----
     1
```
b)
```
        .1666 ...
  6)1.0000 ...
    6
  ----
    40
    36
  ----
    40
    36
  ----
    40
    36
  ----
     4
```

$$\tfrac{1}{9} = .111 \cdots \qquad \tfrac{1}{6} = .1666 \cdots$$

In a repeating decimal a dot is sometimes placed over the first and the last digit of the cycle that repeats, or a bar is drawn over that cycle.

Examples:

$$\tfrac{1}{3} = .\dot{3} \quad \text{or} \quad .\overline{3}; \qquad \tfrac{1}{7} = .\dot{1}4285\dot{7} \quad \text{or} \quad .\overline{142857}; \qquad \tfrac{1}{6} = .1\dot{6} \quad \text{or} \quad .1\overline{6}.$$

It is interesting to observe how a fraction such as $\tfrac{1}{9}$ can be expressed as the sum of a set of fractions which have denominators that are powers of ten:

$$\tfrac{1}{9} = \tfrac{10}{90} = \tfrac{9}{90} + \tfrac{1}{90} = \boxed{\tfrac{1}{10}} + \tfrac{1}{90}$$

and

$$\tfrac{1}{90} = \tfrac{10}{900} = \tfrac{9}{900} + \tfrac{1}{900} = \boxed{\tfrac{1}{100}} + \tfrac{1}{900}$$

and

$$\tfrac{1}{900} = \tfrac{10}{9000} = \tfrac{9}{9000} + \tfrac{1}{9000} = \boxed{\tfrac{1}{1000}} + \tfrac{1}{9000}, \text{ etc.}$$

Thus:              $\frac{1}{9} = \frac{1}{10} + \frac{1}{100} + \frac{1}{1000} + \cdots$

or:                $\frac{1}{9} = .1 + .01 + .001 + \cdots = .111 \cdots$

## Notation

The decimal point is only a device to indicate the place of the ones. The ones place is the center in our system of notation, as can be inferred from the following diagram.

| 1000 | 100 | 10 | 1 | .1 | .01 | .001 |
|------|-----|-----|-----|-----|-----|------|
| $10^3$ | $10^2$ | $10^1$ | $10^0$ | $10^{-1}$ | $10^{-2}$ | $10^{-3}$ |
| thousands | hundreds | tens | ones | tenths | hundredths | thousandths |
| 1 | 1 | 1 | 1 | 1 | 1 | 1 |

$\times 10 \div 10$

$\times 100 \div 100$

$\times 1000 \div 1000$

The tens are located one place to the left of the ones, and the place of the tenths is one step to the right of the ones. The hundreds are located two places to the left of the ones, and the place of the hundredths is two steps to the right of the ones, etc.

From the diagram, the following statement can be derived:

$$1111.111 = 1(10^3) + 1(10^2) + 1(10^1) + 1(10^0)$$
$$+ 1(10^{-1}) + 1(10^{-2}) + 1(10^{-3})$$
$$= 1000 + 100 + 10 + 1 + \tfrac{1}{10} + \tfrac{1}{100} + \tfrac{1}{1000}$$
$$= 1000 + 100 + 10 + 1 + .1 + .01 + .001$$
$$= 1111.111$$

In the diagram (see top of facing page), the positional value of each of the digits in the numeral 2222.222 is shown.

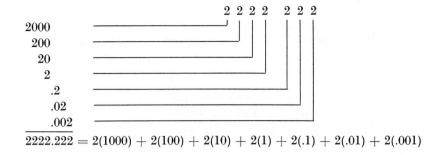

$$\overline{2222.222} = 2(1000) + 2(100) + 2(10) + 2(1) + 2(.1) + 2(.01) + 2(.001)$$

## Equivalents

Numerals that express the same number are called *equivalents*. Thus the fraction $\frac{1}{10}$ and the decimal .1 are equivalents.

In the preceding chapter we decided that $\frac{5}{10} = \frac{50}{100} = \frac{500}{1000}$, etc. Since $\frac{5}{10} = .5$, $\frac{50}{100} = .50$, and $\frac{500}{1000} = .500$, we may write $.5 = .50 = .500$. It will not be difficult to decide why $.500 = .50 = .5$. We call .5, .50, and .500 *equivalent decimals*. Thus we may annex as many zeros to the end of a decimal, or take off as many zeros from the end of a decimal, as we wish.

### Changing a fraction to an equivalent decimal

EXAMPLE 1:
*Problem:* Write $\frac{3}{5}$ as a decimal.
*Solution: Step 1:* Rename $\frac{3}{5}$ to get a fraction with a denominator of a power of ten:
$$\frac{3}{5} = \frac{2 \times 3}{2 \times 5} = \frac{6}{10}$$
*Step 2:* Write $\frac{6}{10}$ as a decimal: $\frac{6}{10} = .6$.
$$\frac{3}{5} = \frac{6}{10} = .6$$
EXAMPLE 2:
*Problem:* Write $\frac{3}{4}$ as a decimal.
*Solution: Step 1:* Rename $\frac{3}{4}$ to get a fraction with a denominator of a power of ten. Four is not a factor of 10, but it is a factor of 100. Thus the new fraction will have 100 as denominator:
$$\frac{3}{4} = \frac{25 \times 3}{25 \times 4} = \frac{75}{100}$$
*Step 2:* Write $\frac{75}{100}$ as a decimal: $\frac{75}{100} = .75$.
$$\frac{3}{4} = \frac{75}{100} = .75$$

EXAMPLE 3:

*Problem:* Write $\frac{7}{8}$ as a decimal.

*Solution: Step 1:* Rename $\frac{7}{8}$ to get a fraction with a denominator of a power of ten. Eight is not a factor of 10, and it is not a factor of 100, but it is a factor of 1000. Thus the new fraction will have 1000 as denominator:

$$\frac{7}{8} = \frac{125 \times 7}{125 \times 8} = \frac{875}{1000}$$

*Step 2:* Write $\frac{875}{1000}$ as a decimal: $\frac{875}{1000} = .875$.

$$\frac{7}{8} = \frac{875}{1000} = .875$$

The decimal equivalent of a fraction can also be obtained by performing the division indicated by the fraction, as was shown before.

*Note:* The decimal equivalent of $\frac{7}{8}$ is expressed as .875 and not as $.87\frac{1}{2}$. Similarly, $\frac{1}{8} = .125$ and not $.12\frac{1}{2}$. Notations such as $.12\frac{1}{2}$, $.87\frac{1}{2}$, and $.33\frac{1}{3}$ are not decimals and may build faulty concepts.

## Changing a decimal to an equivalent fraction

When changing a decimal to an equivalent fraction, the decimal can be written first in fraction form in the way it is pronounced. Then, if necessary, the fraction is expressed in simplest terms.

EXAMPLE 1:

*Problem:* Write .9 as a fraction.

*Solution:* .9 = nine tenths = $\frac{9}{10}$.

EXAMPLE 2:

*Problem:* Write .675 as a fraction.

*Solution:* .675 = six hundred seventy-five thousandths = $\frac{675}{1000} = \frac{27}{40}$.

## Changing a repeating decimal to a fraction

EXAMPLE:

*Problem:* Write .666 $\cdots$ as a fraction.

*Solution: Step 1:* Represent the unknown fraction by $n$:

$$n = .666 \cdots$$

*Step 2:* We need to find a multiple of .666 $\cdots$ such that the difference between this multiple and .666 $\cdots$ is a whole number. Since 6.666 $\cdots$ satisfies this condition, we multiply both members of the equation $n = .666 \cdots$ by 10: $10n = 6.666 \cdots$.

*Note:* If the cycle that repeats consists of two or more digits, both members of the equation must be multiplied by a higher power of ten.

*Step 3:* Find the difference between $10n$ and $n$:

$$10n = 6.666\cdots$$
$$-\quad n = \phantom{6}.666\cdots$$
$$\overline{\phantom{-}9n = 6}$$

*Step 4:* Find $n$: Since $9n = 6$, $n = \frac{6}{9} = \frac{2}{3}$. Thus $.666\cdots = \frac{2}{3}$.

## Typical Grade Placement of Decimals

*Grades Kgt.–IV:*    1. Readiness activities, including the use of decimals in the the monetary system.

*Grade V:*   
1. Meaning of tenths and hundredths.
2. Reading tenths and hundredths.
3. Writing tenths and hundredths.
4. Adding tenths and hundredths.
5. Subtracting tenths and hundredths.
6. Relating fractions to decimals.

*Grade VI:*   
1. Maintaining skills and extending decimals.
2. Multiplying with decimals.
3. Dividing with decimals.
4. Relating decimals to per cents.
5. Rounding decimals.

## Introducing Decimals

When specific instruction in decimals is undertaken, the pupils are already acquainted with the decimal point from experiences with money situations. They have used the decimal point to indicate the digits which stand for dollars. They have also performed operations involving money numbers and are supposed to know that decimal points must be aligned in vertical addition and subtraction. Such experiences have prepared the children for formal instruction in decimals.

For the introduction of decimals the teacher has several devices available.

### Odometer

The car odometer shows the numerals which represent the tenths in a contrasting color. In the illustration below, the square reserved for the tenth is shaded. After a complete rotation of the tenths dial, a numeral appears in the ones dial which represents the number that is one unit larger than the preceding one in the ones dial.

| 0 | 0 | 1 | 2 | 3 | 5 |
|---|---|---|---|---|---|

## Number line

The units on the number line which is used to introduce decimals are sub-divided into tenths. The marks on the line representing the tenths are labeled with both fractions and decimals:

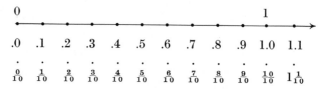

## Ruler and tape

An engineer's ruler and a surveyor's tape, both graduated in inches and tenths of inches, are used by the pupils to measure lengths and distances.

## Diagrams

Diagrams on graph paper and worksheets with mimeographed squares and divided squares can be used effectively to introduce the meaning of decimals and to illustrate simple operations involving decimals. An empty square represents a unit of one, a square divided into ten strips the tenths, and a hundred square the hundredths:

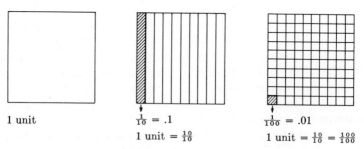

If the pupils understand the meaning of decimals and can work with tenths and hundredths, it will probably not be necessary to introduce thousandths in the same way as tenths and hundredths have been presented. The child will usually be able to extend the decimals to thousandths by applying the knowledge he has already acquired. If there is a need to introduce thousandths separately, the meter graduated in decimeters, centimeters, and millimeters is recommended as a device, provided that the pupils have already been introduced to the metric system of measures. Another device which can be used is the micrometer, which measures the width of small objects in thousandths of an inch.

## Reading Decimals

In learning to read decimals the pupils must realize that the ones digit is the center of our system of notation. Thus in 45.6 the 5 stands for ones, the 4 for tens, and the 6 for tenths. A diagram on the chalkboard will be helpful to emphasize that the decimal point is only a device to indicate the place of the ones.

In reading a decimal, its denominator must be determined. Starting with the first digit to the right of the decimal point, the names are assigned to each position (tenths, hundredths, etc.), and the name of the position of the last digit agrees with the denominator of the decimal.

The rule to reserve the conjunction "and" for the decimal point in a mixed decimal has become widely accepted.

EXAMPLES:

| | | |
|---|---|---|
| 4578 | — | four thousand, five hundred, seventy-eight |
| .7 | — | seven tenths |
| .07 | — | seven hundredths |
| .007 | — | seven thousandths |
| .77 | — | seventy-seven hundredths |
| .777 | — | seven hundred seventy-seven thousandths |
| 6.6 | — | six and six tenths |
| 66.66 | — | sixty-six and sixty-six hundredths |

The decimal point is sometimes read as "point":

5.3   —   five point three

## Writing Decimals

Instruction in the writing as well as the reading of decimals is a necessary part of the program. The tenths are introduced first, and are presented in both decimal and fraction form. When smaller decimals are introduced, the pupils are guided to discover that hundredths are expressed by two digits to the right of the decimal point, and thousandths by three digits to the right of that point. Thus in the decimal .005, the zeros hold the places for the tenths and the hundredths, and consequently .5, .05, and .005 express different numbers. In introductory exercises the number is expressed in words, in fraction form, and in decimal form.

EXAMPLES:

$$\text{One and three tenths} = 1\tfrac{3}{10} = 1.3$$
$$\text{Fourteen and seventeen hundredths} = 14\tfrac{17}{100} = 14.17$$
$$\text{Nine and one hundredth} = 9\tfrac{1}{100} = 9.01$$
$$\text{Seven and eleven thousandths} = 7\tfrac{11}{1000} = 7.011$$
$$\text{Five thousandths} = \tfrac{5}{1000} = .005$$

## The Fundamental Operations with Decimals

Several examples of exercises involving decimals and possible ways of working those exercises are presented in the following paragraphs. Such solutions include methods of finding the answer to the number question by mental computation, by "horizontal addition," by using the standard algorism or "vertical addition," by substituting fraction equivalents and thus applying already acquired knowledge, and by working with devices or aids such as the number line, rulers graduated in inches and tenths of an inch or in decimeters and centimeters, and divided squares. Since various methods of solution are usually available, the teacher will have to select those which fit his program of instruction best. In initial exercises the obtained answer can be checked easily by substituting fractions for decimals and then performing the indicated operations. For more difficult problems, some methods of checking presented in the chapters dealing with the fundamental operations involving whole numbers are easier to use.

## Addition with Decimals

The first exercises are derived from easy problem situations and usually make use of only tenths. The presented types increase gradually in difficulty through the inclusion of more addends, mixed decimals, and so-called ragged decimals. Ragged decimals have denominators which express different powers of ten as in $6.5 + .45 + 3.664$.

EXAMPLE 1:

*Problem:* It is .3 mile from Jack's home to school. How far is it from his home to school and back?

*Number question:* .3 + .3 = □.

*Solutions:*

1. Fractions:

$$.3 + .3 = \tfrac{3}{10} + \tfrac{3}{10} = \frac{3 + 3}{10} = \tfrac{6}{10} = .6$$

2. Horizontal addition:

Since 3 tenths + 3 tenths = 6 tenths, .3 + .3 = .6

3. Number line:

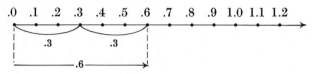

4. Diagram:

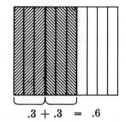

.3 + .3 = .6

5. Vertical addition:

| 3 tenths | and | .3 |
|---|---|---|
| + 3 tenths | | + .3 |
| 6 tenths | | .6 |

The distance from Jack's home to school and back is .6 mile.

EXAMPLE 2:

*Problem:* Add 1.7 and .5.

*Number question:* 1.7 + .5 = □.

*Solutions:*

1. Horizontal addition:

   a) *Think:* How much do I add to 1.7 to get 2?

The answer is .3. If .3 is added, then .2 more must be added, because .5 = .3 + .2.

   1.7 + .3 = 2,    and    2 + .2 = 2.2,    so    1.7 + .5 = 2.2.

b)          $1.7 + .5 = (1 + .7) + .5$     renaming

$= 1 + (.7 + .5)$     associative property

$= 1 + 1.2$     addition

$= 2.2$     addition

2. Number line:

.9 1.0 1.1 1.2 1.3 1.4 1.5 1.6 1.7 1.8 1.9 2.0 2.1 2.2 2.3

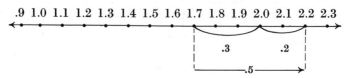

3. Diagrams:

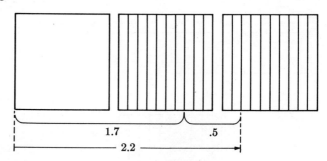

4. Vertical addition:

$\begin{array}{r} 1.7 \\ +.5 \\ \hline 2.2 \end{array}$     7 tenths + 5 tenths = 12 tenths
Ten tenths equal 1 one. Thus 12 tenths = 1.2.
The 1 one in 1.2 is added to the unit in the ones
column.

*Check:* $1.7 + .5 = 1\frac{7}{10} + \frac{5}{10} = 1\frac{12}{10} = 2\frac{2}{10} = 2.2.$

EXAMPLE 3:

*Problem:* Add 2.5, 17.55 and 3.7.

*Number question:* $2.5 + 17.55 + 3.7 = \square$,     or     $\begin{array}{r} 2.5 \\ 17.55 \\ +\;\;3.7 \\ \hline \end{array}$.

*Solution:*

1. The addends are expressed in expanded notation and then added:

$\begin{array}{rl} 2.5 = & 2 + .5 \\ 17.55 = & 10 + 7 + .5 + .05 \\ +\dfrac{3.7 = }{} & 3 + .7 \\ \hline & 10 + 12 + 1.7 + .05 = 10 + 12 + 1 + .7 + .05 = 23.75 \end{array}$

2. Standard algorism:

$$2.5 = 2.50$$
$$17.55 = 17.55$$
$$3.7 = 3.70$$
$$+\overline{\phantom{xxx}23.75}$$

Procedure:

a) Rewrite the addends so that they have like denominators. For this purpose zeros are annexed where necessary. In the exercise under consideration enough zeros are annexed to each addend to make it a 2-place decimal.

b) Add as whole numbers are added.

c) Place the decimal point.

*Note:* The pupils must realize why the decimal points are aligned.

$$Check: \ 2.5 + 17.55 + 3.7 = 2\tfrac{50}{100} + 17\tfrac{55}{100} + 3\tfrac{70}{100}$$
$$= 22\tfrac{175}{100} = 23\tfrac{75}{100} = 23.75.$$

## Subtraction with Decimals

EXAMPLE 1:

*Problem:* Subtract .3 from .7.

*Number question:* $.7 - .3 = \square$.

*Solution:*

1. Horizontal subtraction:

7 tenths $-$ 3 tenths $=$ 4 tenths, so $.7 - .3 = .4$.

2. Number line:

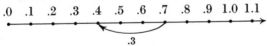

3. Vertical subtraction:

$$\begin{array}{r} .7 \\ - .3 \\ \hline .4 \end{array}$$

Subtract as whole numbers are subtracted. Then place the decimal point.

$$Check: \ .7 - .3 = \tfrac{7}{10} - \tfrac{3}{10} = \tfrac{4}{10} = .4.$$

EXAMPLE 2:

*Problem:* From Mary's home to school is 1.3 miles. From Jane's home to school is .8 mile. What is the difference in distance?

*Number question:* $1.3 - .8 = \square$.

*Solution:*

1. Horizontal subtraction:

First subtract enough from 1.3 to get 1: $1.3 - .3 = 1$. Since $.8 = .3 + .5$, .5 more must be subtracted: $1 - .5 = .5$.

Thus $1.3 - .8 = 1.3 - (.3 + .5) = (1.3 - .3) - .5 = 1 - .5 = .5$.

2. Number line:

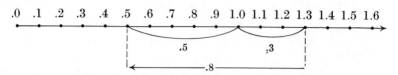

3. Vertical subtraction:

a)
$$1.3 = 1 \text{ one, } 3 \text{ tenths} = 13 \text{ tenths}$$
$$\underline{.8 =} \qquad \underline{\qquad 8 \text{ tenths}}$$
$$5 \text{ tenths} = .5$$

b)
$$\begin{array}{r} 1.3 \\ -\ .8 \\ \hline .5 \end{array}$$     Subtract as whole numbers are subtracted.
Then place the decimal point.

The difference in distance is .5 mile.

*Check:* $1.3 - .8 = 1\frac{3}{10} - \frac{8}{10} = \frac{5}{10} = .5.$

EXAMPLE 3:

*Problem:* Helen planned to walk 4 miles. After she had walked 2.7 miles, how much further did she have to go?

*Number question:* $4 - 2.7 = \square.$

*Solutions:*

1. Horizontal form:

Subtract 2 ones from 4 ones, and then .7 from the remainder:

$$\begin{aligned} 4 - 2.7 &= 4 - (2 + .7) \\ &= (4 - 2) - .7 \\ &= 2 - .7 \\ &= 1.3 \end{aligned}$$

2. Expanded notation:

$$\begin{array}{r} 4 \ \ = 3 + 1.0 \\ -\ 2.7 = 2 + \ \ .7 \\ \hline 1 + \ .3 = 1.3 \end{array}$$

3. Standard algorism:

$$\begin{array}{r} 4.0 \\ -\ 2.7 \\ \hline 1.3 \end{array}$$    a) Write 4 as 4.0.
               b) Subtract as whole numbers are subtracted.
               c) Place the decimal point.

Helen had 1.3 miles to go.

*Check:* $4 - 2.7 = 3\frac{10}{10} - 2\frac{7}{10} = 1\frac{3}{10} = 1.3.$

## Multiplication with Decimals

Multiplication with decimals is best introduced in examples which can be solved by serial addition and by using the number line.

EXAMPLE 1:
*Problem:* When training for track, Jim ran four times around the school building. The distance around the building was .4 mile. How many miles did Jim run?
*Number question:* $4 \times .4 = \square$.
*Solutions:*
1. Number line:

.0  .1  .2  .3  .4  .5  .6  .7  .8  .9 1.0 1.1 1.2 1.3 1.4 1.5 1.6 1.7  1.8

2. Horizontal form:

4 tenths + 4 tenths + 4 tenths + 4 tenths = 16 tenths = 1.6.

$4 \times 4$ tenths = 16 tenths = 1.6.

$4 \times .4 = 1.6$.

3. Vertical form:

$$\begin{array}{r} .4 \\ 4 \\ \times \overline{\phantom{0}} \\ \overline{1.6} \end{array}$$    From the previous solutions, the pupils know that the answer is 1.6. The class then discusses why the answer cannot be 16. With such easy examples the place of the decimal point is determined by inspection and by using common sense in deciding what the answer should be.

Jim ran 1.6 miles.

*Check:* $4 \times .4 = 4 \times \frac{4}{10} = \frac{16}{10} = 1.6$.

The next step is to develop the rule: When multiplying with decimals, point off as many places in the product as there are decimal places in the two factors together. It is recommended that this rule be arrived at inductively by working several exercises in which fractions are substituted for decimals.

EXAMPLES:

$$.2 \times .4 = \tfrac{2}{10} \times \tfrac{4}{10} = \frac{2 \times 4}{10 \times 10} = \tfrac{8}{100} = .08$$

(multiplication of tenths by tenths yields hundredths)

$$.2 \times .04 = \tfrac{2}{10} \times \tfrac{4}{100} = \frac{2 \times 4}{10 \times 100} = \tfrac{8}{1000} = .008$$

(multiplication of hundredths by tenths yields thousandths)

$$.04 \times .2 = \tfrac{4}{100} \times \tfrac{2}{10} = \frac{4 \times 2}{100 \times 10} = \tfrac{8}{1000} = .008$$

(multiplication of tenths by hundredths yields thousandths)

EXAMPLE 2:

*Problem:* Find the product of 1.4 and 3.65.

*Number question:* $1.4 \times 3.65 = \square$.

*Solution:*

| | |
|---|---|
| 3.65 | Procedure: |
| $\times\dfrac{1.4}{\phantom{x}}$ | a) Multiply as whole numbers are multiplied. |
| 1460 | b) Find the total number of decimal places in the |
| 365 | factors. |
| $\overline{5.110}$ | c) Starting at the right, count off the same number of decimal places in the product and place the decimal point. |

## Division with Decimals

In the following presentation of division with decimals four main types will be considered:

| | |
|---|---|
| Type I: | $5.6 \div 4 = \square$ |
| Type II: | $4 \div 5 = \square$ |
| Type III: | $27 \div 4.5 = \square$ |
| Type IV: | $8.5 \div 3.4 = \square$ |

Illustrations of possible methods of solution are presented below.

## Type I

EXAMPLE 1:

*Problem:* Ted walked 9.6 miles in 3 hours. What was his average speed in miles per hour?

*Number question:* $9.6 \div 3 = \square$.

*Solution:*

Procedure: a) Divide as whole numbers are divided.

b) Place the decimal point in the quotient.

The pupils should decide where to place the decimal point in the quotient by using several meaningful methods such as the following:

a) Inspection:

After the division has been worked without considering the decimal point, the class reasons as follows: Since 9.6 expresses a number between 9 (which equals 3 × 3) and 12 (which equals 4 × 3), the quotient of 9.6 ÷ 3 must be a number between 3 and 4. Thus the decimal point must be placed between the 3 and the 2, and the quotient is 3.2.

b) Changing the dividend to tenths:

Since 9.6 = 96 tenths, 9.6 ÷ 3 = 96 tenths ÷ 3 = 32 tenths, or 3.2.

c) Using fractions:

$$9.6 \div 3 = 9\tfrac{6}{10} \div 3 = \tfrac{96}{10} \div 3 = \frac{96 \div 3}{10} = \tfrac{32}{10} = 3\tfrac{2}{10} = 3.2$$

Jim's average speed was 3.2 miles per hour.

Several examples are worked in various ways. These examples should include dividends with hundredths and thousandths. Then the pupils conclude that there are as many decimal places in the quotient as there are in the dividend.

EXAMPLE 2:

*Problem:* Divide 6.2 by 5.

*Number question:* 6.2 ÷ 5 = □.

*Solution:*

In the type of division under consideration, the division is not finished when all the digits in the dividend have been brought down. Thus zeros are annexed to the dividend in order to continue the dividing. In the exercise 6.2 ÷ 5 = □ one zero needs to be annexed during the division process. Since this results in two decimal places in the dividend, there will also be two decimal places in the quotient:

```
        1.24
    5)6.20
      5
      ‾‾
      12
      10
      ‾‾
       20
       20
       ‾‾
        0
```

*Check:*

$$6.2 \div 5 = 6\tfrac{2}{10} \div 5 = \tfrac{62}{10} \times \tfrac{1}{5} = \frac{62 \times 1}{10 \times 5} = \tfrac{62}{50} = 1\tfrac{12}{50} = 1\tfrac{24}{100} = 1.24.$$

EXAMPLE 3:

*Problem:*  Divide 1.5 by 3.

*Number question:*  $1.5 \div 3 = \square$.

*Solution:*  Since the quotient of $1.5 \div 3$ is not a whole number, 1.5 is changed to 15 tenths and then divided by 3: 15 tenths $\div$ 3 = 5 tenths = .5. Thus $1.5 \div 3 = .5$. The sentence $1.5 \div 3 = .5$ can be illustrated on graph paper and on the number line.

$$\text{Check: } 1.5 \div 3 = 1\tfrac{5}{10} \div 3 = \tfrac{15}{10} \div 3 = \frac{15 \div 3}{10} = \tfrac{5}{10} = .5.$$

The pupils should first estimate the quotient of a division problem. By using common sense, they will decide that the answer to $1.5 \div 3 = \square$ cannot be 5. The application of the method of checking the answer by determining whether the product of the quotient and the divisor equals the dividend will also assist them in placing the decimal point correctly.

EXAMPLE 4:

*Problem:*  Divide .15 by 3.

*Number question:*  $.15 \div 3 = \square$.

*Solution:*  15 hundredths $\div$ 3 = 5 hundredths. Thus $.15 \div 3 = .05$. The use of the zero in the quotient often causes difficulties. It is recommended to use graph paper to illustrate why the quotient is .05, and not .5. The necessity of using the zero as a placeholder in the tenths place is also emphasized by working the exercise with common fractions:

$$.15 \div 3 = \tfrac{15}{100} \div 3 = \frac{15 \div 3}{100} = \tfrac{5}{100} = .05$$

After the pupils have worked several exercises and understand what it is that they are doing, they are guided to reason as follows:

a) There are no ones in the dividend. Thus a decimal point is placed in the quotient.

$$3\overline{)\overset{.}{.15}}$$

b) There is only 1 tenth in the dividend. Thus a zero is placed in the tenths place of the quotient.

$$3\overline{)\overset{.0}{.15}}$$

c) There are 15 hundredths in the dividend. 15 hundredths $\div$ 3 = 5 hundredths. Thus a 5 is placed in the hundredths place of the quotient and the division is completed.

$$\begin{array}{r} .05 \\ 3\overline{)\,.15} \\ \underline{15} \\ 0 \end{array}$$

*Check:*  The answer is checked by working the exercise with fractions, as shown above, or by multiplying the quotient and the divisor: $3 \times .05 = .15$.

EXAMPLE 5:
*Problem:* Divide 25.1 by 3.
*Number question:* $25.1 \div 3 = \square$.
*Solution:* When the division indicated by $25.1 \div 3$ is performed, the process does not terminate. The quotient can be expressed as a repeating decimal:

$$8.366\ldots, \text{ or } 8.3\overline{6}$$

$$
\begin{array}{r}
8.366\ldots \\
3\overline{)25.100} \\
24 \\
\hline
11 \\
9 \\
\hline
20 \\
18 \\
\hline
20 \\
18 \\
\hline
\end{array}
$$

A repeating decimal is usually rounded to the nearer one, tenth, hundredth, etc. by applying rules such as the following:
When rounding a decimal to the nearer one:
a) round *down* if the tenths digit is 1, 2, 3, or 4;
b) round *up* if the tenths digit is 5, 6, 7, 8, or 9.
Similar rules can be formulated for rounding a decimal to the nearer tenth, hundredth, or thousandth.
If the quotient of $25.1 \div 3$ is rounded to the nearer tenth, the answer is 8.4.

## Type II

EXAMPLE:
*Problem:* Change the fraction $\frac{3}{4}$ to a decimal fraction.
*Number question:* $3 \div 4 = \square$.
*Solution:* Since the divisor is larger than the dividend, a decimal point is placed behind the 3 and zeros are annexed as necessary for continuing the dividing:

$$
\begin{array}{r}
.75 \\
4\overline{)3.00} \\
2\,8 \\
\hline
20 \\
20 \\
\hline
0 \\
\end{array}
$$

## Type III

EXAMPLE:

*Problem:* Divide 14 by 3.5.

*Number question:* $14 \div 3.5 = \square$.

*Solution:* The decimal point in the divisor presents a new difficulty. Therefore, the answer is first found by using previously learned methods:

a) Serial subtraction. (In order to use serial subtraction, the verbal problem
under consideration should be a measurement type of division.)

$$14 - 3.5 = 10.5 \ (1), \qquad 10.5 - 3.5 = 7 \ (2), \qquad 7 - 3.5 = 3.5 \ (3),$$
$$3.5 - 3.5 = 0 \ (4).$$

Thus four 3.5's equal 14.

b) Number line:

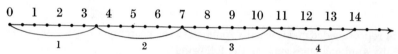

c) Fractions:

$$14 \div 3.5 = 14 \div 3\tfrac{5}{10} = \tfrac{14}{1} \div \tfrac{35}{10} = \frac{\overset{2}{14}}{1} \times \frac{10}{\underset{5}{35}} = \tfrac{20}{5} = 4$$

In order to arrive at the method which is in common use, the teacher
suggests that it would be more convenient if the divisor were a whole number.
It is decided that the divisor (3.5) must be multiplied by 10 to get 35. This
leads to the rule which states that multiplying the dividend and the divisor
by the same number does not change the quotient. Examples such as the
following are presented:

|  | Sentence: | $10 \div 5 = 2$ |
|---|---|---|
| Dividend and divisor are multiplied by 2: | | $20 \div 10 = 2$ |
| Dividend and divisor are multiplied by 5: | | $50 \div 25 = 2$ |
| Dividend and divisor are multiplied by 10: | | $100 \div 50 = 2$ |

After the rule has been understood and tested, the pupils multiply both the
dividend and the divisor in $14 \div 3.5$ by 10 and perform the division:

$$3.5)\overline{14}$$

$$\begin{array}{r} 4 \\ 35)\overline{140} \\ \underline{140} \\ 0 \end{array}$$

## Type IV

EXAMPLE:
*Problem:* A rope which is 10.5 feet long is cut into pieces of 3.5 feet each.
How many pieces of 3.5 feet are there?
*Number question:* 10.5 ÷ 3.5 = □.
*Solution:*

a) Write the division question.

b) Draw a line under the exercise.

c) Decide by which power of ten 3.5 must
be multiplied to get 35.

d) Multiply both the dividend and the divisor
by 10 and rewrite the division question.

e) Proceed with the division.

$$3.5\overline{)10.5}$$

$$\begin{array}{r} 3 \\ 35\overline{)105} \\ 105 \\ \hline 0 \end{array}$$

There are 3 pieces of 3.5 feet each.

*Check:* 3 × 3.5 = 10.5.


## Multiplying and Dividing by Powers of Ten

The multiplication and division of numbers expressed as decimals by powers
of ten is an extension of the cases in which whole numbers are multiplied
and divided by those powers. Such cases should be presented soon during
the study of decimals. In fact, the pupils will already have worked with
sentences such as 10 × $.25 = $2.50 in preceding grades. The rules should
be arrived at inductively. They are then extended to cover other powers of
ten. The rules are applied extensively in mental computation.


## SELECTED RESEARCH

Grossnickle, F. E., "Kinds of Errors in Division of Decimals and Their
Constancy." *Journal of Educational Research*, October, 1943, pp.
110–17.

Grossnickle classified in his study the different kinds of errors made in
division with decimals, and he determined the persistence or constancy of
these errors. The sample consisted of 100 pupils, randomly selected from a
group of approximately 200 pupils who were tested in each of the grades VI

through IX. The investigator concluded that the only constant error in division with decimals results from dividing a whole number by a number expressed as a decimal. He recommended that the pupil be instructed to change the divisor to a whole number before completing the division.

Guiler, W. S., "Difficulties in Decimals Encountered by Ninth-grade Pupils." *The Elementary School Journal*, March, 1946, pp. 384–93. Copyright 1946 by The University of Chicago.

During three years the *Christofferson-Rush-Guiler Analytical Survey Test in Computational Arithmetic* was administered to 936 ninth-grade pupils in five school systems in Ohio. The investigator made a detailed analysis of the pupils' performance on the decimals phase of the test.

Of the several findings, the following are reported:

1. Nearly one-third encountered difficulty in adding and in subtracting with decimals.

2. Three-fifths had difficulty in changing fractions to decimals.

3. More than four-fifths encountered difficulty in dividing with decimals.

## SKILLS TEST

1. $4.6 + 7.9 + 4.2 =$          $104.06 + 2.26 + 3.8 =$
   $21.33 + 25 + 49.6 =$        $200.003 + 1.65 + 9.9 =$

2. $\$150.20 + \$13 + \$16.36 =$      $\$900.41 + \$1.26 + \$.06 =$
   $\$16 + \$.33 + \$1.10 =$         $\$19.96 + \$1.70 + \$2 =$

3. $46.25 - 19.77 =$     $50.56 - 6.9 =$     $71 - 1.19 =$
   $70.02 - 69.65 =$    $290.04 - 13.136 =$    $80 - 15.6 =$

4. $\$100 - \$3.75 =$     $\$60.80 - \$50.90 =$     $\$11 - \$.73 =$
   $\$10 - \$6.84 =$     $\$700.04 - \$555.55 =$     $\$24 - \$5.86 =$

5. $6 \times .9 =$    $.9 \times .8 =$    $1.2 \times 3.65 =$    $.18 \times 9.4 =$
   $.7 \times 8 =$    $.06 \times .4 =$    $.17 \times .77 =$    $1.31 \times 6.1 =$

6. $5 \times \$3.73 =$    $13 \times \$2.57 =$    $29 \times \$.75 =$    $66 \times \$15.20 =$
   $9 \times \$9.04 =$    $17 \times \$1.06 =$    $44 \times \$.19 =$    $78 \times \$10.42 =$

7. $12.5 \div 5 =$    $2.5 \div 5 =$    $38 \div 7.6 =$    $46.2 \div 6.6 =$
   $78.4 \div 7 =$    $3.69 \div 9 =$    $47 \div 9.4 =$    $77.4 \div 8.6 =$

8. $328.7 \div 17.3 =$     $\$47.70 \div 9 =$     $\$1102.20 \div 15 =$
   $543.4 \div 24.7 =$     $\$120.40 \div 7 =$     $\$1531.35 \div 45 =$

9. What decimal part is 6 of 24? What decimal part is 9 of 45?

Find the answers to numbers 10, 11, and 12 by mental computation.

10. $6.5 + 1.7 =$  $4 - 3.2 =$  $6 \times 2.3 =$  $14 \div 5 =$

  $7.2 + 2.8 =$  $9 - 5.6 =$  $3 \times 3.4 =$  $27.9 \div 9 =$

11. $10 \times 15.5 =$  $100 \times \$5.75 =$  $7.5 \div 10 =$  $\$55 \div 100 =$

  $10 \times 2.65 =$  $100 \times \$.25 =$  $9 \div 10 =$  $\$163 \div 100 =$

12. $35.3 + 11.9 + 15.7 =$   $57.6 - 8.1 - 7.6 =$

  $29.5 + 7.8 + .5 =$   $75.4 - 1.2 - 25.4 =$

13. Round to the nearer tenth:

  16.66  25.94  18.47  16.251  6.922

14. Round to the nearer dollar:

  $15.49  $6.50  $8.71  $20.29  $8.62

15. Round to the nearer cent:

  $1.555  $2.375  $6.008  $9.104  $2.906

16. Change these fractions to decimals:

  $\frac{5}{8}$  $\frac{3}{4}$  $\frac{5}{16}$  $\frac{7}{25}$  $\frac{3}{5}$  $\frac{9}{10}$

17. Change these decimals to fractions, and express the fractions in lowest terms:

  .15  .255  .8  .875  .175  .27

18. Write in figures:

   a) five hundred and three thousandths
   b) five hundred three thousandths
   c) fifty-five and fifty-five thousandths
   d) five and five thousandths

## EXERCISES

1. Give two examples of:

   a) a terminating decimal
   b) a repeating decimal
   c) a pure decimal
   d) a mixed decimal

2. Solve .3 + .9 = □ by using:

   a) the number line
   b) squares divided into 10 strips each
   c) fractions
   d) mental computation

3. Solve 3 × .28 by using:

   a) the number line
   b) squares divided into 100 small squares
   c) fractions
   d) mental computation

4. Show .15 on graph paper or on a square divided into 100 small squares.

5. Solve 15.3 ÷ .9 = □ in the way suggested in this chapter.

6. What is the positional value of each digit in the numeral 504.39?

7. In the numeral 126.45, how much more is the positional value of the 1 than that of the 5?

8. Read these decimals:

   15.704     .064     15.015     1400.14     3333.3333

9. Give examples of the four main types of problems in division with decimals.

10. Explain what is meant by "ragged decimals."

**For advanced students**

11. Write out what you would say and do to teach the multiplication of two numbers expressed as decimals.

12. Report on a piece of research pertaining to the teaching of decimals.

13. As assigned by the instructor of the course, report on one or more of the following articles:

   a) Arnold, F. C., "The Decimal Is More than a Dot." *The Arithmetic Teacher*, October, 1955, pp. 80–82.
   b) Benz, H. E., "Note on the Teaching of 'Ragged Decimals.' " *The Arithmetic Teacher*, April, 1958, pp. 149–51.
   c) Broussard, V., "Using the Subtraction Method in Dividing Decimal Fractions." *The Arithmetic Teacher*, May, 1963, pp. 288–89.
   d) Crofts, M. E., "Division of Decimal Fractions." *The Mathematics Teacher*, April, 1946, pp. 178–79.
   e) Grossnickle, F. E., "How to Find the Position of the Decimal Point in the Quotient." *The Elementary School Journal*, April, 1952, pp. 452–57.
   f) Johnson, J. T., "The Use of a Ruler in Teaching Place Value in Numbers." *The Mathematics Teacher*, April, 1952, pp. 264–66.

g) Jones, E., "Historical Conflict—Decimal Versus Vulgar Fractions." *The Arithmetic Teacher*, April, 1960, pp. 184–88.
h) Spencer, P. L., "Do They See the Point?" *The Arithmetic Teacher*, November, 1958, pp. 271–72.

## SELECTED REFERENCES

Banks, J. H., *Learning and Teaching Arithmetic*, 2nd Ed. Boston: Allyn and Bacon, Inc., 1964, Chs. X and XI.

Bell, C., C. D. Hammond, and R. B. Herrera, *Fundamentals of Arithmetic for Teachers*. New York: John Wiley & Sons, Inc., 1962, Ch. XI.

Brumfield, C. F. et al., *Principles of Arithmetic*. Reading, Mass.: Addison-Wesley Publishing Company, Inc., 1963, Ch. XIII.

Buckingham, B. R., *Elementary Arithmetic: Its Meaning and Practice*. Boston: Ginn and Company, 1953, Ch. X.

Corle, C. G., *Teaching Mathematics in the Elementary School*. New York: The Ronald Press Company, 1964, Ch. IX.

Dutton, W. H. and L. J. Adams, *Arithmetic for Teachers*. Englewood Cliffs, N.J.: Prentice-Hall, Inc., 1961, Ch. X.

Grossnickle, F. E. and L. J. Brueckner, *Discovering Meanings in Elementary School Mathematics*. New York: Holt, Rinehart & Winston, Inc., 1963, Ch. XII.

Heddens, J. W., *Today's Mathematics*. Chicago: Science Research Associates, Inc., 1964, Unit XVI.

Howard, C. F. and E. Dumas, *Basic Procedures in Teaching Arithmetic*. Boston: D. C. Heath & Company, 1963, Ch. X.

Larsen, H. D. and H. G. Ludlow, *Arithmetic for Colleges*. New York: The Macmillan Co., 1963, Ch. VIII.

Marks, J. L., C. R. Purdy, and L. B. Kinney, *Teaching Arithmetic for Understanding*. New York: McGraw-Hill, Inc., 1958, Ch. IX.

Mueller, F. J., *Arithmetic: Its Structure and Concepts*, 2nd Ed. Englewood Cliffs, N.J.: Prentice-Hall, Inc., 1964, Units XXI and XXII.

Potter, F. F., *The Teaching of Arithmetic*. New York: Philosophical Library, Inc., 1961, Ch. XIII.

School Mathematics Study Group, *Studies in Mathematics, Vol. IX: A Brief Course in Mathematics for Elementary School Teachers*. Stanford: Leland Stanford Junior University, 1963, Ch. XXIII.

Spitzer, H. F., *The Teaching of Arithmetic*. Boston: Houghton Mifflin Company, 1961, Ch. VIII.

Thorpe, C. B., *Teaching Elementary Arithmetic*. New York: Harper & Row, Publishers, 1962, Ch. XVII.

Ward, M. and C. E. Hardgrove, *Modern Elementary Mathematics*. Reading, Mass.: Addison-Wesley Publishing Company, Inc., 1964, Ch. IX.

# 16

---

# PER
# CENTS

---

SITUATIONS INVOLVING PER CENTS are frequently met in daily life and are often encountered by elementary-school children in their reading materials. Upper-grade pupils, as well as adults, are at a loss on many occasions if they do not understand the language of per cent. The teaching of this part of the mathematics curriculum is therefore essential. Because of the frequent use of per cents in science and in the social studies, it is recommended that the meaning of per cent be introduced in grade V, and that the teaching of computational procedures be undertaken in grade VI.

## Meaning and Terms

The term "per cent" comes from the Latin words *per centum*, which mean "per hundred." A per cent expresses a ratio between a given number and 100. Nine per cent of 200 means 9 per 100, or 18.

In the example $9\%$ of 200 = 18, the *rate* is $9\%$—which can be expressed by the decimal .09, the *base* is 200, and the *percentage* is 18. The difference between the per cent (9) and the percentage (18) should be noted.

A per cent can be easily shown as a fraction with a denominator of 100. For example, $5\%$ of 200 = $\frac{5}{100}$ of 200, or .05 of 200. Since per cents express the ratio between the given number and 100, they can be easily compared. It is easier to compare $14\%$ and $15\%$ than $\frac{7}{50}$ and $\frac{3}{20}$.

The concepts of ratio and proportion are often used in the teaching of per cents. In a *ratio* two numbers are compared. For example, if there are 3 boys and 6 apples, the ratio of the number of boys to the number of apples is written as 3 to 6, or 3:6, or $\frac{3}{6}$. A *proportion* expresses the equality of two ratios. An example of a proportion is $3:6 = 12:24$, or $\frac{3}{6} = \frac{12}{24}$.

306

## Introducing Per Cent

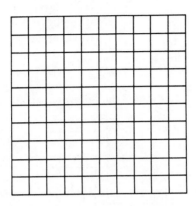

The meaning of per cent can be introduced effectively by using a hundred board. This board consists of 10 rows of 10 movable disks or squares. Each square has a certain color on one side and another color on the other side. Thus, when one or more of the squares are turned over, they show a color which is different from that exposed by the remaining squares on the board. The total of 100 small squares represents 100%, so each small square is .01 or 1% of the total area. When the pupils understand the relationship between 100% and 1% of the board, they are encouraged to do exercises such as: (1) turning over the number of squares corresponding to a given per cent; (2) telling what per cent of all the squares have been turned over; (3) illustrating on the board expressions such as "one out of every ten," and (4) completing sentences such as "1 out of every 10 squares on the hundred board gives a total of □ squares."

The pupils can work individually on worksheets with squares consisting of 10 rows of 10 small squares each. They are directed to write what per cent of a given square has been shaded or to shade a given per cent of a square, as in these examples:

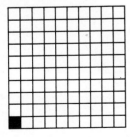

1 small square is shaded.
$\frac{1}{100}$ of the large square is shaded.
.01 of the large square is shaded.
□ % of the large square is shaded.

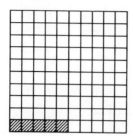

5 small squares are shaded.

$\frac{5}{100}$ of the large square is shaded.

.05 of the large square is shaded.

$\square$ % of the large square is shaded.

What per cent of each of the following squares is shaded?

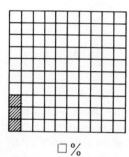 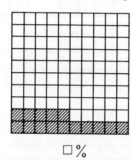 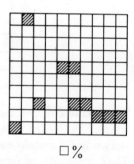

$\square$ %                     $\square$ %                     $\square$ %

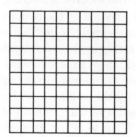

Shade 27 % of the square.

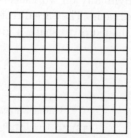

Shade $\frac{1}{2}$ of the square.

$$\frac{1}{2} = \frac{\square}{100}.$$

$$\frac{1}{2} = \square \%.$$

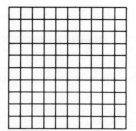

Shade $\frac{1}{5}$ of the square.

$$\frac{1}{5} = \frac{\square}{100}.$$

$$\frac{1}{5} = \square \%.$$

Divided figures are used to illustrate that the total of the component parts of a unit equals 100%. They also suggest the relation between fractions and per cents:

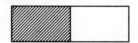

The whole bar represents 100%.

$\frac{1}{2}$ of the bar represents $\square \%$.

The whole circle represents $\square \%$.

$\frac{1}{2}$ of the circle represents $\square \%$.

$\frac{1}{4}$ of the circle represents $\square \%$.

## Equivalents

The number line is an effective aid for showing relationships among fractions, decimals, and per cents:

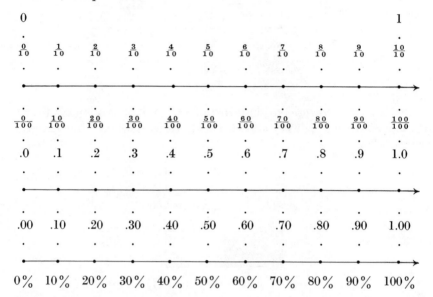

The pupils can also construct such number lines themselves and write sentences such as $\frac{1}{2} = .5 = 50\%$. When they understand the relationships among fractions, decimals, and per cents, they are ready to formulate these rules with the help of the teacher:

1. A decimal is converted to a per cent by moving the decimal point two places to the right and annexing the per cent sign.

EXAMPLES:

$$.17 = 17\% \qquad .5 = .50 = 50\% \qquad .03 = 3\%$$

2. A fraction is converted to a per cent by changing the fraction to a decimal and then changing the decimal to a per cent.

EXAMPLES:

$$\tfrac{1}{5} = .2 = 20\% \qquad \tfrac{1}{10} = .1 = 10\% \qquad \tfrac{3}{8} = .375 = 37.5\%$$

A fraction can often be changed to a per cent more meaningfully by thinking: Since the whole equals $100\%$, $\frac{1}{2} = 50\%$, $\frac{1}{4} = 25\%$, etc.

3. A per cent is changed to a decimal by dropping the per cent sign and moving the decimal point two places to the left.

EXAMPLES:

$$35\% = .35 \qquad 50\% = .50 = .5 \qquad 8\% = .08$$
$$25.5\% = .255 \qquad 100\% = 1.00 = 1 \qquad 250\% = 2.50 = 2.5$$

4. A per cent is changed to a fraction by expressing the per cent as a fraction with a denominator of 100 and, if necessary, writing the fraction in simplest terms.

EXAMPLES:

$$50\% = \tfrac{50}{100} = \tfrac{1}{2} \qquad\qquad 15\% = \tfrac{15}{100} = \tfrac{3}{20}$$

$$\tfrac{1}{5}\% = \frac{\tfrac{1}{5}}{100} = \frac{5 \times \tfrac{1}{5}}{5 \times 100} = \tfrac{1}{500} \qquad 61\% = \tfrac{61}{100}$$

A recommended exercise is the preparation of a table presenting important equivalent fractions, decimals, and per cents. These equivalents should be memorized, in order to facilitate future computations with per cents, and to enable the pupils to interpret immediately common expressions such as "$12\tfrac{1}{2}$ off" which appear frequently in advertisements in newspapers and on price tags.

## Methods of Teaching

There are three cases or types of per cent problems:
Case I, finding a per cent of a number. *Example:* $5\%$ of $800 = \square$.
Case II, finding what per cent one number is of another number. *Example:* $6 = \square\%$ of 24.
Case III, finding a number when a per cent of it is given. *Example:* $8 = 2\%$ of $\square$.

These types of problems can be solved by any of several methods. Some methods are more promising than others and are more commonly taught. The presentation in this chapter deals with:

   I. Formula method.
  II. Equation method.
 III. Unitary analysis method.

### I. Formula method

The formulas are developed after pupils know the meaning of per cent and have had experiences in solving simple per cent problems by using fractions and decimals, or by working with the hundred board and the number line. Two examples follow.

*Example 1:* When 10% of $400 must be found, the number line shown above indicates that 10% = .1. Thus, 10% of $400 = .1 × $400 = $40.

*Example 2:* Twenty-five per cent of $16 is found by taking $\frac{1}{4}$ of $16, since 25% = $\frac{1}{4}$.

After the pupils have learned to identify the *rate, base,* and *percentage,* the formula is developed, in which the letters *r, b,* and *p* are used for these terms:

$$5\% \text{ of } 700 = .05 \times 700 = 35$$

$$r \times b \quad = p$$

The formulas for Cases II and III are derived from the formula for Case I. Problem situations are of the type for which the pupils already know the answers or for which the answers can easily be found.

From the exercise presented above, the pupils know that 5% of 700 = 35. In Case II the rate must be found, and the formula is derived as follows:

$$\square \text{ of } 700 = 35$$

$$5\% \text{ of } 700 = 35$$

$$.05 \times 700 = 35$$

$$.05 = \tfrac{35}{700}$$

$$r = \frac{p}{b}$$

In Case III the base is the unknown. The formula is derived in a similar way:

$$5\% \text{ of } \square = 35$$

$$5\% \text{ of } 700 = 35$$

$$.05 \times 700 = 35$$

$$700 = \frac{35}{.05}$$

$$b = \frac{p}{r}$$

EXAMPLE OF CASE I:

*Problem:* On a snowy day the teacher said that 15% of the 400 pupils enrolled in school were absent. How many pupils were absent?

*Number question:* 15% of 400 = $\square$.

*Formula:* $p = r \times b$.

*Solution:*    $b = 400$

$r = 15\%$, which must be expressed as .15.

$p = .15 \times 400$

$p = 60$

There were 60 pupils absent.

## EXAMPLE OF CASE II:

*Problem:* In a spelling test of 50 words, Bill spelled 10 words incorrectly. What per cent of the words did he spell incorrectly?

*Number question:* $10 = \square\%$ of 50.

*Formula:* $r = \dfrac{p}{b}$ .

*Solution:*

$$p = 10$$
$$b = 50$$
$$r = \tfrac{10}{50} = .20$$
$$r = 20\%$$

Bill spelled 20% of the words incorrectly.

## EXAMPLE OF CASE III:

*Problem:* Tom received a commission of 25% for selling Christmas cards. If Tom earned \$10, how much money did he sell the cards for?

*Number question:* 10 is 25% of $\square$.

*Formula:* $b = \dfrac{p}{r}$ .

*Solution:*    $p = 10$

$r = 25\%$, which must be expressed as .25.

$$b = \frac{10}{.25} = 40$$

The amount of Tom's sales was \$40.

## II. Equation method

The equation method presented below uses a proportion which is a statement that expresses the equality of two ratios.

A per cent expresses the ratio of a number to 100. Therefore, one of the ratios in the proportion is always $\dfrac{\text{number of per cents}}{\text{one hundred}}$ . The other part of the equation expresses the ratio between the percentage and the base. Thus the equation is expressed as $\dfrac{\text{number of per cents}}{\text{one hundred}} = \dfrac{\text{percentage}}{\text{base}}$ , in which the number of per cents, the percentage, or the base is the missing number.

In Case I, the percentage must be found, and the equation is written as: $\dfrac{\text{number of per cents}}{100} = \dfrac{n}{\text{base}}$ .

In Case II, the number of per cents must be found. This is expressed as: $\dfrac{n}{100} = \dfrac{\text{percentage}}{\text{base}}$ .

In Case III, the base is the unknown which is shown in the equation: $\dfrac{\text{number of per cents}}{100} = \dfrac{\text{percentage}}{n}$ .

When a per cent problem is being solved by the equation method, the pupils do not need to identify the case to which it belongs. Yet, for the purpose of organization, the different problem situations will be discussed in the order of the traditional cases.

EXAMPLE OF CASE I:

*Problem:* A salesman earned 5% commission on a sale of $300. How much commission did he receive?

*Number question:* 5% of 300 = □, or 5% of 300 = n.

*Solution:* Equation $\dfrac{5}{100} = \dfrac{n}{300}$ .

In initial exercises the pupils are guided to reason as follows: I multiply 100 by 3 to get 300, so I multiply 5 by 3 to find the missing number. This process is expressed as follows: $\dfrac{5}{100} = \dfrac{3 \times 5}{3 \times 100} = \dfrac{15}{300}$ . Since the missing number is 15, 5% of 300 = 15. (Of course, other approaches can be selected, for example: 5 to 100 = n to 300.)

The salesman received $15.

It is not always possible to multiply a given number by a whole number and get 100. Therefore, at a more advanced stage, the children are taught to solve the problem by applying the principle that the cross products of a proportion are equal. The missing number is then found in this way:

$$\frac{5}{100} = \frac{n}{300}$$

$$100 \times n = 5 \times 300$$

$$100n = 1500$$

$$n = 15$$

The equality of the cross products of a proportion is demonstrated by using an example involving simple computations:

$$\frac{2}{3} = \frac{4}{6} \qquad \text{multiply both } \tfrac{2}{3} \text{ and } \tfrac{4}{6} \text{ by 6.}$$

$$\frac{6 \times 2}{3} = \frac{6 \times 4}{6}$$

$$\frac{6 \times 2}{3} = 4 \qquad \text{multiply both } \frac{6 \times 2}{3} \text{ and 4 by 3.}$$

$$\frac{3 \times 6 \times 2}{3} = 3 \times 4$$

$$6 \times 2 = 3 \times 4$$

EXAMPLE OF CASE II:

*Problem:* When selling Christmas cards, Ted collected $20. If he was allowed to keep $4, what was the rate of his commission?

*Number question:* 4 is □ % of 20.

*Solutions:*

1. Equation: $\dfrac{n}{100} = \dfrac{4}{20}$ , or $\dfrac{4}{20} = \dfrac{n}{100}$ .

Since 20 is multiplied by 5 to get 100, 4 must also be multiplied by 5 to find the missing number: $5 \times 4 = 20$. Thus $n = 20$.

Ted received a commission of 20%.

2. Equation: $\dfrac{n}{100} = \dfrac{4}{20}$ .

$$20n = 400$$
$$n = 20$$

EXAMPLE OF CASE III:

*Problem:* Judy has $10 in her bank. If this is 20% of the money she has, how much money does she have in all?

*Number question:* 10 is 20% of □.

*Solutions:*

1. Equation: $\dfrac{20}{100} = \dfrac{10}{n}$ .

Since 20 is divided by 2 to get 10, 100 must be divided by 2 to find the missing number: $100 \div 2 = 50$.

$n = 50$

Judy has $50 in all.

2. Equation: $\dfrac{20}{100} = \dfrac{10}{n}$ .

$$20n = 1000$$
$$n = 50$$

### III. Unitary analysis method

The unitary analysis method, also called the *unit method*, is easy to understand and apply. When solving a per cent problem, the pupils do not have to determine to which case it belongs.

EXAMPLE OF CASE I:

*Problem:* One day 3% of the 800 pupils of Jefferson School were absent.
How many pupils were absent that day?
*Number question:* 3% of 800 = □.
*Solution:*
a) Find 1% of the given base: 1% of 800 = 8.
b) Find 3% of 800: 3% of 800 = 3 × 8 = 24.
c) There were 24 pupils absent.

EXAMPLE OF CASE II:

*Problem:* One day 8 of the 400 pupils of Grant School were absent. What per cent of the pupils were absent that day?
*Number question:* 8 is □% of 400.
*Solution:*
a) Find 1% of the given base: 1% of 400 = 4.
b) Determine what per cent 8 is of 400: Since 4 = 1% of 400, 8 = 2% of 400.
c) 2% of the pupils were absent.

EXAMPLE OF CASE III:

*Problem:* Twenty per cent of the pupils of Washington School are members of the choir. If the choir has 40 members, how many pupils are enrolled in Washington School?
*Number question:* 40 is 20% of □.
*Solution:*
a) Find 1% of the base: Since 20% of the base = 40, 1% of the base = 40 ÷ 20 = 2.
b) Find 100%: Since 1% of the base = 2, 100% of the base = 100 × 2 = 200.
c) There are 200 pupils enrolled in Washington School.

The unitary analysis method of teaching percentage appears to be a very logical method. The pupils first find one per cent of the base. Then they decide what must be found and compute the answer.

In cases where the per cent is an aliquot part of 100, it is simpler to use the method sometimes called the *fraction method*.

EXAMPLES:

1. $10\%$ of $400 = \frac{1}{10} \times 400 = 40$.

2. $12\frac{1}{2}\%$ of $24 = \frac{1}{8} \times 24 = 3$.

3. $75\%$ of $80 = \frac{3}{4} \times 80 = 60$.


## SELECTED RESEARCH

Brueckner, L. J., *Diagnostic and Remedial Teaching in Arithmetic.* New York: Holt, Rinehart & Winston, Inc., 1930, pp. 242–57.

Brueckner administered a test composed of items in percentage and related topics to 405 seventh-grade pupils. Of the items covering Case I, 41.6 per cent were solved correctly; of Case II, 15.7 per cent; and of Case III, 12.6 per cent. The score for all three cases combined was 24.6 per cent correct responses. The errors were as high as 96.5 per cent for one item.

The investigator gave two chief causes for the large number of errors: (1) The inability of pupils to work decimals correctly, and (2) Their lack of understanding of the processes involved in arriving at the correct answer.

Guiler, W. S., "Difficulties in Percentage Encountered by Ninth-Grade Pupils." *The Elementary School Journal,* June, 1946, pp. 563–75.

From the results of a test administered to 936 ninth-grade pupils, the following findings were reported: Nearly one-half of the pupils manifested incompetency in finding what per cent one number is of another; more than one-half, in finding a per cent of a number; nearly three-fourths, in finding the result of a per cent of increase or decrease on a given number; nearly nine-tenths, in finding a per cent of increase or decrease of one number on another; and more than nine-tenths, in finding a number when a per cent of it is known.

Kenney, R. A. and J. D. Stockton, "An Experimental Study in Teaching Percentage." *The Arithmetic Teacher,* December, 1958, pp. 294–303.

Percentage was taught to three groups of seventh-grade pupils, with a total of 475 pupils. An effort was made to balance the ability of the groups. Three methods or approaches were used:

1. Drill procedures were emphasized, with reliance on rules and repetition. No explanations were given, and no aids were used.

2. Understandings and mathematical reasonings were emphasized. The *why* and *how* were stressed. No rules were taught as such. All kinds of aids were used.

3. A combination of the first two methods was used: procedures were employed to develop understandings, and drill was used to fix and facilitate learning.

A pretest, posttest, and follow-up test, all of equal difficulty, were administered.

Although the results were not conclusive, the combination method appeared to be the best of the three approaches used. One of the clear findings was that the three upper quarters of all three groups made significant progress during the experimental period. Small gains were made by the lowest level.

## SKILLS TEST

1. Change the decimals to per cents:

   .04          .36          .09          .15

   .74          1.15          .99          2.50

2. Change the fractions to per cents:

   $\frac{1}{2}$          $\frac{3}{10}$          $\frac{3}{4}$          $\frac{3}{8}$

   $\frac{1}{4}$          $\frac{2}{5}$          $\frac{1}{20}$          $\frac{3}{50}$

3. Change the per cents to decimals:

   22%          3%          17%          1%

   49%          8%          60%          9%

4. Change the per cents to fractions:

   10%          50%          90%          5%

   15%          75%          60%          25%

5. Find the answers to the following exercises by using the fraction method:

   10% of 60 =          75% of 20 =          80% of 25 =          $37\frac{1}{2}$% of 40 =

   5% of 40 =          $12\frac{1}{2}$% of 32 =          $33\frac{1}{3}$% of 15 =          $87\frac{1}{2}$% of 16 =

6. Find the answers to the following exercises:

   6% of 240 =          12 = _____% of 40          8 = 40% of _____

   28% of 1250 =          150 = _____% of 200          63 = 21% of _____

7. Find the interest on $200 at 5% for 3 months.

8. A school team won 12 of the 20 games played. What per cent of the games played did the team win?

9. A salesman sold a vacuum cleaner for $60 and made a profit of $15. What was the per cent of profit on the selling price?

10. How much money must be invested at 4% to earn a yearly income of $200?

## EXERCISES

1. Explain the meaning of the words "per cent."

2. Explain and illustrate what a per cent expresses.

3. Write a per cent problem; find the answer to it; and identify the rate, the base, and the percentage.

4. Without consulting the text, express in words the proportion which is used in the equation method presented in this chapter.

5. Construct a problem for each of the three presented cases dealing with per cents. Solve each problem in three different ways.

6. What visual aids can serve for the teaching of the meaning of per cent?

**For advanced students**

7. Write an illustrative lesson for sixth-grade pupils in which one of the three types of per cent problems is taught by any one of the methods presented in this chapter.

8. Examine four arithmetic textbook series for the elementary school and report at which grade level per cents are introduced. Report also at which grade level each case is taught and which method is used.

9. Report on an important piece of research dealing with the teaching of per cent.

10. As assigned by the instructor of the course, report on one or more of the following articles:
    a) Brown, E. N., "Per Cent without Three Cases." *School Science and Mathematics*, May, 1943, pp. 428–30.
    b) Hauck, E., "Concrete Materials for Teaching Percentage." *The Arithmetic Teacher*, December, 1954, pp. 9–12.
    c) Rappaport, D., "Percentage—Noun or Adjective?" *The Arithmetic Teacher*, January, 1961, pp. 25–26.
    d) Tredway, D. C. and G. E. Hollister, "An Experimental Study of Two Approaches to Teaching Percentage." *The Arithmetic Teacher*, December, 1963, pp. 491–95.

## SELECTED REFERENCES

Banks, J. H., *Learning and Teaching Arithmetic*, 2nd Ed. Boston: Allyn and Bacon, Inc., 1964, Ch. XI.

Brueckner, L. J., F. E. Grossnickle, and J. Reckzeh, *Developing Mathematical Understandings in the Upper Grades*. New York: Holt, Rinehart & Winston, Inc., 1957, Ch. VII.

Buckingham, B. R., *Elementary Arithmetic*. Boston: Ginn and Company, 1953, Ch. XI.

Corle, C. G., *Teaching Mathematics in the Elementary School*. New York: The Ronald Press Company, 1964, Ch. X.

Dutton, W. H. and L. J. Adams, *Arithmetic for Teachers*. Englewood Cliffs, N.J.: Prentice-Hall, Inc., 1961, Ch. XII.

Harting, M. L. *et al.*, *Charting the Course for Arithmetic*. Chicago: Scott, Foresman and Company, 1960, chapter on Grade VI.

Howard, C. F. and E. Dumas, *Basic Procedures in Teaching Arithmetic*. Boston: D. C. Heath & Company, 1963, Ch. XI.

Larsen, H. D. and H. G. Ludlow, *Arithmetic for Colleges*. New York: The Macmillan Co., 1963, Ch. IX.

Marks, J. L., C. R. Purdy, and L. B. Kinney, *Teaching Arithmetic for Understanding*. New York: McGraw-Hill, Inc., 1958, Ch. X.

Mueller, F. J., *Arithmetic: Its Structure and Concepts*, 2nd Ed. Englewood Cliffs, N.J.: Prentice-Hall, Inc., 1964, Unit XXIV.

Spitzer, H. F., *The Teaching of Arithmetic*. Boston: Houghton Mifflin Company, 1961, Ch. VIII.

Thorpe, C. B., *Teaching Elementary Arithmetic*. New York: Harper & Row, Publishers, 1962, Ch. XVIII.

# 17

# MEASUREMENT

MEASUREMENT IS AN important topic in the elementary-school mathematics program because of its extensive use in life and the numerous occasions when children are faced with measurement situations both in and out of school.

In the primary grades the teacher introduces the meaning and the needed terms of measurement, acquaints the children with the important units of measure, and directs their efforts to use the common tools. As the pupils move up in the grades, he refines the acquired concepts, extends the vocabulary and leads the children from crude comparisons to more refined measurements.[1] The teacher must, therefore, be acquainted with the main principles of measurement and with their applications.

## Meaning

In measurement the ratio between a magnitude—which is a property of an object that is measurable, such as length or weight—and a given *standard unit* of the same nature is expressed by a number. Such a reference unit must necessarily be accurately defined.

When the number of beads in a group is determined, the beads are counted. In this activity a group which consists of *discrete* or separate elements is measured and its cardinal number is determined.

When the length of an object is measured or the measure of a distance is determined, a *continuous property* is considered, and the length of the object

---

[1] The student is referred to: E. M. Churchill, *Counting and Measuring*. (Toronto: University of Toronto Press, 1961), Ch. VII.

or the distance is compared with a continuous scale. A standard unit of the same nature, such as the inch, is selected, and it is decided how many of the selected units approximately equal the length of the object or the distance to be measured. The number that expresses the length of the object in standard units is called a *measure* of the object. Such a measurement cannot be performed exactly—not even by scientists who use refined tools—and the measure decided upon expresses an approximation.

The term "measuring" is used when a continuous property is involved. The term "counting" refers to the activity when the cardinal number of a set is determined.

## Some History of Measurement

In primitive society there was not much need for specific units of measure, since crude comparisons were sufficient. An object under consideration was compared with a known object; for example, an animal was described as being larger or smaller than a deer. When the need for more accurate descriptions arose, man established units of measure for common use. Such units were related to parts of the body, to conspicuous objects, or to natural phenomena, and were therefore not standardized. The different positions of the sun and the moon suggested units of time. Lengths were expressed by referring to dimensions of certain parts of the human body, such as *girth*, the length around the waist; *cubit*, from the elbow to the tip of the middle finger; *palm*, the width of the hand; *span*, from the tip of the thumb to the tip of the little finger when the hand is spread out; *digit*, the width of the finger; *ell*, from the tip of the middle finger on an outstretched arm to the middle of the body; and *fathom*, from the tip of one middle finger to the tip of the other when the arms are outstretched. Common units for measuring distances were *foot*, *step*, and *pace* (a double step). Longer distances were compared with an *arrow's flight* or a *day's journey*. The Romans called a distance of 1000 paces a *mille passum*, which equaled approximately 5000 feet.[2]

Unstandardized units of measure have been employed for a long time, and some are still in use. For example, it is common to refer to a handful of sand, a pinch of salt, and an armful of firewood, but such measures are not reliable, since they vary with different people and on different occasions. Thus the need for standardized units of measure arose. People gradually became more specific in their descriptions until, finally, governments defined standard units of measure by law.

---

[2] For a study of the origin of units of measure the student is referred to a more extensive treatment of the topic—for example, to H. G. Wheat, *How to Teach Arithmetic.* (New York: Harper & Row, Publishers, 1956), Ch. XII.

## Direct and Indirect Measurement

In direct measurement the selected standard unit is applied directly to the object under consideration. For example, determining the length of a table by using a foot ruler is direct measurement.

In indirect measurement the standard unit is not applied directly to the object to be measured. The altitude of a mountain top, for instance, is measured indirectly by application of a proper formula.

## Precision in Measurement

The measurement of a continuous magnitude results in a measure that expresses the ratio between the considered magnitude of the object and the selected unit. Such a number expresses an approximation of that ratio and, since it names the selected unit of measure, it is usually called a *denominate number*.

A measurement is assumed to be precise to the smallest unit reported. If the length of an object is reported to be 9.6 inches, the last significant digit indicates tenths, and it is assumed that the measure of the length has been reported to the nearer tenth of an inch. Thus 9.6 expresses an approximate number and may represent any number from 9.55 to 9.65. If the length is given as 9.75 inches, the last significant digit indicates hundredths, and it is assumed that the measure of the length has been rounded to the nearer hundredth of an inch. Thus 9.75 may represent any number from 9.745 to 9.755. Since the number in the first example has been rounded to the nearer tenth, the error may be as much as .05 inch, whereas in the second example the *maximum error* is .005.

## Foundation Experiences

The primary-grade teacher who wants to provide suitable activities for his pupils will first determine the quantity and the quality of the concepts of measurement which the children have already acquired. He may administer a self-made test and record each pupil's knowledge and abilities on a check-sheet. With this information, he will then attempt to help the children refine concepts they already possess, develop new ones, and extend their measurement vocabulary.

Many exercises in the pupil's textbook and workbook will serve the teacher in providing proper experiences in measurement. Yet it will often be necessary to supply additional activities. Several foundation experiences from which the teacher may make a selection have been suggested in Chapter 9.

## Linear Measures

A rich program in foundation experiences will gradually lead the child from unstandardized units to a meaningful use of standard units. Foot rulers, yardsticks, and tape measures are used, and lengths and distances are expressed in increasingly smaller units. Examples of activities are:

Comparing lengths and distances.

Comparing line segments.

Identifying various measurement instruments and comparing them.

Measuring the dimensions of the schoolroom and of objects in the room.

Measuring the distance that a pupil can jump.

Determining the growth of a plant during a period of time.

Measuring the height of pupils and comparing the answers.

Estimating the length of an object and verifying the result.

Selecting the appropriate unit of measure to be used for measuring the lengths of small and large objects.

Measuring the length of the schoolbuilding by using a tape measure or a rope of a given length.

Drawing a line segment of a given length.

Measuring the length of a line segment.

Estimating the length of a line segment and verifying the result.

Drawing a line segment of a given length without using a foot ruler and verifying the result.

Performing computations with linear measures.

Working with simple fractional units of measure.

Translating one unit of measure into another.

Rounding reported measures.

Working with linear metric units.

Through frequent use of common measuring tools the children will become well enough acquainted with equivalents such as 1 foot = 12 inches,

1 yard = 3 feet, and 1 yard = 36 inches to construct their own table of measures. Such equivalents as 1 mile = 5280 feet are provided by the teacher.

## Perimeters

The perimeter of a polygon equals the sum of the measures of its sides. Thus if the letters "$l$" and "$w$" stand for the measures of the length and the width of a rectangle, the formula for its perimeter can be expressed as $P = l + w + l + w$. The pupil should develop the formula $P = 2l + 2w$. Since a square is a quadrilateral with four congruent sides, the formula for its perimeter is written as $P = 4s$.

## Circumference of a circle

After the teacher has introduced or reviewed the needed common terms such as circumference, diameter, and radius by presenting and discussing an illustration as shown in Figure 17-1, he directs the pupils to find the measure

*Figure 17-1*

of the circumferences of cans, baskets, or wooden disks by using a tape measure. The answers are pooled and compared, and the ratio of the circumference to the diameter is approximated. It is suggested that a reasonable approximation of the number which expresses the ratio between the circumference and the diameter of a circle is 3.14 or $3\frac{1}{7}$. The teacher tells the pupils that the exact ratio is expressed by the symbol $\pi$ (read "pie") but that in computations the approximations 3.14 or $3\frac{1}{7}$ may be used. The formula is then written as $C = \pi d$ or $C = \pi 2r$.

# Area

The area of a surface is found by determining how many of the selected units of measure are needed to cover that surface. In initial teaching unstandardized units are used—the child determines how many books will cover the surface of a desk, how many selected squares it takes to cover the surface of a book, or how many tiles are needed to cover the surface of a certain part of the floor. After these exercises the teacher directs the class discussion so that the need for standard units of area becomes apparent. The square inch—a square region with sides measuring 1 inch each—and the square foot are introduced. The pupil manipulates these units and determines, for example, how many units of one square inch it takes to cover the surface of a book, or how many units of one square foot are needed to cover the surface of a table top. Such activities prepare the child for a meaningful development of the needed formulas. The square yard is usually introduced at a later time.

### Rectangle

The area of the rectangle[3] illustrated in Figure 17-2 is first determined by covering its surface with models measuring one square unit and counting the number of units needed. The pupil is then led to the shorter way in which the

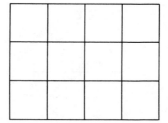

*Figure 17-2*

number of units in one row is multiplied by the number of rows: $3 \times 4$ square units = 12 square units or $4 \times 3$ square units = 12 square units. This leads to the development of the formula: Area = length $\times$ width ($A = l \times w$).

    It should be understood that when the formula $A = l \times w$ is applied, the *number* of square units in a row is multiplied by the *number* of rows in the width to find the *number* of square units in the area.

### Square

A square is a rectangle with congruent sides. Therefore, when its area is determined by finding how many selected square units it takes to cover its surface, there prove to be as many rows as there are columns. This leads to the formula: Area = side $\times$ side ($A = s \times s$ or $A = s^2$).

---

[3] When reference is made to the area of a plane figure, the plane figure and its interior is meant.

## Parallelogram

A nonrectangular parallelogram as shown in Figure 17-3 can be converted into a rectangle with the same amount of surface. This is done by moving

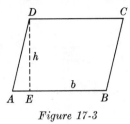

*Figure 17-3*

triangle *AED* to the right of the parallelogram to form triangle *BFC*, as illustrated in Figure 17-4. The parallelogram *ABCD* has been converted into

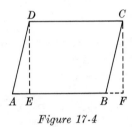

*Figure 17-4*

rectangle *EFCD* with the same area. Thus the formula for the area of a parallelogram can be written as Area = base × height (or altitude), or $A = b \times h$.

## Triangle

The parallelogram *ABCD* shown in Figure 17-5 is divided into two congruent triangles by the diagonal *BD*. The pupils verify that the area of

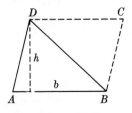

*Figure 17-5*

triangle $ABD$ is equal to one-half of the area of parallelogram $ABCD$. Since the formula for the area of a parallelogram can be expressed as $A = b \times h$, the formula for the area of a triangle can be written as $A = \dfrac{b \times h}{2}$ or as $A = \frac{1}{2} \times b \times h$.

## Trapezoid

In the illustration in Figure 17-6, trapezoid $ABCD$ has been divided into two triangles, $ABD$ and $DCB$, respectively, with the bases $b_1$ and $b_2$. The base

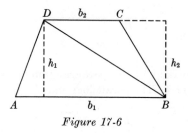

*Figure 17-6*

of triangle $DCB$ ($b_2$) has been extended, and $h_2$ represents the altitude of that triangle. Since the opposite sides $AB$ and $DC$ are parallel, $h_1 = h_2$. The area of a trapezoid may thus be expressed as the sum of the areas of two triangles:

Area of triangle $ABD$:     $\dfrac{b_1 \times h}{2}$

Area of triangle $DCB$:     $\dfrac{b_2 \times h}{2}$

$+\ \rule{3cm}{0.4pt}$

Area of trapezoid $ABCD$:     $\dfrac{(b_1 + b_2) \times h}{2}$

## Circle

The formula for the area of a circle is $\pi r^2$. The reasonableness of this formula may be accepted by examining a circle inscribed in a square, as shown in

*Figure 17-7*

Figure 17-7. The area of one fourth of the square is expressed as $r^2$. By comparing the area of the circle with that of the square, the pupils are led to see that the total area of three small squares ($3r^2$) is not enough to cover the area of the circle. (If necessary, this can be illustrated more accurately on graph paper by making a count of the small square units needed to cover the area of the circle and also of those needed to cover the area of the square.) Since it is obvious that four small squares include much more area than that of the circle, $3.14 \times r^2$ or $\pi r^2$ appears to be a sensible formula.

## Volume

A solid is a figure with three dimensions: length, width, and height. A measure of a solid is its volume. The most frequently used unit for measuring volume is the cube, which is a solid with six congruent square faces. Commonly used standard units of volume are the cubic inch, the cubic foot, and the cubic yard.

When the concept of volume is introduced, the pupils engage in such activities as filling various boxes with units, and are led to conclude that the volume of a solid is determined by finding how many of the selected units are needed to fill the box. The differences in the various units used suggest the need for standard units of measure, and the cubic inch, the cubic foot, and the cubic yard are introduced. If time permits, the pupils should construct some of these units from cardboard or construction paper.

Terms such as rectangular prism, cylinder, cone, pyramid, and sphere are reviewed or introduced if needed.

### Rectangular solid

The volume of a box as illustrated in Figure 17-8 is initially determined by counting the number of cubic-inch blocks it takes to fill the box. After several similar activities, the rule for finding the volume of a rectangular solid

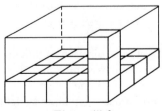

*Figure 17-8*

is developed by the pupils or suggested by the teacher while pursuing these steps:

1. The number of cubic-unit blocks (for example, cubic-inch blocks) in the bottom layer is determined by multiplying the number of cubes in one row by the number of rows. (Base = length × width. This is abbreviated as $B = l \times w$.)

2. The number of cubes in the bottom layer is multiplied by the number of layers (height × base).

3. The volume ($V$) of a rectangular solid can then be expressed as: $V = l \times w \times h$ or $V = B \times h$.

## Cube

Experiments with filling a cubical box or frame with cubic-inch blocks leads to the formula for the volume of a cube: $V = s^3$.

If enough cubic-inch blocks are available, the pupils can discover that 1728 cubic inches are contained in a cubic foot: 12 × 12 cubic-inch blocks comprise the bottom layer, and there are 12 such layers. Similarly, it is determined that a cubic yard equals 27 cubic feet: 3 layers of 9 cubic-foot blocks each are placed in a frame that measures one cubic yard.

## Measures of Capacity

In England, the basic unit of measure for dry materials and liquids is the British imperial gallon, which contains approximately 277 cubic inches. In the United States, the basic unit for liquid measure is the gallon, which contains 231 cubic inches. Thus the gallon in this country is approximately five sixths of the British imperial gallon. Other liquid measures are the quart ($\frac{1}{4}$ gallon); the pint ($\frac{1}{2}$ quart); and the cup ($\frac{1}{2}$ pint). The capacity of bottles or cans is often expressed in fluid ounces; a fluid ounce equals one-sixteenth of a pint.

Our basic unit for dry measure is the bushel, which is defined as 2150.42 cubic inches. Other dry measures are the peck ($\frac{1}{4}$ bushel); the quart ($\frac{1}{8}$ peck); and the pint ($\frac{1}{2}$ quart).

Efforts to improve the standardization of units of capacity in the United States have not led to satisfactory results, and there is still much confusion concerning various measures. A liquid quart is less than a dry quart, and several types of bushels are in use. Attempts to define the bushel by weight have resulted in various definitions in different states. Consequently, there is a great need for improvement.

The young child frequently comes into contact with units of liquid measure. As early as in the primary grades he manipulates gallons, quarts, and pints, fills them with water, and observes simple relationships between the units.

Although the child has little need for using units of dry measure, he should be acquainted with the bushel basket, quart, and peck. Only in some rural areas may there be a need for more extensive computations involving such units.

As enrichment exercises, the interested pupil may study some of the history of the development of units of measure of capacity; he may also investigate the origin and meaning of less frequently used terms, such as "barrel" and "hogshead."

## Measures of Weight

Under certain specified conditions, one cubic inch of distilled water weighs 252.458 grains. Seven thousand grains is legally defined as the avoirdupois pound, which is the standard pound in common use in the United States. This pound is divided into 16 ounces of 437.5 grains each.

The hundredweight, which equals 100 pounds, is used for weighing heavy commodities, such as livestock. The ton of 2000 pounds, which is the legal ton in the United States and Canada, is used for weighing goods sold in large bulk—coal, for instance. It is sometimes called the short ton to distinguish it from the British long ton of 2240 pounds.

Other units are the troy pound and the apothecaries' pound, each of which weighs 5760 grains, although they are differently subdivided. The troy pound is seldom used; the apothecaries' pound is used by pharmacists.

The modern teacher engages his pupils in activities in which they perform measurements and verify the obtained answers. For this purpose the following activities are suggested:

Weighing objects.

Comparing the weight of objects.

Estimating the weight of an object and verifying the answer by weighing.

Filling bags with sand to weigh 1 pound, 2 pounds, 5 pounds, $\frac{1}{2}$ pound, etc., and labeling the bags.

Investigating and reporting which articles are sold by the pound, in a bag of 10 pounds, etc.

Comparing and using different types of weighing instruments.

Keeping a record of one's weight.

## Measures of Time

The three main units of time are the year (the period of time needed for one revolution of the earth around the sun); the month (the period of time needed for one revolution of the moon around the earth); and the day (the period of time needed for one rotation of the earth on its axis). The fact that none of these units can be expressed as an integral part of another has created great difficulties for the makers of calendars all through the centuries. Though the presently used Gregorian calendar has some weaknesses, it is quite usable. Scientists favor the adoption of the "World Calendar," which would be an improvement upon the Gregorian calendar.[4]

Time has been determined in the past by observing the position of the sun in the sky or by measuring the lengths of shadows, and also by using instruments such as sundials, water clocks, and sandglasses. Later, clocks that were first run by weights and pendulums, then by springs and balance wheels were invented. Clocks and watches were gradually improved and equipped with an hour hand, a minute hand, and often with a second hand.

In the present system of measuring time, the following units are in common use:

| | |
|---|---|
| 1 century | = 100 years |
| 1 common year | = 365 days |
| 1 leap year | = 366 days |
| 1 common year | = 52 weeks and 1 day |
| 1 year | = 12 calendar months |
| 1 calendar month | = 28, 29, 30, or 31 days |
| 1 week | = 7 days |
| 1 day | = 24 hours |
| 1 hour | = 60 minutes |
| 1 minute | = 60 seconds |
| 1 solar year | = 365 days, 5 hours, 48 minutes and 46 seconds |

---

[4] The student is referred to: H. F. Spitzer, *The Teaching of Arithmetic.* (Boston: Houghton Mifflin Company, 1961), pp. 238–42.

Elementary-school pupils receive systematic instruction in reading the calendar, and in telling and measuring time by consulting the clock. They must develop concepts of commonly used units of time and become acquainted with the common vocabulary.

The hour hand of the clock revolves twice during the period of one day. One set of twelve hours is designated as A.M. (ante meridiem), and the other set as P.M. (post meridiem). In the armed forces of the United States and in some foreign countries the 24-hour clock is used. On this clock the hours and minutes lapsed since midnight are registered by a four-figure numeral. The first two figures indicate the hour and the last two the minutes. Thus midnight is indicated as 2400, 6:30 P.M. as 1830, 2 A.M. as 0200, etc.

Other topics of interest related to time are time zones in the United States, conversion of units of longitude into units of time, and the history of the development of calendars and time pieces.

## Measures of Temperature

Temperature is measured indirectly by observing the change it produces in, for example, the volume of mercury in a narrow tube. Two different scales are prominent in this country: the Fahrenheit thermometer, which is used in daily activities; and the centigrade thermometer, which is employed in scientific work.

Fahrenheit indicates the temperature at which water freezes under certain specified conditions as 32° and the temperature at which water boils—again under specified conditions—as 212°. Thus there is a difference of 180 degrees between the two points.

On the centigrade scale, the freezing point of water is 0° and the boiling point is 100°.

Upper-grade children are introduced to the two thermometers. Pupils with sufficient ability derive and use formulas for converting a temperature reading from one scale into the other.

EXAMPLE:
*Problem:* 60° C = □ °F.
*Solution:* The freezing point on the Fahrenheit scale is designated as 32°, and the distance between the freezing point and the boiling point of water is represented by 180°. Since the centigrade scale has 100 degrees between the freezing point and the boiling point, there are 9° on the Fahrenheit scale for every 5° on the centigrade scale. Thus the equation $F - 32 = \frac{9}{5}C$ can be

used to solve the problem:

Since $\qquad$ C = 60, $\qquad$ F $-$ 32 $= \frac{9}{5} \times 60$

$$5(\text{F} - 32) = 9 \times 60$$
$$5\,\text{F} - 160 = 540$$
$$5\,\text{F} = 700$$
$$\text{F} = 140$$

Thus 60° C = 140° F.

## Measuring Lumber

The standard unit for measuring lumber is the board foot. It is a board 1 inch thick, 1 foot wide, and 1 foot long, as illustrated in Figure 17-9. A

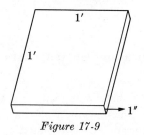

*Figure 17-9*

model of a board foot should be available in the classroom.

If the number of board feet contained in a board that is $\frac{5}{8}$ inch thick, 4 inches wide, and 9 feet long is to be determined, the width of the board is expressed in feet, and the dimensions are written $\frac{5}{8}'' \times \frac{1}{3}' \times 9'$. Since for measurement purposes a thickness of less than one inch is considered to be one inch, the board is said to contain $(1 \times \frac{1}{3} \times 9) \times 1$ board foot = 3 board feet.

Usually the price of lumber is quoted per 1000 board feet. Thus lumber that is priced at $260 per M costs $260 per 1000 board feet.

Not all lumber is sold by the thousand board feet. Some materials are sold by the square yard, others by the linear foot.

## The Metric System of Measures and Weights

The metric system is the official system of measures and weights in almost all the important countries of the world. Though it has been legal in the United

States for approximately a century, it is not in common use. But it is employed by scientists, and measures of several articles, such as guns, films, and drugs, are reported in metric units. These facts, and its use in international trade and in the Olympic games, make the teaching of the main principles of the system mandatory. Many people advocate its universal adoption on the grounds that it is—in contrast to the English system—a logical and scientific system that is in world-wide use.

The superiority of the metric system to the English system is implied by two main characteristics: (1) it is a decimal system in which the ratios between the units are expressed by numbers that are powers of ten; and (2) its units of length, area, volume, weight, and capacity are related.

The standard unit of measure in the metric system is the meter, which was originally intended to equal one ten-millionth part of a meridian between the North Pole and the Equator. It was later discovered that the measure was not correct, and the meter was defined as the distance between two lines on a platinum-iridium bar under specified conditions. At present the meter is defined in terms of wave lengths of red cadmium light waves. The meter equals 39.37 inches.

**Linear measures**

Decimal multiples of units are designated by Greek or Latin prefixes:

| Prefixes and Their Meaning | Equivalents | Abbreviations |
|---|---|---|
| kilo = 1000 | 1 kilometer = 1000 meters | 1 km = 1000 m |
| hecto = 100 | 1 hectometer = 100 meters | 1 hm = 100 m |
| deka = 10 | 1 dekameter = 10 meters | 1 dam = 10 m |
| deci = .1 | 1 decimeter = .1 meter | 1 dm = .1 m |
| centi = .01 | 1 centimeter = .01 meter | 1 cm = .01 m |
| milli = .001 | 1 millimeter = .001 meter | 1 mm = .001 m |

The student who is acquainted with the prefixes can find the relation between units in the following diagram. Each unit equals ten times the next smaller unit and is one one-tenth part of the next larger unit.

km    hm    dam    m    dm    cm    mm

*Examples:*
$$1 \text{ m} = 10 \times 10 \text{ cm} = 100 \text{ cm}$$
$$1 \text{ km} = 10 \times 10 \times 10 \text{ m} = 1000 \text{ m}$$
$$1 \text{ cm} = .1 \times .1 \text{ m} = .01 \text{ m}$$
$$1 \text{ mm} = .1 \times .1 \times .1 \text{ m} = .001 \text{ m}$$

## Capacity

The cubic decimeter (dm³) equals a liter (l). The relation between units of capacity can be read from this diagram:

|  | kl | hl | dal | l | dl | cl | ml |
|---|---|---|---|---|---|---|---|

*Examples:*      1 kl = 10 × 10 dal = 100 dal

1 cl = .1 × .1 l = .01 l

## Weight

The weight of one cubic centimeter of pure water at a specified temperature is defined as one gram (g). The gram is the basic unit of weight and other units are derived from it:

|  | kg | hg | dag | g | dg | cg | mg |
|---|---|---|---|---|---|---|---|

*Examples:*      1 kg = 10 × 10 dag = 100 dag

1 dg = .1 × .1 dag = .01 dag

## Area

The units for measuring area are the linear measures squared. In the following diagram each unit equals one hundred times the next smaller unit and is one one-hundredth part of the next larger unit.

|  | km² | hm² | dam² | m² | dm² | cm² | mm² |
|---|---|---|---|---|---|---|---|

*Examples:*      1 dm² = 100 × 100 mm² = 10,000 mm²

1 dm² = .01 × .01 dam² = .0001 dam²

The centiare (1 m²), are (1 dam²), and hectare (1 hm²) are units of measure used for measuring land.

*Examples:*      1 ha (hectare) = 100 a (are)

1 ca (centiare) = .01 a

## Volume

The units for measuring volume are the linear measures cubed. In the following diagram each unit equals one thousand times the next smaller unit and is one one-thousandth part of the next larger unit.

|  | m³ | dm³ | cm³ | mm³ |
|---|---|---|---|---|

*Examples:*    $1 \text{ m}^3 = 1000 \times 1000 \text{ cm}^3 = 1{,}000{,}000 \text{ cm}^3$
$1 \text{ mm}^3 = .001 \times .001 \text{ dm}^3 = .000001 \text{ dm}^3$

## Selected approximate equivalents for English and metric units

| 1 kilometer | = .62 mile | 1 mile | = 1.61 kilometers |
|---|---|---|---|
| 1 meter | = 39.37 inches | 1 yard | = .91 meter |
| 1 centimeter | = .39 inch | 1 foot | = .30 meter |
| 1 kilogram | = 2.20 pounds | 1 inch | = 2.54 centimeters |
| 1 liter | = 1.06 liquid quarts | 1 pound | = .45 kilogram |
| 1 liter | = .91 dry quart | 1 liquid quart | = .95 liter |

## Teaching the Metric System

The metric system of measures and weights is rightly included in an increasing number of mathematics curricula. In the primary and middle grades only the main principles are taught, and the pupils engage in simple measuring exercises in which the meter stick—graduated in decimeters and centimeters—is used. In the upper grades the exercises become more difficult.

Suggested activities are:

Measuring small objects with a decimeter ruler graduated in centimeters.

Measuring large objects and distances with a meter stick graduated in decimeters and centimeters.

Determining the weight of objects in kilograms and hectograms.

Determining the capacity of containers in liters.

Comparing units such as the kilometer and the mile, the meter and the yard, the centimeter and the inch, the liter and the quart, and the kilogram and the pound.

Discussing reports of Olympic games.

Determining the length of line segments in metric units.

Discussing the decimal nature of the metric system.

Showing the relationship between metric units.

Converting measures from one system to the other.

Expressing metric units in larger or smaller units.

## Scale Drawings

In a scale drawing a given actual dimension is represented by a drawing. For example, if a distance of 20 inches is represented by a line segment of 1 inch, the ratio may be expressed as "scale 1/20." If a small unit stands for a large one, as when an inch is substituted for a mile, the ratio may be indicated as "1 inch equals 1 mile."

Plans of the classroom or of garden plots can be interpreted and constructed by primary-grade pupils; middle-grade children construct and interpret simple maps. More difficult tasks are assigned to upper-grade pupils; these include selecting convenient scales for proposed drawings, interpreting detailed maps, and drawing plans according to given scales with a high degree of accuracy.

## Tables

Sometimes a large number of mathematical facts can be understood and interpreted better and more quickly if they are organized and presented in a table. Data presented in such a way are classified and ordered to make the task of the interpreter more convenient. Information can be presented in a table in detail. Each table must have a title that tells what kind of data it presents.

The teacher may tabulate the pupils' scores on a test from the highest to the lowest, or prepare a grouped frequency distribution indicating the number of scores falling within selected equal intervals. The pupils may prepare tables presenting data such as the heights of children in the class, the number of absentees on each school day of a week, the temperature readings on each school morning of a month, the results of a class election, etc. An example of a table follows:

*Distance Between Selected Cities in Miles*

|               | Boston | Chicago | Cleveland | Detroit | New York City |
|---------------|--------|---------|-----------|---------|---------------|
| Boston        |        | 998     | 648       | 716     | 218           |
| Chicago       | 998    |         | 346       | 269     | 832           |
| Cleveland     | 648    | 346     |           | 170     | 500           |
| Detroit       | 716    | 269     | 170       |         | 628           |
| New York City | 218    | 832     | 500       | 628     |               |

# Graphs

Graphs are designed to show relationships in such a way that the user can easily read and interpret the illustrated data. Several types of graphs can be used. The type selected depends upon the situation that is to be pictured and the data that are to be summarized. Each graph must have a title telling the reader what the information is about.

## Line-segment graphs

In a line-segment graph, numerical data that tend to fluctuate are shown graphically. The graph in Figure 17-10 shows the results of Jane Brown's

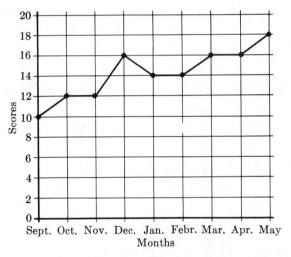

*Figure 17-10. Results of Jane Brown's Mathematics Tests.*

mathematics tests taken each month during the school year. The highest possible score on each test was 20.

In the graph two perpendicular lines, the horizontal axis and the vertical axis serve as the reference lines. On the vertical line the selected units of length have been marked off, and the numerals represent possible scores. The horizontal axis is the reference line for the nine months during which the tests were taken. Lines drawn parallel to the horizontal axis intersect the vertical axis at points representing the scores. Lines parallel to the vertical axis intersect the horizontal axis at points representing the months. The data have been graphed by plotting points at the appropriate locations.

For example, Jane's mathematics score for September was 10; thus that point has been graphed which is the intersection of the horizontal line representing a score of 10 and of the vertical line reserved for the September score. The points graphed have been connected by line segments.

A major difficulty in the construction of a graph is the selection of the proper scale. This choice will be influenced by such factors as the number of data to be graphed, the size of the numbers to be pictured and the difference between them, the degree of accuracy required, and the number of units available on the graph paper. These elements should be considered in the class discussion; different plans should be compared and the best selected.

## Bar graphs

Bar graphs vividly show differences among groups of data. For example, a bar graph is an effective means of comparing amounts of money collected for a certain cause by various grades. Either horizontal or vertical bar graphs can be used. In order to avoid a distorted picture of the data, the bars must be of equal width and must be placed equally far apart.

Figure 17-11 allows the reader to compare at a glance the differing amounts of money contributed to the March of Dimes by grades III, IV, V, and VI of Arlington School. From this graph it cannot be determined

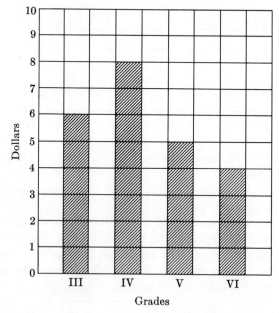

*Figure 17-11. Contributions to the March of Dimes by Grades III–VI.*

whether the amounts of money contributed have been rounded to whole dollars.

Parts of dollars can be pictured by extending the bar part of a unit. In this case, the interpreter of the graph must estimate the amount of money pictured.

**Circle graphs**

The comparative sizes of the component parts of a unit or a group can be pictured clearly in a circle graph. The segments of the circle are in proportion to the sizes of the parts which they represent. Thus, when examining a circle graph, the reader can compare quickly the relative sizes of the represented parts.

Before the pupil is introduced to the circle graph, he should be acquainted with the simple characteristics of a circle, with angular measurement, and preferably with per cents.

EXAMPLE:

*Exercise:* Bill White earned $50 during his summer vacation. He spent $25 on a trip, $10 on books, $5 on presents, and $10 on records. Draw a circle graph that shows how Bill spent his money.

*Solution:* First the pupil prepares a table such as Table 17-1. After the table has been prepared, all the information needed for constructing the

*TABLE 17-1. How Bill Spent His Money*

| Money Spent | | Part of Earnings | Measure of Segment |
|---|---|---|---|
| Trip | $25 | $\frac{1}{2}$ | $\frac{1}{2} \times 360° = 180°$ |
| Books | 10 | $\frac{1}{5}$ | $\frac{1}{5} \times 360° = 72°$ |
| Presents | 5 | $\frac{1}{10}$ | $\frac{1}{10} \times 360° = 36°$ |
| Records | 10 | $\frac{1}{5}$ | $\frac{1}{5} \times 360° = 72°$ |

circle graph as shown in Figure 17-12 is available. The entire circular region represents Bill's total earnings, and each segment stands for a specific amount of money Bill has spent. The solution can be checked as follows:

$$\tfrac{1}{2} + \tfrac{1}{5} + \tfrac{1}{10} + \tfrac{1}{5} = \frac{5 + 2 + 1 + 2}{10} = 1.$$

The sum of the measures in degrees must equal 360:

$$180° + 72° + 36° + 72° = 360°$$

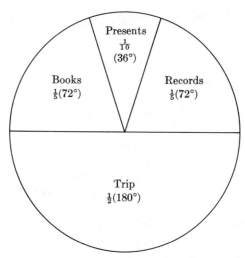

*Figure 17-12. How Bill Spent His $50.*

## Pictographs

In a pictograph, pictures are used to represent unit values; the picture of one automobile tire may stand for 1,000,000 or even many more tires manufactured. In order to obtain a convenient scale, numbers are usually rounded before they are pictured, which may result in a lack of accuracy. When a part of a unit is shown, the pupil has to estimate the number which that part represents. In the graph in Figure 17-13 one picture represents 100 books. The number of books has been rounded to the nearer hundred.

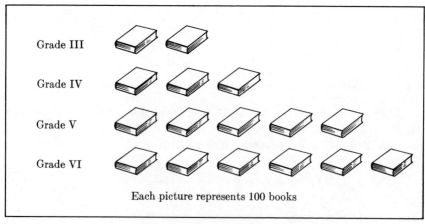

*Figure 17-13. Number of Library Books of Grades III–VI of Grant School.*

## Measures of Central Tendency

From a set of organized numerical data, numbers that represent the center of the distribution can be derived. Such descriptive statistics are called "measures of central tendency." There are three common measures of central tendency: the arithmetic mean, usually called the mean; the median; and the mode.

### The mean

The mean of a set of measures is determined by adding the measures and dividing the obtained sum by the number of observations.

*Example:* The mean of 6, 9, 10, and 11 is $\dfrac{6 + 9 + 10 + 11}{4} = \dfrac{36}{4} = 9.$

### The median

The median of a set of measures arranged in order of size is the middle measure.

*Example:* The weights of five children are 60, 65, 66, 70, and 80 pounds, respectively. The median or middle measure is 66 pounds, since two of the children weigh less and two weigh more than 66 pounds. It should be understood that the median of six measures placed in order of size falls halfway between the third and fourth measure.

### The mode

The mode is the most frequently observed measure in a set of measures.

*Example:* The scores on a mathematics test are 25, 30, 24, 25, 33, 21, 22, 25, 24, 25, 29, 30, and 25. The mode is 25, since the score of 25 occurs most frequently in the set. There is no mode when all the scores are different.

The presented measures of central tendency are introduced in the intermediate and upper grades of the elementary school in real situations. If the pupil's textbook does not provide enough problem situations, the teacher can supply additional problems, such as finding the mean, median, and mode of a set of scores or of temperature readings at each Monday noon during a certain period of time.

# SELECTED RESEARCH

Corle, C. G., "A Study of the Quantitative Values of Fifth and Sixth Grade Pupils." *The Arithmetic Teacher*, November 1960, pp. 333–40.

This study attempted to determine the nature and extent of the functional knowledge of measures among fifth-grade and sixth-grade pupils by having them estimate and measure the following quantities:

(1) The weight of a bar of plumber's lead ($4\frac{1}{2}$ pounds).

(2) The weight of a blackboard eraser (2 ounces).

(3) The weight of a block of wood (8 ounces).

(4) The length of a piece of rope (16 feet).

(5) The thickness of a lead pencil ($\frac{5}{16}$ inch).

(6) The circumference of a basketball (30 inches).

(7) The room temperature.

(8) The outdoor temperature.

(9) Time required for sand to run through an egg timer (3 minutes).

(10) The amount of water in a half-filled pail (6 quarts).

The sample consisted of 108 sixth-graders and 39 fifth-graders. The children estimated each quantity during an individual interview after having been allowed to manipulate objects, use aids or devices, or assist themselves as they saw fit. After the estimates had been completed, each child selected from a table a measuring device that he thought suitable for each measuring task assigned to him.

In order to determine the index of estimate error and of measurement error, the amount of error was divided by the actual measure of the quantity. Thus if a block of lead weighing $3\frac{1}{2}$ pounds was estimated to be $10\frac{1}{2}$ pounds, the error of 7 pounds yielded an index of $\dfrac{7}{3\frac{1}{2}} = 2$. Per cents of estimate error and measurement error were also computed.

Of the presented findings, the following are reported:

(1) Boys estimated more accurately than girls.

(2) Sixth-grade pupils were more effective in estimating and in measuring quantities than were fifth-graders.

(3) Fifth-graders missed the correct estimate by approximately 6 times and sixth-graders by almost $1\frac{1}{2}$ times the actual values.

(4) Errors in measurement averaged 2.39 times the actual values for fifth-graders and .78 of the actual values for sixth-graders.

(5) When the gross error in the index of measurement was reduced to per cents not exceeding 100, there was still substantial evidence that the pupils were unable to work effectively with common measuring tools.

(6) The smallest discrepancy in estimating and in measuring occurred in temperature, the greatest in weighing.

(7) Pupils appeared to be more accurate in estimating linear distance than in measuring it.

The findings reveal that fifth-graders and sixth-graders make a great number of errors in both estimating and actually measuring quantities. Many common quantitative concepts needed for successfully working several textbook problems have not been acquired by the pupils. Teachers appear to have made a limited use of common measuring tools in the teaching of practical applications of measures, which results in a lack of functional knowledge of measures among the pupils. However, the better performance of sixth-graders in estimating and measuring quantities indicates that the pupils' ability in these skills increases during the school year.

## SKILLS TEST

1. 1 ft. 8 in. $+$ 1 ft. 7 in. $=$      3 $\times$ 3 ft. 5 in. $=$
   6 lb. 5 oz. $-$ 2 lb. 7 oz. $=$      7 bu. 2 pk. $\div$ 3 $=$

2. 2 lb. 11 oz. $+$ 3 lb. 8 oz. $=$      3 $\times$ 3 gal. 2 qt. $=$
   3 mi. 600 ft. $-$ 1 mi. 900 ft. $=$      2 hr. 40 min. $\div$ 4 $=$

3. 52 oz. $=$ _____lb. _____oz.      1 cu. ft. $-$ 200 cu. in. $=$ _____cu. in.
   205 sq. in.      1 cu. yd. $-$ 1 cu. ft. $=$ _____cu. ft.
       $=$ _____sq. ft. _____sq. in.

4. 6000 ft. $=$ _____mi. _____ft.      2 cu. ft. $+$ 1 cu. yd. $=$ _____cu. ft.
   1280 acres $=$ _____sq. mi.      1 cu. ft. $-$ 500 cu. in. $=$ _____cu. in.

5. 3 km $+$ 2 hm
      $+$ 4 dam $+$ 1 m $=$ _____m      4 cm $=$ _____m
   6 kl $+$ 5 hl
      $+$ 2 dal $+$ 7 l $=$ _____l      9 g $=$ _____hg

6. 8 km $+$ 1 hm
      $+$ 9 dam $+$ 4 m $=$ _____m      8 dm $=$ _____dam
   7 kg $+$ 8 hg
      $+$ 1 dag $+$ 2 g $=$ _____g      5 l $=$ _____hl

7. $5 \text{ dm}^3 =$ _____ l $\qquad$ $30 \text{ m}^2 =$ _____ $\text{dm}^2$

    $2 \text{ a} =$ _____ ca $\qquad$ $800 \text{ dm}^3 =$ _____ $\text{m}^3$

8. $17 \text{ l} =$ _____ $\text{dm}^3$ $\qquad$ $90 \text{ dm}^2 =$ _____ $\text{cm}^2$

    $9 \text{ ha} =$ _____ a $\qquad$ $700 \text{ mm}^3 =$ _____ $\text{cm}^3$

9. The sides of a triangle measure $1\frac{1}{2}$ yd., 7 ft., and 60 in. What is the perimeter of the triangle in feet?

10. What is the circumference in inches of a circle with a radius of 1 ft.?

11. How many tiles 9 inches square are needed to cover a floor 12 ft. by 15 ft.?

12. The base of a parallelogram measures 7 yd. and its altitude $3\frac{1}{2}$ yd. What is its area in square feet?

13. Find the area in square inches of a triangle with a base of 10 in. and an altitude of $8\frac{1}{2}$ in.

14. The bases of a trapezoid measure $1\frac{1}{2}$ ft. and $12\frac{1}{2}$ in., and its altitude is 8 in. What is the area in square inches of the trapezoid?

15. Find the area in square inches of a circle with a diameter of 5 inches.

16. The excavation for the basement of a house that is to be constructed is 39 ft. long, 33 ft. wide, and $7\frac{1}{2}$ ft. deep. Find the number of cubic yards of earth which have been removed to make the excavation.

17. The volume of a cube is 64 cubic inches. What is the surface area of each of its bases?

18. A cylindrical tank is $2\frac{1}{2}$ ft. in diameter and 6 ft. long. How many gallons of water will the tank hold? (1 cu. ft. $= 7\frac{1}{2}$ gal.)

19. What is the total surface area of a cube with an edge of 8 in.?

20. Find the mean, the median, and the mode of these scores: 17, 15, 12, 16, 8, 17, 13, 17, 19, 18, and 13.

## EXERCISES

1. Explain and illustrate what is meant by a unit of measure and by a standard unit of measure.

2. Explain and illustrate the difference between direct and indirect measurement.

3. Suggest some activities in linear measurement for the kindergarten and the primary grades.

4. Describe how you would develop with the pupils the formulas for the perimeter of a rectangle and for the circumference of a circle.

5. Develop the formulas for the area of a rectangle, square, parallelogram, triangle, trapezoid, and circle.

6. Develop the formulas for the volume of a rectangular solid and a cube.

7. List main standard units of measure for measuring lumber, time, capacity, weight, and volume.

8. Show how the units of length, area, volume, weight, and capacity are related in the metric system.

9. Show by means of a circle graph how you spend a typical 24-hour day.

10. State pros and cons of universal adoption of the metric system of measures.

11. Describe and give examples of three measures of central tendency.

**For advanced students**

12. Preview some filmstrips or films on the teaching of measurement in the elementary school and list their strengths and weaknesses.

13. Outline a lesson plan for the introduction of bar graphs at a grade level to be selected by you.

14. Report on a piece of research pertaining to the teaching of measurement in the elementary school.

15. As assigned by the instructor of the course, report on one or more of the following articles:
    a) Anderson, S. E., "A Simple Device for Illustrating the Size of a Cubic Yard." *The Mathematics Teacher*, December, 1953, pp. 578–79.
    b) Bowles, D. R., "The Metric System in Grade 6." *The Arithmetic Teacher*, January, 1964, pp. 36–38.
    c) Eddy, C. F., "What Weights and Measures Should be Taught in the Elementary School?" *Education*, April, 1951, pp. 483–86.
    d) Jenkins, J., "Teaching the Formula for Circle Area." *The Mathematics Teacher*, November, 1956, pp. 548–49.
    e) Johnson, J. T., "The Metric System." *School Science and Mathematics*, November, 1944, pp. 717–21.
    f) Luchins, A. S. and E. H. Luchins, "A Structural Approach to the Teaching of the Concept of Area in Intuitive Geometry." *Journal of Educational Research*, March, 1947, pp. 528–33.
    g) McKeen, G., "Measures Make Arithmetic Meaningful." *The Arithmetic Teacher*, December, 1956, pp. 247–48.

h) Meadows, G. C., "Let's Modernize Graph Teaching." *The Arithmetic Teacher*, May, 1963, pp. 286–87.
i) Parker, H. C., "Teaching Measurement in a Meaningful Way." *The Arithmetic Teacher*, April, 1960, pp. 194–98.

## SELECTED REFERENCES

Banks, J. H., *Learning and Teaching Arithmetic*, 2nd Ed. Boston: Allyn and Bacon, Inc., 1964, Chs. XII and XIII.

Buckingham, B. R., *Elementary Arithmetic: Its Meaning and Practice*. Boston: Ginn and Company, 1953, Chs. XIII–XX.

Churchill, E. M., *Counting and Measuring*. Toronto: University of Toronto Press, 1961, Ch. VII.

Corle, C. G., *Teaching Mathematics in the Elementary School*. New York: The Ronald Press Company, 1964, Chs. XI, XII, and XIII.

Dutton, W. H. and L. J. Adams, *Arithmetic for Teachers*. Englewood Cliffs, N.J.: Prentice-Hall, Inc., 1961, Ch. VI.

Heddens, J. W., *Today's Mathematics*. Chicago: Science Research Associates, Inc., 1964, Units XX, XXI, and XXII.

Howard, C. F. and E. Dumas, *Basic Procedures in Teaching Arithmetic*. Boston: D. C. Heath & Company, 1963, Chs. V and XII.

Marks, J. L., C. R. Purdy, and L. B. Kinney, *Teaching Arithmetic for Understanding*. New York: McGraw-Hill, Inc., 1958, Ch. XI.

McSwain, E. T. and R. J. Cooke, *Understanding and Teaching Arithmetic in the Elementary School*. New York: Holt, Rinehart & Winston, Inc., 1959, Chs. IX and X.

Morton, R. L., *Teaching Children Arithmetic*. Morristown, N.J.: Silver Burdett Company, 1953, Chs. IX and X.

Mueller, F. J., *Arithmetic, Its Structure and Concepts*, 2nd Ed. Englewood Cliffs, N.J.: Prentice-Hall, Inc., 1964, Units XXV and XXVI.

School Mathematics Study Group, *Mathematics for the Elementary School, Grade VI*, Teacher's Commentary, Part II. New Haven: Yale University Press, 1963, Chs. VII and VIII.

Spitzer, H. F., *The Teaching of Arithmetic*. Boston: Houghton Mifflin Company, 1961, Ch. IX.

Swenson, E. J., *Teaching Arithmetic to Children*. New York: The Macmillan Co., 1964, Ch. XIX.

Thorpe, C. B., *Teaching Elementary Arithmetic*. New York: Harper & Row, Publishers, 1962, Chs. XIX and XX.

Wheat, H. G., *How to Teach Arithmetic*. New York: Harper & Row, Publishers, 1956, Ch. XII.

Wilson, G. M., *Teaching the New Arithmetic*. New York: McGraw-Hill, Inc., 1951, Ch. XXI.

# 18

# VERBAL-
# PROBLEM
# SOLVING

ONE OF THE main objectives in the teaching of elementary-school mathematics is the development of the ability to solve verbal problems. The child meets such problems in school and in daily life and, as he grows older, he will encounter numerous additional situations in which this ability is required. Thus the modern teacher should be acquainted with promising techniques for improving the child's ability to solve verbal problems. This chapter includes the presentation of several techniques, which should be considered as suggestions and not as prescriptions.

## Terms

A problem has been described by John Dewey as anything that perplexes and challenges the mind so that it makes belief uncertain. The individual faced with a problem must analyze the situation, gather facts that point toward a solution, decide which of those facts are pertinent to the problem, and then, by reasoning logically with these data at hand, make an intelligent choice that terminates his confusion.

A quantitative problem may be expressed as a number question, the answer to which cannot be given by a habitual response of the individual who faces the problem. Depending upon the mathematical maturity of the person who is confronted with a quantitative situation, a number question is an enigma, a problem, or an exercise. The number question $4 + 3 = \square$ is an enigma to the typical three-year-old child, since the question has no meaning for him. To the first-grade pupil who understands the situation but cannot supply an automatic response, it is a problem. To a fourth-grade pupil who can give the answer immediately, it is an exercise.

A verbal quantitative problem is considered to be a described situation that involves a quantitative question for which the individual has no ready answer. In this chapter a verbal quantitative problem is called a "verbal problem" or a "word problem."

## The Process of Verbal-problem Solving

Though a definite pattern in the process of verbal-problem solving has not been discerned, some steps in the process can be identified. First the problem is recognized and a goal is set. This is followed by the realization of a difficulty, since the existence of a problem excludes an automatic response. A problem can be compared with a situation in which an individual has to unlock a door without readily knowing which key to use. Thus the person starts the process of deliberation and tries to decide which key must be used to open the door and reach the goal. In using the drill method, the teacher would furnish the key and urge the pupil to practise opening the door until he could do so automatically. The teacher who uses the meaning method encourages the pupil to size up the situation, gather and analyze the data that are available, perceive the relations, and decide upon a possible solution or hypothesis. Comparing the problem again with the situation of the locked door, the pupil is to use all the available information and select with discrimination the key that he thinks might fit the door. When a key has been selected, the tentative solution is tested and either accepted or rejected. If it is rejected, another solution or hypothesis must be formulated and tested.

When the pupil has unlocked the problem and found the correct solution, he has pursued a meaningful learning process. It is anticipated that in future problems similarities or common relations will be perceived. Ideally, the pupil should repeat the meaningful process of unlocking various problems so that he will become skillful in organizing data, identifying relations, and testing tentative solutions.

## The Importance of the Teaching of Verbal-problem Solving

Teaching pupils to solve verbal problems is an integral part of a good mathematics curriculum and is to be emphasized for several reasons:

1. Situations in which verbal problems must be solved arise frequently in daily life, and ability to cope with them is often crucial. An individual's success in his occupation may well depend upon his skill in this area. Adults' performance in solving verbal problems is to a great extent related to the thoroughness of the mathematics instruction they received in school.

2. Verbal problems arise repeatedly in other subjects which the pupil pursues in school. His success in interpreting quantitative situations presented in subjects such as science and social studies depends upon his skill in problem solving. Verbal problems also occur frequently in various school activities in which the child is engaged. In such situations dividends are gathered from a sound investment in the mathematics program.

3. The word problem may serve to demonstrate the importance of and the need for a skill introduced in the problem and may thus motivate the child to learn the skill.

4. Verbal problems are meaningful material that provides practice in computational skills. Generalizations formed inductively are applied deductively in such situations.

## Suggested Procedures in the Solving of Verbal Problems

When a word problem is presented for solution, the pupil needs a sufficient amount of time for reading it. He must identify the number question and proceed to find, check, and interpret the answer. This procedure is illustrated in the following example:

*Verbal problem:* Jim gave 7 of his 25 marbles to his friend. How many marbles did Jim have left?
*Number question:* $25 - 7 = \square$.
*Solution:* $25 - 7 = 18$
*Check:* $18 + 7 = 25$
*Interpretation:* Jim had 18 marbles left.

If the problem presented is an application of a learned process or a review of a previously mastered skill, the pupil should have no difficulty in finding the answer to a correctly stated number question. The anticipated difficulty for some pupils is the identification of the number question itself. Even this difficulty is reduced to a minimum in one-step problems, such as the one resented above, in which the numerals and the word "left" suggest that 7 must be subtracted from 25. Techniques for removing such cues from the statement of a problem are described elsewhere in this chapter.

Multi-step problems are situations that must be interpreted by finding the relationship between "what is given" and "what is to be found." A definite pattern for solving such problems can hardly be prescribed, since children seem to find the relationships in different ways and conditions in word problems differ. Consequently, the procedure of teaching verbal-problem solving by directing the child to pursue a series of prescribed steps is not a panacea. However, the teacher may want to design some systematic plan of procedure for the benefit of pupils who experience difficulties. The following suggestions for such a plan of attack should serve as guidelines rather than as a definite prescription. Ideally, the pupil is assisted in the development of his ability to solve word problems by the presentation of examples that illustrate how it can be done, and by being encouraged to find and use alternate methods of solution. He is stimulated to "think out loud" so that the teacher can assist him by asking proper guide questions. The teacher's interpretations, often aided by diagrams presented on the chalkboard, will help the pupil in discovering relationships in the problem situation.

The following procedure in the solving of multi-step verbal problems may assist the pupil who encounters difficulties:

(1) Reading the problem.

(2) Identifying what is given.

(3) Deciding what is asked.

(4) Deliberating, if necessary with the help of diagrams, in order to find the relationship between what is given and what is asked, and to determine which operations must be performed.

(5) Writing the number question—also called "open mathematical sentence."

(6) Finding the answer.

(7) Checking the answer.

(8) Interpreting the answer.

The following numbered paragraphs illustrate the suggested procedure:

*Verbal problem:* Mr. Ames owns $1\frac{3}{4}$ acres of land. He keeps $\frac{1}{2}$ acre and sells the remainder in lots of $\frac{1}{8}$ acre each. How many lots does Mr. Ames sell?

(1) *Reading the problem:* The pupil reads the problem carefully. The teacher may ask him to interpret the situation in his own words.

(2) *Identifying what is given:* Of his $1\frac{3}{4}$ acres of land, Mr. Ames keeps $\frac{1}{2}$ acre and sells what is left in lots of $\frac{1}{8}$ acre each.

(3) *Deciding what is asked:* How many lots does Mr. Ames sell?

(4) *Deliberating:* First, $\frac{1}{2}$ acre must be subtracted from $1\frac{3}{4}$ acres. Then it must be determined how many lots of $\frac{1}{8}$ acre each are contained in the remainder.

(5) *Writing the number question:* $(1\frac{3}{4} - \frac{1}{2}) \div \frac{1}{8} = \square$.

(6) *Finding the answer:*

$$(1\frac{3}{4} - \frac{1}{2}) \div \frac{1}{8} = 1\frac{1}{4} \div \frac{1}{8} = \frac{5}{4} \div \frac{1}{8} = \frac{5 \times \overset{2}{\cancel{8}}}{\underset{1}{\cancel{4}} \times 1} = \frac{10}{1} = 10.$$

(7) *Checking the answer:*

$$10 \times \frac{1}{8} = \frac{10}{8} = 1\frac{2}{8} = 1\frac{1}{4} \text{ and } 1\frac{1}{4} + \frac{1}{2} = 1\frac{3}{4}.$$

(8) *Interpretation:* When the pupil computes the answer, he works with numbers. Thus, when the equation has been solved, the answer is interpreted: Mr. Ames sells 10 lots of $\frac{1}{8}$ acre each.

## Possible Causes of Poor Performance in the Solving of Verbal Problems

Elementary-school teachers often complain about the poor performance of their pupils in verbal-problem solving. Frequently discrepancies are evident between the pupils' proficiency in computation and their ability to solve word problems as measured by standardized tests and as observed by the teacher in regular classwork. Many pupils have acquired computational skills which they cannot apply promptly in verbal situations. On the other hand, there are pupils who display an understanding of verbal quantitative problems but who are unable to perform the required computations. The causes of such deficiencies should be determined and effective techniques should be applied to improve the pupils' proficiency.

The following possible causes of poor performance in verbal-problem solving are suggested for the teacher's consideration:

1. *The teacher overemphasizes computation at the expense of problem solving.* The importance of considerable practice in problem solving is not always realized, and the time allotted to it is frequently insufficient. More than mere knowledge of numbers is needed for the solving of word problems. Pupils may master mathematical skills without being able to apply them because of their inability to understand the meaning of the fundamental operations and the interrelationships among those operations. Such deficiencies may be the result of a lack of experience in applying mathematical knowledge and skills in situations. It seems logical to assume that practice in problem solving will result in more proficiency in this area. In attempting to determine the effect understanding the fundamental operations has upon problem-solving ability, Pace[1] concluded that such understanding is a vital factor in the

---

[1] A resumé of this study is presented at the end of the chapter.

improvement of problem-solving ability and that consequently the teacher should provide for the development of understanding of the fundamental operations.

2. *The wording of many verbal problems in textbooks does not encourage analytical thinking, and these books do not suggest enough promising techniques for problem solving.* The way in which some word problems are stated in textbooks allows the pupils to determine at a glance—or just by skimming the sentences—which operation is to be performed on what numbers. Such word problems are not much more than computation exercises. Preferably, word problems should be stated so that the child is forced to analyze the presented situation. Spitzer and Flournoy[2] suggest that the typical textbook program for improving or developing problem-solving ability should be supplemented by providing more promising techniques.

3. *The pupil lacks skills needed to read and interpret the word problem.* The child whose reading ability is below average is at a disadvantage when he must read and solve word problems. In fact, interpreting quantitative situations requires skills beyond those needed for reading sentences in stories. The child must be able to locate within the problem the information that is pertinent, discard the data that are irrelevant, and thus discriminate between expressions that are essential to solving the problem and those that are not. He must be thoroughly acquainted with the presented mathematical vocabulary so that he can decide which operations are inferred by "clue words" in expressions such as the "total" of 5 and 9; the "product" of 4 and 13; 5 "per cent" of 300; $\frac{3}{4}$ "of" 8; etc. If the child is deficient in such skills, he cannot be expected to perform well in solving verbal problems.

4. *The time allotted for the child to solve a verbal problem presented in class is insufficient.* The solving of a problem requires time for analyzing the situation, deliberating upon the steps that should be followed, identifying the number question, and computing the answer. Striving to cover a specified amount of subject matter in too little time, and evaluating the child's progress by quantity covered instead of quality of work accomplished is at least questionable. The teacher must take time to encourage the pupil to "think out loud," to show a visual representation of the situtation, and to correct faulty thinking.

5. *The pupil lacks knowledge of mathematical vocabulary.* As shown by Treacey,[3] pupils who are well acquainted with the special vocabulary of mathematics do better in solving verbal problems than the pupils to whom these

---

[2] H. F. Spitzer and F. Flournoy, "Developing Facility in Solving Verbal Problems." *The Arithmetic Teacher*, November, 1956, pp. 177–82.

[3] A resumé of this study is presented at the end of this chapter.

words convey little or inappropriate meaning. Johnson[4] concluded that vocabulary instructional materials should be used regularly and systematically as an integral part of the classroom procedure.

6. *The pupil is not proficient in estimating answers.* Kliebhan[5] studied the problem-solving ability of sixth-grade boys and found that the principal differences between high and low achievers originated in differences in ability to estimate answers to problems.

7. *The pupil cannot perform simple computations mentally.* The child who is completely dependent upon paper and pencil for the solving of common problems involving small numbers does not show evidence that he understands the processes. Flournoy[6] found that intermediate-grade pupils who had finished a program in mental computation had made significant gains both in mental computation and in problem solving.

8. *The pupil lacks ability to perform the required computations.* With the exception of word problems used to introduce a new skill, verbal problems should not involve computations that have not yet been taught, so that the pupil is free to concentrate on the problem situation.

9. *The situations presented in the word problems are not appealing to the age level for which they are intended.* The child should have at least some interest in the situations that are presented so that he will be motivated for his task. This does not mean that all the presented verbal problems must be real situations. Banks,[7] reporting on a study conducted by Welch, presents evidence showing that pupils prefer fantasy problems to problems describing real-life situations. Even ridiculous situations were not found to be a distraction. Pupils performed as well on the unreal problems as they did on the real problems.

10. *The classroom climate is not conducive to a proper learning situation.* The way in which the teacher directs the class discussions may be of such a nature that the child hesitates to volunteer an answer for fear of making a mistake. In such a situation the teacher has not succeeded in establishing a relaxed atmosphere in which the child's thinking is stimulated and constructively corrected. The master teacher strives toward the ideal situation, where each

---

[4] A resumé of this study is presented at the end of the chapter.

[5] M. C. Kliebhan, *An Experimental Study of Arithmetic Problem-Solving Ability of Sixth Grade Boys.* (Washington, D.C.: The Catholic University of America Press, 1955.)

[6] M. F. Flournoy, "The Effectiveness of Instruction in Mental Arithmetic." *The Elementary School Journal*, November, 1954, pp. 148–53.

[7] J. H. Banks, *Learning and Teaching Arithmetic*, 2nd Ed. (Boston: Allyn and Bacon, Inc., 1964), p. 407.

child is actively engaged in the learning process, volunteers answers, challenges solutions, and experiences some degree of success. The teacher who understands and likes mathematics and who attempts to stimulate the children's thinking will motivate his pupils intrinsically.

## Techniques for Improving Problem Solving

Several techniques for the improvement of problem solving are available. The degree of success with which pupils use each of these will depend upon the kind of problems used, the ability and enthusiasm of the teacher, and the mathematical maturity and motivation of the pupils. The following techniques are suggested:

1. *Applying the method of analysis.* The procedure followed in the solving of verbal problems by the analysis method has been described elsewhere in this chapter.

2. *Applying the method of analogy.* After a pupil has worked a problem that makes use of easy numbers, he can attack a more difficult problem containing cumbersome numbers but requiring the use of the same operations. This technique allows the pupil to concentrate on the relationship between the numbers in the problem without being hampered by unwieldy computations. After the relationships have been detected, and the pupil has ascertained that the solution of the easier problem is correct, the more difficult problem is solved by applying the same principles.
EXAMPLE:
*Word problem:* In a spelling test Judy spelled $12\frac{1}{2}\%$ of the 56 words incorrectly. How many words did she spell correctly?
*Alternate problem:* In a spelling test Judy spelled one-tenth of the the 60 words incorrectly. How many words did she spell correctly?

3. *Devising problems by interpreting pictures.* In the primary grades pictures illustrating simple numerical data are interpreted and translated into number questions.

4. *Solving verbal problems with the help of visual representations.* Number lines and diagrams may assist the pupils in visualizing the problem situation.
EXAMPLE 1:
Linda has 11 coins. She has only pennies and nickels. If she has 8 pennies, how many nickels does she have?

The mathematical sentence $11 = 8 + \square$ or $11 = 8 + n$ can be illustrated on the number line:

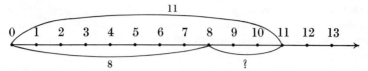

EXAMPLE 2: Mr. Right sold $1\frac{1}{4}$ of his 2 acres of land. How much land did Mr. Right have left?

The situation can be represented in a diagram:

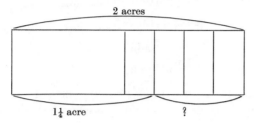

5. *Solving simple problems by mental computation.* Most quantitative problems that arise in daily life and classroom activities are common problems, and the computations required for their solution are usually simple. The pupil should acquire skill in solving such easy problems without the use of paper and pencil. His experiences with simple situations will deepen his understanding of the relationships involved, and the success he experiences will motivate him to attack problems requiring written computations.

The results of research conducted in this area point clearly to the need for a systematic program in mental computation in the elementary school. Flournoy[8] stated that mental arithmetic seems to be more prevalent in daily life than is written computation. Hall[9] discovered a positive correlation between general intelligence and ability to solve verbal arithmetic problems without the use of paper and pencil.

Because of the great importance of mental computation in the modern mathematics curriculum, provision should be made for a sequential program that presents both mental-computation exercises and verbal problems in all the grades at levels that become gradually more difficult.

In the teaching of mental computation, number properties are applied when feasible, and mathematical sentences are pictured on the number line

---

[8] F. Flournoy, "Providing Mental Arithmetic Experiences." *The Arithmetic Teacher*, April, 1959, pp. 133–39.

[9] J. V. Hall, "Solving Verbal Arithmetic Problems without Pencil and Paper." *The Elementary School Journal*, December, 1947, pp. 212–17.

or by arrays. The pupil should discover how the application of number properties can simplify difficult mathematical sentences.

EXAMPLES:

1. *Verbal problem:* Tom added 13 rocks to his collection of 49 rocks. How many rocks did Tom then have in all?

*Number question:* $49 + 13 = \square$.

*Solution 1:* $49 + 13 = 49 + (10 + 3) = (49 + 10) + 3 = 59 + 3 = 62$

Tom had 62 rocks in all.

*Mathematical justification:*

$$49 + 13 = 49 + (10 + 3) \text{ renaming}$$
$$= (49 + 10) + 3 \text{ associative property}$$
$$= 59 + 3 \text{ addition}$$
$$= 62 \text{ addition}$$

*Solution 2:* $49 + 13 = (40 + 10) + (9 + 3) = 50 + 12 = 62$

The mathematical justification for this procedure was presented in Chapter 10.

2. *Verbal problem:* Mrs. House bought 4 dozen eggs. How many eggs did she buy?

*Number question:* $4 \times 12 = \square$.

*Solution:* $4 \times 12 = 4 \times (10 + 2) = (4 \times 10) + (4 \times 2) = 40 + 8 = 48$

Mrs. House bought 48 eggs.

*Mathematical justification:*

$$4 \times 12 = 4 \times (10 + 2) \text{ renaming}$$
$$= (4 \times 10) + (4 \times 2) \text{ distributive property}$$
$$= 40 + 8 \text{ multiplication}$$
$$= 48 \text{ addition}$$

3. *Verbal problem:* Rex read 78 pages in his reader in 6 days. How many pages did he read on an average per day?

*Solution:* $78 \div 6 = (60 + 18) \div 6 = (60 \div 6) + (18 \div 6) = 10 + 3 = 13$

On an average, Rex read 13 pages per day.

*Mathematical justification:*

$$78 \div 6 = (60 + 18) \div 6 \text{ renaming}$$
$$= (60 \div 6) + (18 \div 6) \text{ distributive property}$$
$$= 10 + 3 \text{ division}$$
$$= 13 \text{ addition}$$

4. *Verbal problem:* On three different days, the Johnson family traveled 165 miles, 159 miles, and 41 miles, respectively. How many miles did the family travel in all?

*Number question:* $165 + 159 + 41 = \square$.

*Solution:* $165 + 159 + 41 = 165 + (159 + 41) = 165 + 200 = 365$

The Johnson family traveled 365 miles in all.

*Mathematical justification:*

$$165 + 159 + 41 = 165 + (159 + 41) \text{ associative property}$$
$$= 165 + 200 \text{ addition}$$
$$= 365 \text{ addition}$$

6. *Estimating answers to verbal problems.* Estimating the answer to a problem requires mental computation with rounded numbers. The sum of 29, 71, and 42 is estimated by adding 30, 70, and 40. The product of 48 and $7\frac{1}{2}$ is estimated by multiplying 50 by 7. Skill in estimating answers is a help to the pupil in checking the reasonableness of an answer to a problem, and applying this skill may prevent him from supplying answers that are not sensible. Many textbooks do not include a sufficient amount of exercises in estimation. Thus the teacher may have to provide additional word problems constructed for the specific purpose of developing the child's ability in this skill.

EXAMPLE: On a trip of 196 miles, Mr. Green's car traveled, on an average, 20 miles on one gallon of gasoline. Approximately how many gallons of gasoline were needed for the trip?

7. *Formulating questions fitting given quantitative situations.* A serious limitation of many verbal problems in textbooks is the presence of strong cue words that practically tell the pupil what operation to use. Such cues allow the child to find the answer to the problem without carefully reading it. Consider the following problem: "David worked 36 arithmetic exercises in the morning and 15 in the afternoon. How many exercises did Dave work that day in all?" The answer can be found by skimming the sentences, noticing the numerals "36" and "15" and the words "in all," and then adding 15 to 36. Thus the problem has been reduced to a mere computational exercise. The technique of omitting the question and having the pupil formulate it forces the child to read the problem carefully.

EXAMPLE: Ken had 45 customers on his paper route. He got 16 new customers.

The child formulates a question such as "How many customers did Ken then have in all?" and he proceeds to find the answer.

8. *Identifying superfluous data in given problems.* The inclusion of superfluous information in the problem requires the pupil to read it carefully and to select the pertinent data.

EXAMPLE: Mr. Red estimated that he had to spend $2500 on house improvements and a new garage. If he figured that the improvements on his house would cost $1800 and if he had $1300 in his bank account, how much did he estimate the garage would cost?

The pupil who understands the problem situation realizes that the amount of money in Mr. Red's bank account need not be considered when the problem is solved. The identification of the superfluous information is a guarantee that the pupil has isolated the relevant data.

9. *Identifying the kind of additional data needed.* When situations are presented which lack data needed to answer the number question, the pupil must identify the kind of needed additional information. He can do this only if he understands the problem and is thus required to analyze the situation.
EXAMPLE: Mr. Brown bought a radio. He paid $25 down and the remainder in monthly payments of $10 each. What was the total cost of the radio?

The pupil must realize that the number of monthly payments is not given. If he has spotted this lack of information he has understood the problem situation.

10. *Working with problems in which no numbers are used.* In the lower grades such problems are simple, one-step situations. The pupil is to identify the operation that must be performed.
EXAMPLE: Ted knows how many baseball cards he has and how many his brother has. How can Ted find out how many he will have if he gets all his brother's cards?

In the middle grades the problems become more difficult and involve more than one step.
EXAMPLE: Mary wants to buy as many rings as she can with the money she has in her purse. How can she find out how many rings she can buy and how much money she will have left?

In the upper grades the problems involve several steps.
EXAMPLE: Mr. Grant wants to estimate the cost of the gasoline needed for driving his car from New York to Chicago. What must Mr. Grant know and do to arrive at a reasonable estimate of the cost?

It is anticipated that the pupil will list these steps:

(1) Find out how many miles it is from New York to Chicago.
(2) Find out how many miles Mr. Grant's car travels on one gallon of gasoline.
(3) Determine how many times the number of miles Mr. Grant's car travels on one gallon of gasoline is contained in the total number of miles traveled.
(4) Estimate the average price of a gallon of gasoline.
(5) Estimate the total cost of the gasoline by multiplying the average price of one gallon by the number of gallons needed.

After these steps have been outlined, the pupil supplies numbers in the problem situation and finds the answer. The problem may be rewritten as follows:

Mr. Grant plans to drive from New York to Chicago, which is a distance of approximately 832 miles. His car travels about 16 miles on one gallon of gasoline and the average cost of one gallon of gasoline is estimated to be 33¢. Find the approximate cost of all the gasoline needed for the trip.

11. *Translating the given problem situation into a mathematical sentence.* The basic difficulty encountered in the solving of a verbal problem is the translation of the situation into a number question—also called an open mathematical sentence. To construct such a sentence, the pupil must analyze the situation, isolate the pertinent facts, state the question, and identify the needed mathematical symbols. He must further determine the relationship between the facts and the unknown, and arrange the symbols in the form of a mathematical sentence.

EXAMPLES:

(1) Betty had 8 flowers. She picked 5 more. How many flowers did Betty then have in all?

      *Mathematical sentence:* $8 + 5 = \square$

(2) Ann had 7 flowers. After she picked some more, she had 12 flowers. How many flowers did Ann pick?

      *Mathematical sentence:* $7 + \square = 12$

(3) After Tim received 3 marbles, he had a total of 11 marbles. How many marbles did Tim have to begin with?

      *Mathematical sentence:* $\square + 3 = 11$

(4) Three of the twelve teachers in Lincoln School are men. How many lady teachers are there in Lincoln School?

      *Mathematical sentence:* $12 = 3 + \square$

(5) Ann gave 7 of her 13 picture cards to her sister. How many cards did Ann have left?

      *Mathematical sentence:* $13 - 7 = \square$

(6) After Larry gave some of his 15 baseball cards to his friend, he had 9 cards left. How many cards did Larry give to his friend?

      *Mathematical sentence:* $15 - \square = 9$

(7) After Lois spent 8¢ she had 7¢ left. How much money did Lois have to begin with?

      *Mathematical sentence:* $\square - 8 = 7$

(8) How many days equal 3 weeks?

      *Mathematical sentence:* $3 \times 7 = \square$

(9) Mother bought 5 boxes of apples. If she bought a total of 20 apples, and there were the same number of apples in each box, how many apples were in each box?

*Mathematical sentence:* $5 \times \square = 20$

(10) Linda bought some packages of chocolate bars. There were 5 bars in each package. If Linda bought 15 bars in all, how many packages did she buy?

*Mathematical sentence:* $\square \times 5 = 15$

(11) There are 45 chairs in a room. The chairs are placed in rows of 9 chairs each. How many rows of chairs are there?

*Mathematical sentence:* $45 = \square \times 9$

(12) How many committees of 5 children each can be formed in a group of 15 children?

*Mathematical sentence:* $15 \div 5 = \square$

(13) Mrs. Bird divided 12 cupcakes equally among some girls. If each girl got 3 cupcakes, how many girls were there?

*Mathematical sentence:* $12 \div \square = 3$

(14) A number of pictures were equally divided among 5 girls. If each girl got 3 pictures, how many pictures were there to be divided?

*Mathematical sentence:* $\square \div 5 = 3$

In the following example a two-step verbal problem is presented. The answer to the problem is obtained by performing the necessary operations in a specific order, which must be expressed in the mathematical sentence. EXAMPLE: Tony bought a composition book for 25¢ and a pen for 35¢. He gave the clerk a one-dollar bill. How much change did Tony receive?

*Mathematical sentence:*    $100 - (25 + 35) = \square$

The mathematical sentence that is a translation of a verbal problem is not necessarily an equation, as is shown below.
EXAMPLE: After Jim received 2 marbles, he had fewer than 8 marbles. How many marbles could Jim have had before he got the 2 marbles?

*Mathematical sentence:*    $n + 2 < 8$ or $\square + 2 < 8$

12. *Devising verbal problems to fit given mathematical sentences.* Composing a verbal problem that is a description of a situation expressed in a given mathematical sentence causes the pupil to study the meaning of the abstract symbols and to translate the mathematical idea into a concrete situation. Thus the pupil moves from number operations to daily-life problems. It is anticipated that such activities will deepen the child's understanding of the abstract symbols and will prove to be of help to him when he must express a verbal problem in symbolic form.

EXAMPLE: *Mathematical sentence:* $85 - \square = 60$
*Possible word problem:* Ann had to read a book of 85 pages. After she had read several pages, she discovered that there were 60 pages left to read. How many pages had Ann read?

13. *Providing "brain teasers" for capable pupils.* Rapid learners often finish their assigned work in less than the allotted time. These pupils need additional assignments that are interesting and stimulating. Most children like enrichment exercises that are called "brain teasers." Such problems are designed to improve skill in reasoning.
EXAMPLE: Ray had a square piece of cardboard with a side measuring half a yard. Ron had a piece with an area of half a square yard. Which boy had the larger piece of cardboard?

14. *Teaching reading skills that are essential in the solving of verbal problems.* The nature of verbal problems requires that ideas included therein be expressed accurately and exactly. This can often be accomplished only by using sentences that are somewhat complicated in structure. The interpretation of such sentences requires skill in analytical reading, including locating pertinent information given, classifying concepts presented, drawing inferences, and retaining data. Treacy[10] conducted a study on the relationship of reading skills to the ability to solve verbal problems in arithmetic. He stated that his findings suggest that the development of several reading skills is of help in the improvement of problem-solving ability. He also concluded that help which enriches the meanings the pupil gets as he reads may have a beneficial effect on his performance in problem solving.

15. *Devising various questions fitting a given quantitative situation.* Sometimes several questions can be derived from a quantitative situation. The pupil tries to frame as many questions as he can.
EXAMPLE: Ted spelled 20 out of 30 words correctly in a spelling test. Ray took the same test and made 5 mistakes.
*Some possible questions:*

(1) How many words did Ray spell correctly?

(2) How many mistakes did Ted make?

(3) How many more mistakes did Ted make than Ray?

(4) What was the total number of mistakes Ted and Ray made?

(5) What fractional part of the total number of words did Ted spell correctly?

---

[10] A resumé of this study is presented at the end of the chapter.

# SELECTED RESEARCH

Johnson, H. C., "The Effect of Instruction in Mathematical Vocabulary upon Problem Solving in Arithmetic." *Journal of Educational Research,* October, 1944, pp. 97–110.

The purpose of this study was to determine whether improvement in specific mathematical vocabulary leads to an improvement in the solution of problems involving the use of these specific mathematical terms.

The sample consisted of 28 seventh-grade classes in three junior-high schools; 316 pupils were in the experimental group and 282 in the control group. It was demonstrated that these pupils came from the same general population.

The instructional program for both groups comprised these topics: decimals, per cents, measurement, graphs, and common uses of per cents. The experiment had a duration of fourteen weeks, which was divided into three periods. Each period was preceded and followed by tests in vocabulary and problem solving based upon the material taught during the respective periods. Whereas the control group had to rely solely upon the textbook and class discussions for learning mathematical terms, the experimental group was provided with additional mimeographed materials. These contained exercises so designed that words relating to a common topic were grouped and discussed to bring out their individual meanings and inter-relationships.

The author reported several findings; of his conclusions, the following are presented:

(1) The use of instructional materials in mathematical vocabulary leads to significant growth in the knowledge of the specific terms included in these materials, as well as in the solution of numerical problems involving the use of these terms. Values derived from such study are applicable to pupils of practically all levels of ability.

(2) In order to insure an adequate retention of learning contributed by vocabulary instructional materials, they must be used regularly and systematically as an integral part of the classroom procedure.

Pace, A., "Understanding and the Ability to Solve Problems." *The Arithmetic Teacher,* May, 1961, pp. 226–33.

The investigator's purpose was to determine the effect of understanding the fundamental operations upon problem-solving ability in arithmetic.

The sample comprised two groups of children from the fourth grade of a training school: Group I, the control group, and Group II, the experimental group. The exact size of the sample was not reported. The groups were equated with respect to chronological age, mental ability, and performance in arithmetic reasoning and computation.

During the experimental period of eight weeks, systematic instruction in understanding of processes in arithmetic was provided for Group II only by using twenty-four sets of problems—three sets for each week—as a basis for discussions. Each set contained two one-step verbal problems for each of the operations of addition, subtraction, multiplication, and division. The children in the experimental group had to read each problem, tell how it was to be solved, and defend their choice of the operation. The children in the control group merely solved the problems without any discussion of the work. At the end of the experimental period, an alternate form of the arithmetic reasoning test used as pretest was administered. The scores made on these alternate forms were compared and the gains determined. Added information was obtained by administering to both groups four special "Problem Tests" constructed for use at spaced intervals during the experimental period. Each test contained ten problems of the conventional variety and five problems with distorted cues. The administration of these tests was accompanied by individual interviews with the children in order to determine how children solve problems and what effect understanding has upon the ability to solve problems.

Of the results reported by the investigator, the following are presented:

(1) The gains in performance on the Arithmetic Reasoning Test administered at the end of the experimental period, as compared with performance on the alternate form used initially, were negligible for Group I but were statistically significant for Group II.

(2) On the Problem Tests both groups showed improvement from Test I to Test IV in the number of correct methods of solutions used to solve both the conventional problems and the problems with distorted cues. Group II showed greater improvement than Group I.

The implications of the results of the study which the investigator presented are summarized as follows:

(1) Children should be given many opportunities to solve problems.

(2) Children should be allowed to solve problems in various ways, since there is more than one correct way of solving a problem. Pupils should be led gradually to use more mature and efficient processes.

(3) The teacher should provide for the development of understanding of the four fundamental operations, since this is a vital factor as far as improvement in problem solving is concerned. Such development of understanding is a gradual process, and is to take place as the fundamental operations are presented and as problems are solved.

Treacy, J. P., "The Relationship of Reading Skills to the Ability to Solve Arithmetic Problems." *Journal of Educational Research*, October, 1944, pp. 86–96.

The purpose of this study was to determine the relationship of certain reading skills to ability to solve verbal problems in arithmetic.

Several tests were administered to a sample of 244 7B pupils of two junior-high schools to collect a total of 18 items of information. These tests were tests of (1) problem solving—"problems" and "arithmetic reasoning"; (2) mental ability; and (3) reading ability—silent reading tests, analytical scales of attainment, and diagnostic examination of silent reading abilities.

On the basis of performance on the tests on problem solving, pupils were designated as "good achievers" (the 80 best performers) and "poor achievers" (the 80 lowest performers).

Chronological age was found to correlate $-.299$ with problem-solving ability, and mental age correlated $.758$ with this ability.

The good achievers and the poor achievers were compared on each of the reading skills tested.

Among the findings of the investigator were the following:

(1) Good achievers were found to perform better than poor achievers at the 1 per cent level of significance in Quantitative Relationships; Perception of Relationships; Vocabulary in Context; and Integration of Dispersed Ideas.

(2) Good achievers were found to perform better than poor achievers at the 5 per cent level of significance in Arithmetic Vocabulary; Vocabulary (Isolated Words); Retention of Clearly Stated Details; Drawing of Inferences from Context; and Reading Level.

(3) No significant differences were found between good and poor achievers in the Prediction of Outcomes; Understanding of Precise Directions; Rate of Comprehension; General Information; Grasp of Central Thought; and Interpretation of Content.

Of the educational implications of the findings that the author presented, the following are quoted:

(1) The results of this study indicate that in studying the causal relationships between reading and problem solving in arithmetic, and in planning procedures for helping pupils through reading instruction to improve their ability in problem solving, reading should be regarded as a composite of specific skills rather than as a generalized ability.

(2) Teachers should consider the reading skills that are significantly related to success in this subject, especially in their diagnostic and remedial work. Tests covering reading skills related to problem solving might well precede some exercises in problem solving. Remedial teaching should follow where weaknesses in reading skills related to success in problem solving are discovered.

(3) Four of the reading skills on which good and poor achievers in problem solving differed were associated in one way or another with vocabulary (Quantitative Relationships; Vocabulary in Context; Vocabulary, Isolated Words; and Arithmetic Vocabulary). This fact suggests the need for stressing the meaning of terms, general and mathematical, as an approach to improving pupils' ability in problem solving.

(4) Three of the reading skills on which good and poor achievers differed significantly (Perception of Relationships, Integration of Dispersed Ideas, and Drawing Inferences from Content) require that the pupil carefully associate, immediately and remotely, the elements of the reading material that he reads. This finding may be one explanation of the fact that Rate of Comprehension was not found to be a significant factor in problem solving. It also suggests that help given a pupil which enriches the meanings of what he reads may have a beneficial effect on his problem-solving ability.

(5) Good and poor achievers differed significantly on Retention of Clearly Stated Details. This suggests the possibility that pupils may be troubled in problem solving by *inability to retain* significant facts as well as by inability to understand what is read, and that instruction should be designed accordingly.


## SKILLS TEST


1. In a college there are 2878 male and 1943 female students enrolled. By how many students must the enrollment increase to make the total enrollment 5000?

2. Mr. Ex earned $9432 last year. During the first three quarters of the year he earned $2476, $2109, and $2563, respectively. How much did Mr. Ex earn during the last quarter of the year?

3. Mr. Jackson had $7275 saved for building a house. The lot cost $1750, the construction of the house $8055, the garage $1400, and the miscellaneous expenses amounted to $1794. How much money did Mr. Jackson have to borrow to pay the total bill?

4. Last year Mr. Thomas drove his car 11,232 miles. He used 624 gallons of gasoline and paid an average of 32.4¢ per gallon.

    a) What was the average number of miles traveled by Mr. Thomas in his car per month?
    b) How many miles did Mr. Thomas' car travel, on an average, on one gallon of gasoline?
    c) How much money did Mr. Thomas pay that year for gasoline?

5. Mrs. Right bought $1\frac{7}{8}$ pounds of meat and another piece of meat weighing $2\frac{3}{4}$ pounds. She paid 88¢ per pound. How much money did Mrs. Right have to pay for the meat in all?

6. Susan has $3\frac{1}{4}$ yards of cloth, She uses $1\frac{7}{8}$ yards. How many yards does Susan have left?

7. Ted made a hike of $2\frac{1}{2}$ hours. He averaged $3\frac{1}{8}$ miles per hour. How many miles did Ted hike?

8. Ray wanted to make a hike of $12\frac{1}{4}$ miles. He figured that he could walk an average of $3\frac{1}{2}$ miles per hour. How many hours would the walk take?

9. Mrs. Rex bought groceries for the following amounts: $1.46; $2.57; $3.98; $0.13; $0.81; and $1.38. She had to pay 2% sales tax on the total amount. How much change did she receive from a $20 bill?

10. At the end of a month Mr. Fine had $125.67 in his checking account. He deposited $541.08 and paid by check the following amounts: $94.02; $3.65; $46.21; $40.00; $6.44; and $19.79. What was the balance in his checking account after these transactions had taken place?

11. What rate of earnings is the better: $75.50 per week or $342 per month?

12. During a vacation trip, the Green family traveled the following distances: 114.5 miles; 256.6 miles; 65.9 miles; and 303.3 miles. What was the total distance covered by the Green family on that trip?

13. The odometer of a car registers 74,378.6 miles. How many more miles does the car have to travel before the odometer registers 100,000 miles?

14. Mr. Eaton buys 15.8 gallons of gasoline at 33.9¢ per gallon. How much money does Mr. Eaton have to pay?

15. Mrs. Red paid $5.55 for a turkey of 12.9 pounds. How much was the price per pound?

16. Ray wrote 36 of the 40 spelling words correctly. What per cent of the words did Ray spell incorrectly?

17. A salesman earned $544 one month. If his rate of commission was 8% of the sales, what was the amount of his sales during that month?

18. One day 4% of the 850 pupils of Lincoln school were absent. How many pupils were present?

19. Find the interest on $650 at $4\frac{1}{2}$% per year for 8 months.

20. A refrigerator priced at $325 was sold for $299. What per cent of discount was given?

21. A boy bought a bicycle at 80% of the regular price. If he paid $36 for the bicycle, what was the regular price?

22. A radio station can broadcast programs over a distance of 70 miles. Over what area may the programs be received?

23. John can do a job in 3 hours, Bill in 4 hours, and Ray in 6 hours. How long will it take the three boys working together to do the job?

24. Two railroad stations, *A* and *B*, are 780 miles apart. A train leaves *A* at 9:00 A.M. and travels toward *B* at an average speed of 60 miles per hour. Another train leaves *B*, also at 9:00 A.M., and travels toward *A* at an average speed of 70 miles per hour. At what time will the trains meet?

25. A scale distance of $2\frac{1}{2}$ in. on some map represents an actual distance of 200 miles. What actual distance is represented by a scale distance of $3\frac{7}{8}$ in.?

# EXERCISES

1. Explain these terms: problem, quantitative problem, verbal quantitative problem, exercise, enigma.

2. Describe the steps that you think can be identified in the process of problem solving.

3. Describe the way in which a verbal problem can be used in the introduction of a new case in elementary-school mathematics.

4. React to this statement: In elementary-school mathematics generalizations should be formed inductively and applied deductively.

5. Why should the teaching of problem solving receive major attention in the mathematics curriculum of the elementary school?

6. Construct a one-step verbal problem and present a proper question, solution, check, and interpretation of the answer.

7. Construct a multi-step verbal problem and solve it by pursuing the several steps presented in this chapter.

8. What, in your opinion, are five major causes for poor performance in the solving of verbal problems?

9. Translate each of the following verbal problems into an open mathematical sentence:

   a) After Ronald had bought 30 postage stamps, he had a total of 150 stamps. How many stamps did Ronald have before he bought the 30 stamps?

   b) Mr. Nelson had $350 in his checking account. After he paid a debt by check he had $310 left. For what amount did Mr. Nelson write the check?

   c) Mary filled 8 pages in her scrapbook with pictures. She pasted the same number of pictures on each page. If she put a total of 48 pictures in her book, how many pictures did she paste on each page?

    d) A number of baseball cards was divided equally among 8 boys. If each boy got 7 cards, how many cards were there to be divided?

    e) Ed owned 35 books. After he received some more books he had a total of 42 books. How many books did Ed receive?

    f) Ken bought a bag of potato chips for 29¢. He paid 1¢ sales tax. How much change did Ken receive from a half dollar?

10. In this chapter several techniques for improving problem solving were presented. Describe and illustrate the following methods:

    a) The method of analogy.

    b) The method by which the pupil formulates a proper question fitting a presented situation.

    c) The method by which superfluous data must be identified.

    d) The method of presenting insufficient data.

    e) The method of using verbal problems without numbers.

    f) The method by which verbal problems are solved with the help of visual representations.

    g) The method by which verbal problems that fit a given mathematical sentence are devised.

11. Explain how organized instruction in mental computation could improve the pupils' ability to solve verbal problems.

## For advanced students

12. Select an important piece of research dealing with problem solving and report on it.

13. Suppose that you are responsible for the improvement of the mathematics curriculum in a typical elementary school. Assume that achievement-test scores indicate that most pupils are not performing as well in problem solving as might be expected. Describe in detail what you would do in attempting to correct the situation.

14. Criticize the construction of several verbal problems in a randomly selected elementary-school mathematics book. Offer suggestions for improvement.

15. As assigned by the instructor of the course, report on one or more of the following articles:

    a) Balow, I. H., "Reading and Computation Ability as Determinants of Problem Solving." *The Arithmetic Teacher*, January, 1964, pp. 18–22.

    b) Blecha, M. K., "Helping Children Understand Verbal Problems." *The Arithmetic Teacher*, March, 1959, pp. 106–7.

    c) Burch, R. L., "Formal Analysis as a Problem-solving Procedure." *Journal of Education*, November, 1953, pp. 44–47.

d) Faulk, C. J. and T. R. Landry, "An Approach to Problem-solving." *The Arithmetic Teacher*, April, 1961, pp. 157–60.

e) Flournoy, M. F., "The Effectiveness of Instruction in Mental Arithmetic." *The Elementary School Journal*, November, 1954, pp. 148–53.

f) Grossnickle, F. E., "Verbal Problem Solving." *The Arithmetic Teacher*, January, 1964, pp. 12–17.

g) Hansen, C. W., "Factors Associated with Successful Achievement in Problem Solving in Sixth Grade Arithmetic." *Journal of Educational Research*, October, 1944, pp. 111–18.

h) Johnson, H. C., "The Effect of Instruction in Mathematical Vocabulary upon Problem Solving in Arithmetic." *Journal of Educational Research*, October, 1944, pp. 97–110.

i) Karstens, H., "Effective Guidance in Problem Solving." *The Mathematics Teacher*, April, 1946, pp. 172–75.

j) Klas, W. L., "Problems without Numbers." *The Arithmetic Teacher*, January, 1961, pp. 19–20.

k) Koenker, R. H., "Twenty Methods for Improving Problem Solving." *The Arithmetic Teacher*, March, 1958, pp. 74–78.

l) Pace, A., "Understanding and the Ability to Solve Problems." *The Arithmetic Teacher*, May, 1961, pp. 226–33.

m) Pierro, P. S., "Using the 'Problem-Solving' Method." *The Arithmetic Teacher*, April, 1959, p. 160.

n) Spitzer, H. F. and F. Flournoy, "Developing Facility in Solving Verbal Problems." *The Arithmetic Teacher*, November, 1956, pp. 177–82.

o) Thorpe, C. B., "The Equation: Neglected Ally of Arithmetic Processes." *The Elementary School Journal*, March, 1960, pp. 320–24.

p) ——, "Those Problem-solving Perplexities." *The Arithmetic Teacher*, April, 1961, pp. 152–56.

q) Van Engen, H., "The Child's Introduction to Arithmetic Reasoning." *School Science and Mathematics*, May, 1955, pp. 358–63.

r) ——, "The Reform Movement in Arithmetic and the Verbal Problem." *The Arithmetic Teacher*, January, 1963, pp. 3–6.

## SELECTED REFERENCES

Banks, J. H., *Learning and Teaching Arithmetic*, 2nd Ed. Boston: Allyn and Bacon, Inc., 1964, Ch. XIV.

Brownell, W. A., "Problem Solving." *Forty-first Yearbook*, Part II, National Society for the Study of Education. Bloomington, Ill.: Public School Publishing Co., 1942, pp. 415–43.

Cronbach, L. J., "The Meanings of Problems." *Arithmetic 1948*. Supplementary Educational Monographs, No. 66. Chicago: University of Chicago Press, 1948, pp. 32–43.

Dewey, J., *How We Think.* Boston: D. C. Heath & Company, 1933, Ch. I.

Dutton, W. H. and L. J. Adams, *Arithmetic for Teachers.* Englewood Cliffs, N.J.: Prentice-Hall, Inc., 1961, Ch. VII.

Grossnickle, F. E. and L. J. Brueckner, *Discovering Meanings in Elementary School Mathematics.* New York: Holt, Rinehart & Winston, Inc., 1963, Ch. XIV.

Hartung, M. L., "Advances in the Teaching of Problem Solving." *Arithmetic 1948.* Supplementary Educational Monographs, No. 66. Chicago: University of Chicago Press, 1948, pp. 44–53.

Henderson, K. B. and R. E. Pingrey, "Problem Solving in Mathematics." *The Learning of Mathematics, Twenty-first Yearbook,* National Council of Teachers of Mathematics. Washington, D.C.: The Council, 1953, Ch. VIII.

Howard, C. F. and E. Dumas, *Basic Procedures in Teaching Arithmetic.* Boston: D. C. Heath & Company, 1963, Ch. XIII.

Marks, J. L., C. R. Purdy, and L. B. Kinney, *Teaching Arithmetic for Understanding.* New York: McGraw-Hill, Inc., 1958, Ch. XII.

Morton, R. L., *Teaching Children Arithmetic.* Morristown, N. J.: Silver Burdett Company, 1953, Ch. XI.

Spencer, P. L. and D. H. Russell, "Reading in Arithmetic." *Instruction in Arithmetic, Twenty-fifth Yearbook,* National Council of Teachers of Mathematics. Washington, D.C.: the Council, 1960, Ch. IX.

Spitzer, H. F., *The Teaching of Arithmetic.* Boston: Houghton Mifflin Company, 1961, Ch. X.

Thorpe, C. B., *Teaching Elementary Arithmetic.* New York: Harper & Row, Publishers, 1962, Ch. XXIII.

# 19

---

# EVALUATION

---

IN EVALUATING PUPIL progress in elementary-school mathematics, the teacher first wants to appraise how successful the teaching and learning processes have been in developing the pupils toward the specific goals. The next step is to determine where improvement is needed.

After interpreting the findings of evaluation, the results are—ideally— put to use in these ways:

(1) Weaknesses in the teaching procedures are diagnosed and removed.

(2) Pupil deficiencies are remedied.

(3) Pupils are informed of their progress so that proper motivation takes place.

(4) Parents are supplied with information about their children's progress by written reports and by discussing these reports with them at regular intervals.

(5) Pupils' records are kept up to date by entering all necessary information on the proper forms.

Traditionally, the scope of evaluation in arithmetic has been narrow. It has been concerned mainly with the pupils' speed and accuracy in computation and their skill in problem solving. At present, evaluation also seeks to determine the pupils' understanding of concepts and processes, their ability in applying skills, and their attitude toward the subject. In good programs an attempt is made to assess the children's skill in mental computation and their ability to decide whether the answer to a written computation makes sense.

In Chapter 1 the following general objectives for the teaching of elementary-school mathematics were suggested:

The pupil should acquire:

1. An *understanding* of the structure of the real number system, of basic geometric ideas, and of principles underlying the presented mathematical processes.

2. Functional *knowledge* of quantitative terms and symbols; of graphs, scale drawings, charts, and tables; of simple geometric terms and figures; and of common measures.

3. *Skill* in—
   a) thinking critically by following and building patterns of organized thought;
   b) performing with reasonable speed and accuracy common written and mental computations;
   c) appraising the correctness of acquired results;
   d) applying acquired techniques intelligently in verbal problems, in other school subjects, and in daily life.

4. Favorable *attitudes* toward mathematics and an awareness of the place and importance of mathematics in life.

5. *Confidence* in his ability to reason independently.

The teacher who agrees with these objectives will attempt to determine the degree to which his pupils have acquired such understandings, knowledge, skills, and attitudes.

A general set of objectives is not sufficient for the teacher. Thus the faculty of the school has the responsibility to evaluate and adopt a set of desired outcomes for each grade. These outcomes should be stated in specific and realistic terms, so that the teacher can keep them in mind while he evaluates his pupils' work. The need for regular reevaluation of the adopted outcomes should be realized. The teacher's continuing professional reading, his daily observation of the pupils, and his study of the results of standardized tests administered to his pupils will aid him in making the necessary improvements.

## Evaluation Methods

Several methods and techniques are used in evaluating pupils' progress in elementary-school mathematics. Both subjective appraisal and objective measurement are included in a good evaluation program. Each of these methods has advantages and disadvantages, and they should therefore supplement each other.

When appraisal is made subjectively by using instruments that the teacher himself constructs, there is a strong tendency to consider the child with his strengths and weaknesses and to evaluate the pupil's understandings, skills, knowledge, and attitudes according to what the teacher considers important. In doing this, the teacher may overlook or ignore important outcomes, or he may make premature and unreliable generalizations. When measures are taken objectively with instruments carefully constructed by experts, teacher bias is eliminated; however, there may be a tendency to treat the child as a number or a case, since local and personal conditions cannot be weighted proportionately.

By pooling information obtained from several sources and by applying different techniques, broad appraisal and narrow measurement are combined into a comprehensive program. Suggested techniques and methods include: (1) observation, (2) analysis of daily written work, (3) testing, and (4) interviewing.

## Observation

In the evaluation program of elementary-school mathematics, observation plays an important role. In the primary grades, where objective measurement is a difficult task because of the maturity level of the children, observation is the best single method of evaluation; in fact, many standardized tests in mathematics are not designed for use below the third-grade level.

One advantage of evaluation by observation is that the pupils are not necessarily aware of the fact that evidence is being obtained for appraisal purposes. The children react more naturally than they do when a written test is administered or when specific questions on an attitude scale are to be answered. Another advantage is the sequential nature of observation. Each arithmetic period offers new opportunities to note changes in the children's behavior, and, consequently, to encourage or discourage such behavior.

On the other hand, teacher bias reduces the value of evaluation by observation. It should also be realized that even a minor change in a situation may make pupils behave differently. For these reasons, great care should be taken in making generalizations based on the observed behavior of children. Proper evaluation by observation requires a skillful and experienced teacher who realizes the dangers of subjective judgment. Observers should have the outcomes of their teaching in mind when they observe pupil performance.

When the teacher detects characteristics that are not desirable, he should try to determine the causes and plan individual help and guidance whenever this appears necessary. In some cases, a personal conference may have to be scheduled. It should be realized that gifted pupils, as well as children who are remedial cases, may need extra attention.

The teacher should see the need for gradual improvement in his ability to appraise pupils by means of observation. He should approach his task positively by determining what knowledge and which understandings, skills, and attitudes should be anticipated. His preparation in a course on the teaching of elementary-school mathematics, his experience and common sense, the presentations and directions in the textbook manual, and the local course of study should guide him in setting up a definite plan for observation.

Check lists, stating desired outcomes or specific characteristics of behavior, are sometimes used by teachers who want to approach the task methodically and keep records of observed behavior for future reference. Items on the list are checked off for each individual pupil when he meets the goal or shows a trait mentioned on the list. Other instruments used to record pupil behavior are anecdotal records and rating scales. The interested teacher can locate information on the use of these instruments in books on educational psychology or evaluation in education. Such methods are mostly too time-consuming to be effective in the typical classroom, but they are often essential when exceptional children must be evaluated.

## Analysis of daily written work

The daily written work in mathematics of elementary-school pupils is an important source of information in evaluating the performance and the progress of the children. This work reveals what the pupils have done day by day. If the teacher has sufficient time and energy to examine the written work carefully and is able to observe the pupils closely, he can do an excellent job of evaluation with a minimum of testing.

By analyzing the children's work, the teacher may detect careless work habits, faulty thinking, consistent mistakes, or errors resulting from poor handwriting. He will also identify the pupils whose speed needs to be improved. Such daily analyses result in evaluation at its best. The regular appraisal of the children's work and, if necessary, subsequent interviews or informal talks, will enable the teacher to evaluate his pupils effectively and to motivate them to improve their performance.

Such analyses and evaluations should also result in an improvement of the pupils' handwriting. Teachers readily agree that the penmanship of the typical pupil is of poor quality, and some of his wrong answers result from his inability to read his own writing. In order to correct such situations, the answers should not only be marked wrong; the teacher should also explain why such work cannot be accepted and make the child understand that he could have performed better by applying more effort. The teacher should never cease trying to correct poor work habits and improve careless handwriting.

Since many mistakes can be traced to careless attitudes and poor hand-writing, pupils' performance in elementary-school mathematics would be improved by requiring careful work and legible writing. Daily work should be written neatly in an arithmetic notebook, checked regularly, and graded for performance on mathematics and, if necessary, for a quality of hand-writing that the pupil himself can read easily. Problems that were worked incorrectly should be reworked under the guidance of the teacher and checked again. The notebooks are to be kept during the school term to serve the teacher in his evaluation of the pupils at regular intervals, and to be shown to and discussed with the parents during interviews or at parent-teachers' meetings.

Proper evaluation of the children's daily work makes the child aware of the interest and consistency of the teacher; it uncovers weaknesses quickly, and allows a timely diagnosis of deficiencies. Such evaluation serves as a wholesome stimulus for the children to improve their performance, especially when they understand that the purpose of evaluation is not to find fault with them, but to help them improve their performance.

## Tests

There is a great variety of tests, and the terms used to identify these tests are often confusing. Tests serving the same purpose are sometimes called by different names. For example, inventory tests serve practically the same purpose as readiness tests and pretests, since all three kinds are designed to determine a degree of readiness reached by the pupils.

A general classification of elementary-school mathematics tests is presented below:

1. Tests with different purposes:
   a) achievement test
   b) diagnostic test

2. Tests of different origins:
   a) textbook test
   b) teacher-made test
   c) standardized test

3. Tests evaluating different abilities:
   a) speed test
   b) power test

4. Tests containing different kinds of content:
   a) concepts and understandings
   b) computation
   c) problem solving

5. Tests in which the character of the required responses differs:
   a) essay test
   b) problem-solving test
   c) short-answer test
   d) multiple-choice test
   e) matching test
   f) true-false test

ACHIEVEMENT TESTS.  Achievement tests are intended to measure such outcomes as factual knowledge, skills, ability to solve word problems, understanding of numbers and processes, and ability to apply skills in situations.

According to origin, there are three kinds of achievement tests:

1. Tests that are included in or accompany the textbook.

2. Tests that are constructed by the teacher himself.

3. Standardized achievement tests.

Achievement tests may serve one of two purposes:

1. Assess the level of achievement before study.  Such tests appear under different names.  They are called, for example, readiness tests, inventory tests, or pretests.

2. Assess the level of achievement after study.  These tests are called survey tests, end-of-the-chapter tests, semester tests, standardized achievement tests, posttests, progress tests, and mastery tests.

DIAGNOSIS.  The timely diagnosis of pupil deficiencies in elementary-school mathematics, followed by remediation, will prevent much frustration and save time.  It should be the teacher's goal to locate difficulties early by using as many of the following techniques as practicable:

1. Daily observation of activities and critical evaluation of oral responses.

2. Analytical study of the daily written work in order to detect faulty reasoning. The pupil's specific deficiency in making an error such as $\begin{array}{r} 48 \\ +\ 27 \\ \hline 615 \end{array}$ can easily be identified.  Here the teacher should not only mark the mistake but also note the failure to regroup, and he should reteach that process.

3. The administration of general diagnostic and survey tests presented in textbooks.

4. The administration of teacher-made diagnostic tests.

5. An analysis of the mistakes made by the pupils in a standardized achievement test.

6. The administration of a standardized analytical diagnostic test.

In order to be effective, the administration of a standardized analytical diagnostic test must be followed by individual remediation.  The time element makes such diagnosis and remediation impractical for widespread use by the typical teacher. These tests are, therefore, used only with specific cases, such as a child who can no longer follow the instruction with a reasonable measure of success, or a pupil who has come from another school system and does not perform well.

TEXTBOOK TESTS. Modern textbook series usually present quite complete testing programs, which include tests to assess the level of achievement before study, tests to assess the level of achievement after study, and diagnostic tests. Some of the tests are intended to measure speed, others to measure power. The books not only provide instruments that evaluate achievement in computation and problem solving; there are also tests that are intended to assess the understanding of processes. Knowledge of quantitative terms, symbols, and formulas is usually evaluated by matching tests, short-answer tests, and true-false tests. Pupils are occasionally required to write short essays on how certain processes are performed. Thought questions, which require children to explain why a given statement is true, are often asked.

TEACHER-MADE TESTS. Though modern textbooks generally provide proper testing programs, the need for teacher-made tests arises occasionally. There are outcomes that can be evaluated more accurately by using a test constructed by the teacher himself than by administering a commercial test. This may be the case when the following understandings and skills must be appraised: (1) the understanding of mathematical processes and concepts, (2) the ability to compute mentally, (3) the ability to appraise the correctness of written computations, and (4) the ability to apply skills in situations. Because of the nature of these outcomes, such tests may have to be administered orally and, perhaps, individually.

When reteaching necessitates retesting, there may also be a need for the construction of a test by the teacher. Moreover, the teacher is usually responsible for the preparation of evaluation materials for the gifted pupils and for pupils who receive remedial instruction.

STANDARDIZED ACHIEVEMENT TESTS. A standardized arithmetic achievement test comprises a sample of the content presented in textbooks used widely at the grade levels for which the test is intended. Such a test is necessarily objective.

When constructing a standardized achievement test, the steps taken by the authors include the following:

1. Items are selected by analyzing several textbooks and courses of study. These items must be representative of the knowledge, concepts, and skills to be tested.

2. The items are administered to pupils in corresponding grade levels in order to determine which ones should be eliminated, changed, or retained. This process may have to be repeated several times before there is a sufficient number of usable items available.

3. The final draft of the test is administered to a very large number of pupils at the grade level for which the test is intended in different types of communities and schools, covering as large a geographical area as necessary or feasible.

If the standardization sample is selected at random on a countrywide basis and is large enough to be representative, and if statistical treatment so indicates, the norms are considered to be national. If the sample is taken in only one city, the norms are norms for that city.

A standardized test is accompanied by a manual in which directions for the administration and scoring of the test are presented. The scores made by an individual pupil are interpreted by comparing them with the given norms. Such scores can be converted to percentiles or grade equivalents by consulting the manual.

*Advantages of a standardized test*

1. The test is constructed by experts and is free of teacher bias.

2. An analysis of the results of the test may reveal areas or topics that have been neglected by the teacher.

3. Norms obtained from a nationwide sample provide useful information for comparison.

4. The test is usually administered and scored easily.

5. The scores made by an individual pupil and the average performance of the class can be converted to grade equivalents and percentile ranks.

6. There are usually two or more equivalent forms of the test available. One form can be administered before and another after a teaching process so that the result of instruction given during a limited period of time can be appraised.

7. The results of a test can be recorded on a profile chart. This chart is filed, is brought up to date each school term, and is a basis for an intelligent discussion with parents of the pupil's progress and performance.

8. A profile chart on which the performance of the various classes is plotted provides the teachers, the administration, the Board of Education, and interested citizens with objective information about the academic level of the school.

*Disadvantages of a standardized test*

1. When rating teachers, supervisors may overemphasize the importance of the results of standardized tests.

2. Teachers may be tempted to teach only that content which the test covers and omit other items of importance.

3. Since norms are based on average results, teachers and parents may be unduly satisfied or disappointed with the rank obtained by their pupils or children. A class in a wealthy school district, with experienced teachers who enjoy excellent working conditions and parents who are greatly interested in their children's education, may be expected to perform better than one in a district where opposite conditions exist.

4. National norms may be deceptive, since it is difficult to secure a nationwide representative sample. City norms, however, are narrow in scope and do not reflect the level of performance in a large geographical area.

5. It is difficult to measure in a written test such outcomes as understanding and ability to compute mentally.

6. The standardized test is necessarily limited in length. As a result, the number of items covering a specific concept is often too small to yield reliable scores.

7. The standardized achievement test samples content that is common in widely-used textbooks and courses of study. Since there are differences in the grade placement of many topics in the various series of textbooks, some of the content included in the standardized test may not yet have been presented in the class in which that test is administered. In this case the test lacks curricular validity.

## The administration of a standardized achievement test

Before the test is administered, the teacher should acquaint himself with the directions presented in the manual and the test booklet. It is recommended that the administration of the test be discussed at a special meeting of teachers who are to participate in the testing program. During the test there should be extra pencils and erasers available, and pupils should be separated as much as the seating arrangement in the room allows. Close adherence to the standard directions as given in the manual is necessary. Comparisons of the results are valid only if uniform rules have been followed.

In many schools the standardized achievement test is administered both at the beginning and at the end of the school year, so that the teacher can detect deficiencies in arithmetic at an early date and plan his instruction accordingly. In other schools the test is given only once a year, at the end of the first semester. In this case teaching and learning is evaluated after half a year's work, and revealed deficiencies can be corrected during the second semester. Because of the difficulty of objective evaluation in the primary grades, many schools administer the standardized achievement test for the first time in grade III or grade IV.

## Selection of a standardized arithmetic achievement test

There are several standardized arithmetic achievement tests available. Teachers should be acquainted with the *Mental Measurements Yearbooks*, edited by Oscar K. Buros, which describe and appraise most of the standard-ized tests. *The Twenty-sixth Yearbook* of the National Council of Teachers of Mathematics presents in an appendix an annotated bibliography of mathe-matics tests, including tests for the elementary school.

Standardized achievement tests that can be used (some in part) for testing arithmetic performance in the elementary school include the following:

| Title and Publisher | Available for Grades |
| --- | --- |
| 1. *Analytical Scales of Attainment in Arithmetic* Educational Test Bureau Oak St. and Washington Ave., S.E. Minneapolis, Minn. | 3–8 |
| 2. *California Arithmetic Test* California Test Bureau Del Monte Research Park Monterey, Calif. | 1–14 |
| 3. *Coordinated Scales of Attainment* Educational Test Bureau | 4–8 |
| 4. *Cooperative Sequential Tests of Educational Progress* (STEP) Educational Testing Service Princeton, N.J. | 4–14 |
| 5. *Functional Evaluation in Mathematics* Educational Test Bureau | 4–9 |
| 6. *Iowa Tests of Basic Skills* Houghton Mifflin Company 2 Park St. Boston, Mass. | 3–9 |
| 7. *Metropolitan Achievement Test* Harcourt, Brace & World, Inc. 757 Third Ave. New York, N. Y. | 3–9 |
| 8. *SRA Achievement Test: Arithmetic* Science Research Associates 259 E. Erie St. Chicago, Ill. | 1–9 |
| 9. *Stanford Achievement Test* Harcourt, Brace & World, Inc. | 1–9 |
| 10. *Sueltz Functional Evaluation in Mathematics* Educational Test Bureau | 4–9 |

Most college libraries have a good collection of tests that are in common use. Upon request, publishers will send information about their tests to potential users.

A standardized achievement test should be selected with great care. Factors to be considered include:

1. Purpose of testing.

2. Grades to be tested.

3. Curricular validity of the test.

4. Type of test items.

5. Time allotments.

6. Kind of help and information given in the manual.

7. Size and nature of the sample used for standardization of the test.

8. Amount of work required for administering and scoring the test.

9. Availability of equivalent forms.

10. Reliability of the test.

11. Auxiliary materials accompanying the test.

12. Publication date of the test.

TYPES OF TEST ITEMS IN ELEMENTARY-SCHOOL MATHEMATICS.   Several types of test items can be used in the evaluation of elementary-school mathematics. The types that are frequently used are presented and illustrated below.

*Essay items* require little time to construct and allow pupils to express themselves as well as they can. The pupils' understanding and thinking can be checked. Usually, responses to these items are difficult to score.
*Example:* Develop the formula for the area of a rectangle.

*Problem-solving items* necessarily appear with high frequency in elementary-school mathematics tests, since it is desirable to determine whether the pupil can use computational skills in specific situations. It is difficult to decide how much credit should be given to a pupil who uses the correct procedure but makes a mistake in his computation.
*Example:* The cost of a telegram between two cities is 65¢ for the first 15 words and 2¢ for each additional word. At this rate, how much would a telegram consisting of 24 words cost?

*Short-answer items* such as computation exercises are typical test items in mathematics books. They are easy to score.
*Example:* Find the sum of 34, 29, 46, and 51.

*Multiple-choice items* are popular items for standardized tests. When a pupil has to make a choice among four or five responses, the chance of guessing is reduced. Moreover, the administration of such test items does not require much time, and the answers can be scored quickly and objectively.
*Example:* Which of these is an even number?

$$(1)\ 25; \qquad (2)\ 33; \qquad (3)\ 109; \qquad (4)\ 22$$

*Matching items* are presented in two columns. Each item in the first column must be linked to the proper item in the second. There should be more responses than questions so that guessing is reduced. The matching test is generally used to test the pupils' knowledge of vocabulary, formulas, and measures.
*Example:* Match each term in column A with the proper examples in column B by writing the numbers of the examples in the blank following the term.

|                      A                        |              B                                          |
|  :---:  |  :---:  |
|                  *Terms*                      |          *Examples*                                     |
| Improper fractions_____ | $(1)\ \ \frac{1}{4};\ \ \frac{3}{12}$ |
| Like fractions_____ | $(2)\ \ \frac{1}{5};\ \ \frac{7}{7}$ |
| Mixed fractions_____ | $(3)\ \ \frac{7}{5};\ \ \frac{4}{4}$ |
| Equivalent fractions_____ | $(4)\ \ \frac{3}{5};\ \ \frac{4}{5}$ |
|  | $(5)\ \ 1\frac{3}{4};\ \ 5\frac{1}{2}$ |

*True-false items* are either-or situations that can be rapidly administered and easily scored.
EXAMPLES:

$$\text{True or false:} \qquad 4 \times 7 > 6 \times 5$$
$$14 + 7 = 20 + 1$$
$$15 \div 3 \neq 25 \div 5$$
$$51 - 11 < 30 + 12$$

*Completion items* are frequently used to test the pupils' ability in supplying mathematical symbols to make a statement true. Such items are also used when pupils must supply missing numerals or provide words to complete a sentence.
*Example 1:* Replace each frame by the symbol $=$, $>$, or $<$ to make the statement true.

$$15 + 8 \ \square\ 23$$
$$6 \times 3 \ \square\ 20$$
$$20 - 7 \ \square\ 11$$

*Example 2:* Write the correct number in the box.

$$8 + \square = 14$$
$$13 = 10 + \square$$

*Example 3:* The common point of origin of two rays is called_____.

SUGGESTIONS FOR TEST CONSTRUCTION

1. Make an outline of the subject matter to be tested.

2. By using the outline, write concepts, terms, computation combinations, etc., on cards, using a separate card for each item. Taking the cards one by one, decide which type of test can be used best for each item. Proceed to formulate the selected type of test question

3. Check off in the outline each concept, skill, etc., which has been covered and consider whether each part is represented properly in the test.

4. When constructing multiple-choice items, vary the placement of the correct response among the responses given under the items.

5. State the question, statement, stem, and response clearly.

6. Avoid giving clues to the answer in the question or in the stem of the item.

7. If possible, present the statement or question in a way which is different from that presented in the textbook. This will reward pupils who understand the problem rather than those who have crammed for the test.

8. Make sure that the vocabulary of the items is not too difficult. An arithmetic test is not a reading test.

9. Select items and responses that will discriminate between pupils who know or understand and those who don't. After the test has been administered, analyze the items. Responses that were not selected by any pupil and items that were answered correctly or incorrectly by all the children do not discriminate and should be discarded.

10. Begin and end the test with a few easy items.

11. Make the test as long as feasible for the grade level to be tested.

12. Determine the number of items to be used in testing a given concept or skill by considering the amount of instructional time devoted to that item in class.

13. Don't confuse the pupils by shifting frequently from one type of test item to another—for example, from multiple-choice items to true-false items.

14. Avoid "catch" questions.

15. If the pupils are not acquainted with the type of test to be administered, supply some illustrative items and discuss them before the test is started.

16. Allow a liberal amount of time for pupils to take a power test.

17. Test computational ability and ability to solve word problems frequently.

18. Type on cards items that have proven their usefulness and file these cards for future use.

19. Discuss test construction during staff meetings and request and offer constructive criticism on items used.

## Interviews

Interviews, conferences, and informal talks between teacher and pupil are time-consuming but should be worth the effort of the teacher. The personal relation will stimulate the child more than casual association in the classroom, especially when the pupil realizes that the teacher is really interested in him and his problems. Through skillful questioning, the teacher may discover causes of undesirable attitudes or of faulty reasoning in mathematical processes. Gifted pupils can and should be assisted when the teacher discovers more than usual interest and ability, or when he finds out that the gifted pupil does not perform as well as could be expected. Ideally, the teacher schedules several interviews with each child during the school year. However, this may be difficult to accomplish in the typical classroom with its overcrowded schedule. The best the teacher usually can do is to confer individually with each child whose problems cannot be easily dealt with in the regular classroom situation.

During the interview, the teacher should not dominate the discussion but should give the child the opportunity to speak; he should encourage the pupil to express himself freely. If causes of consistent errors must be determined, the child should explain the procedure he follows while computing the answer. If undesirable attitudes are the reason for the interview, the causes of such behavior should be traced, so that the interviewer can take the necessary steps to correct the situation. During an interview that is conducted to determine the causes of frequent mistakes made in computation and problem solving, it may appear that the child is deficient in many areas and that a systematic approach is needed to determine his weaknesses. If so, the teacher may decide to administer a standardized analytical diagnostic test. Commercial diagnostic tests are available for such purposes.

Undesirable attitudes on the part of the pupil can be studied in a more direct and systematic manner by using an attitude scale. Some work has been done in preparing attitude scales for older pupils. The elementary-school teacher will probably have to prepare his own scale. He can consult available literature on the topic and can use scales prepared for older children as a guide.

Through continuous practice, the interviewer attains skill in the technique. He should never hesitate to call on more experienced people for help when a case appears to be too difficult.

## Some Terms in Evaluation

*Validity.* A test is valid if it measures accurately what it claims to measure. The validity of a test indicates how true the test is to its purpose. The results of a test that lacks validity present a distorted picture, since the test does not tell the truth about a pupil's ability in what the test purports to measure.

*Reliability.* A test is reliable if it is consistent. Reliability means consistency. High reliability is suggested if equivalent forms rank the pupils in the same order.

*Power test.* A power test emphasizes performance and has a liberal time allotment or no time limit at all.

*Speed test.* A speed test emphasizes speed and must be finished within an allotted time. The length of the allotted time determines the degree to which the test is a speed test.

*Speed and power test.* In a standardized test, both speed and power usually are considered important. Such a test is intended to be a sampling of skills learned and knowledge acquired. It tests one of the common objectives: skill in performing common computations with reasonable speed and accuracy.

*Percentile ranks.* In the manual accompanying a standardized achievement test, tables are provided for converting scores of individual pupils into percentile ranks. If a pupil has a percentile rank of 50, his score on the test is higher than that of 50 per cent of the pupils in the standardization sample.

*Grade equivalents.* Grade equivalents or grade norms for test scores are also usually provided in the test manual. If the score of a pupil equals the average score of the fourth-grade pupils in the standardization sample at the end of the first semester, his grade equivalent is 4.5. If the grade equivalent of a pupil is 4.1, he did as well as the average pupil in the standardization sample did at the end of the first month in the fourth grade.

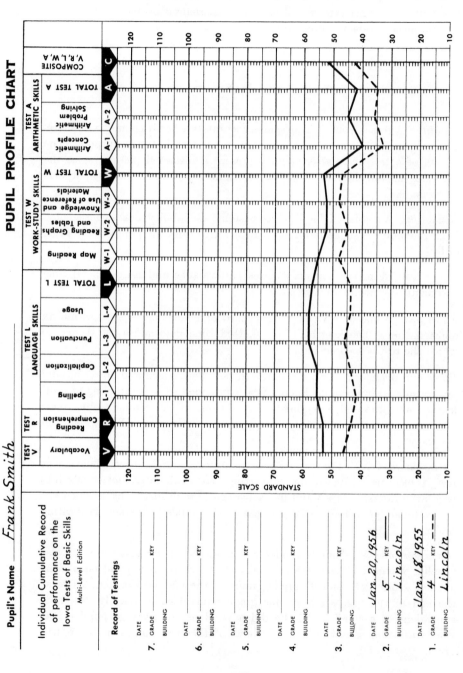

Figure 19-1

*Profiles.* Profile charts are used by teachers to summarize the pupils' achievement graphically, so that their strengths and deficiencies stand out clearly. A copy of the profile chart accompanying the Iowa Tests of Basic Skills[1] is presented in Figure 19-1.

# EXERCISES

1. Set up a testing program in elementary-school mathematics for a selected grade level.

2. List the purposes of testing in elementary-school mathematics.

3. Compare the testing programs in elementary-school mathematics in the traditional and the modern school.

4. Which methods and techniques can be used in the evaluation of pupil progress in elementary-school mathematics?

5. List different kinds of arithmetic achievement tests.

6. Describe some diagnostic techniques in elementary-school mathematics.

7. Describe in general the content and the function of an analytical diagnostic arithmetic test.

8. What is your opinion of the quality of the typical textbook tests?

9. Describe the standardized arithmetic achievement test—construction, content, sample to be used in standardization, advantages, disadvantages, administration, use of findings, and selection of a test.

10. Describe and give an example of different types of test items that can be used in an arithmetic test.

11. How can the interview be conducive to the improvement of instruction in elementary-school mathematics?

12. Explain the following terms: reliability, power test, speed test, percentile rank, grade equivalent, profile, appraisal, measurement, stem, response, ambiguous item, mastery test, pretest, equivalent forms of a test.

## For advanced students

13. Set up a testing program in elementary-school mathematics for grades I through VI of a school of which you would be the principal.

---

[1] Iowa Tests of Basic Skills, *Teacher's Manual* (Boston: Houghton Mifflin Company, 1964), p. 22.

14. Prepare an outline for a talk to the parents on the testing program in elementary-school mathematics in your school.

15. Prepare a good and a poor item for an arithmetic test for each of the following types of test: multiple-choice, true-false, short-answer.

16. Examine three standardized arithmetic achievement tests and select the one that you consider the best for your school. List the reasons why you made the choice.

17. Examine two mathematics textbook series for the elementary school and report on the evaluation program in each series.

18. As assigned by the instructor of the course, report on one or more of the following articles:

    a) Brueckner, L. J., "Evaluation in Arithmetic." *Education*, January, 1959, pp. 291–94.

    b) Buswell, G. T., "Methods of Studying Pupils' Thinking in Arithmetic," *Arithmetic 1949*. Chicago: University of Chicago Press, 1949, pp. 55–63.

    c) Dutton, W. H., "Measuring Attitudes Toward Arithmetic." *The Elementary School Journal*, September, 1954, pp. 24–31.

    d) Glennon, V. J., "Testing Meanings in Arithmetic," *Arithmetic 1949*. Chicago: University of Chicago Press, 1949, pp. 64–74.

    e) Koenker, R. H., "Measuring the Meanings of Arithmetic." *The Arithmetic Teacher*, February, 1960, pp. 93–96.

    f) Rappaport, D., "Testing for Meanings in Arithmetic." *The Arithmetic Teacher*, April, 1959, pp. 140–43.

    g) Spitzer, H. F., "Techniques for Evaluating Outcomes of Instruction in Arithmetic." *The Elementary School Journal*, September, 1948, pp. 21–31.

    h) Sueltz, B. A., "The Measurement of Understandings and Judgments in Elementary School Mathematics." *The Mathematics Teacher*, October, 1947, pp. 279–84.

    i) Wilson, G. M., "Types of Tests in Arithmetic." *Education*, April, 1960, pp. 493–94.

    j) Wrightstone, J. W., "Constructing Tests of Mathematical Concepts for Young Children." *The Arithmetic Teacher*, April, 1956, pp. 81–84.

## SELECTED REFERENCES

Dutton, W. H. and L. J. Adams, *Arithmetic for Teachers*. Englewood Cliffs, N.J.: Prentice-Hall, Inc., 1961, Ch. XV.

Grossnickle, F. E. and L. J. Brueckner, *Discovering Meanings in Elementary School Mathematics*. New York: Holt, Rinehart & Winston, Inc., 1963, Chs. XVII and XVIII.

Marks, J. L., C. R. Purdy, and L. B. Kinney, *Teaching Arithmetic for Understanding*. New York: McGraw-Hill, Inc., 1958, Ch. XIII.

Morton, R. L., *Teaching Children Arithmetic*. Morristown, N.J. : Silver Burdett Company, 1953, Ch. XII.

National Council of Teachers of Mathematics, *Arithmetic in General Education*, Sixteenth Yearbook. New York: Bureau of Publications, Teachers College, Columbia University, 1941, Ch. X.

———, *Emerging Practices in Mathematics Education*, Twenty-second Yearbook. New York: Bureau of Publications, Teachers College, Columbia University, 1954.

———, *Evaluation in Mathematics*, Twenty-sixth Yearbook. New York: Bureau of Publications, Teachers College, Columbia University, 1961.

National Society for the Study of Education, *Educational Diagnosis*, Thirty-fifth Yearbook. Chicago: University of Chicago Press, 1936.

———, *Measurement of Understanding*, Forty-fifth Yearbook. Chicago: University of Chicago Press, 1946, Part I.

Spitzer, H. F., *The Teaching of Arithmetic*. Boston: Houghton Mifflin Company, 1961, Ch. XII.

Thorpe, C. B., *Teaching Elementary Arithmetic*. New York: Harper & Row, Publishers, 1962, Ch. XXV.

# 20

---

# INDIVIDUAL
# DIFFERENCES

---

ONE OF THE main problems of the teacher of mathematics in the elementary school is to select and devise methods and techniques that will assist each pupil to make reasonable progress.

Children differ in intelligence, achievement, maturity, learning rate, emotional and social behavior, physical condition, and aptitude for and interest in mathematics. They come from various backgrounds and environments and thus have been motivated differently. There are also variations in traits within each individual. All these differences—and many more— influence the children's progress in mathematics and may cause serious problems when the teacher attempts to teach the subject to some thirty pupils during a daily period of time ranging from 30 to 60 minutes.

Some pupils benefit sufficiently from class instruction, but many others need a great deal of individual attention. Helpful variations in instruction must be made for the second group especially.

## Findings of Research

The teacher of elementary-school mathematics must be acquainted with the important findings of research concerning individual differences among pupils and trait differences within each child to enable him to select the proper techniques that provide for such differences. He should also know what effect the applications of certain techniques may have on the child. Ignorance of such important research findings may result in hampering the

392

child in his mathematical and emotional development. The following statements and data should be considered:

1. There is a wide range in mathematical ability among children of the same chronological age.

Grossnickle and Brueckner[1] found a range of approximately four years in ability in arithmetic reasoning in typical fifth-grade classes totaling 73 pupils. The range for the same pupils in performance on arithmetic fundamentals was three years.

2. When equal amounts of practice are assigned to pupils, individual differences tend to increase.

Stroud[2] presents data taken from a report on an Iowa testing program in the basic skills which show that the amount of grade overlapping in arithmetic increased from the third to the sixth grade. However, the amount of overlapping for arithmetic was much less than that for reading or language usage.

3. Though an intelligent child usually performs quite well in mathematics, the pupil's IQ does not appear to be an infallible basis for predicting his success in mathematical computation and problem solving.

Brueckner[3] found relatively low correlations between general IQ and computational ability and between IQ and arithmetic problem solving.

4. Often there appear to be great differences in the performance of an individual pupil on the various phases of arithmetic.

Brueckner and Grossnickle[4] present data which show that the scores made by a single individual on different phases of arithmetic often indicate a wide range.

5. There is evidence that middle-grade.pupils whose progress is below the usually accepted minimum for their grade level do not profit from non-promotion.

Stroud[5] reports a study conducted by Coffield who followed through to the seventh grade the progress of groups of pupils who failed in the third grade.

---

[1] F. E. Grossnickle and L. J. Brueckner, *Discovering Meanings in Elementary School Mathematics* (New York: Holt, Rinehart & Winston, Inc., 1963), p. 389.

[2] J. B. Stroud, *Psychology in Education* (New York: David McKay Co., Inc., 1956), pp. 376–77.

[3] L. J. Brueckner, *Adapting Instruction in Arithmetic to Individual Differences* (Minneapolis: University of Minnesota Press, 1941), pp. 6–7.

[4] L. J. Brueckner and F. E. Grossnickle, *Making Arithmetic Meaningful* (New York: Holt, Rinehart & Winston, Inc., 1953), pp. 453–54.

[5] Stroud, *op. cit.*, p. 387.

When the progress of these groups was compared with that of a matched un-failed group it was found that the children who had repeated a grade, and thus had one more year of schooling, did not perform better on achievement tests when they reached the seventh grade than those who had not failed.

## Identifying Individual Differences

At the beginning of the school year the teacher identifies the striking individual differences in mathematics among the pupils in his class. There will be differences in general ability, attitudes, interests, and in the level of mathematical development both in computation and problem solving.

The cumulative folder of each pupil is examined, scores made on tests are considered, and special entries are studied. The evaluation provided by the child's previous teacher is carefully considered. During the school year performance on intelligence tests and achievement tests are analyzed, and reactions to such instruments as interest inventories are taken into consideration. The information collected during the daily observation of the pupil and during interviews will also guide the teacher in deciding what extra help or additional assignments are best for the child. Scores made on daily written work and on progress tests administered during the year will provide some indications as to the effectiveness of the techniques used. When test scores are discussed with the pupil for motivational purposes, the teacher will get additional information concerning the needs and interests of the child.

## Providing for Individual Differences

The failure of the graded school to care adequately for individual differences has gradually become recognized during the last century; especially during the last few decades. Several methods and techniques have been devised and used to gear instruction to the individual child; these include methods of grouping, visual aids, various promotion policies, special services, and educational media such as television and teaching machines. All methods tested have demonstrated strengths and weaknesses, and no method has been identified as a panacea. Thus no agreement has been reached on what kind of classroom organization provides best for individual differences. The methods or techniques selected will depend upon such factors as the ability of the pupils; the financial resources of the school district; the attitude of the parents; the experience, skill, and creativity of the teachers; the possibility to fix a schedule that fits the proposed plan; and other local conditions.

Provisions that are made for individual differences can be classified under three headings: grouping by schools, grouping within the school, and making provisions within the classroom.

1. *Grouping by schools.* Mentally retarded and other groups of handicapped children are sometimes assigned to a special school. Rarely are schools established for only highly gifted children, and when this does take place, it is usually the result of action by private enterprise.

2. *Grouping within the school.* This kind of grouping may take several forms: grouping by classes in multi-track programs; permitting semi-annual and quarterly promotions; applying administrative acceleration and non-promotion; multi-grade grouping; applying the dual-progress plan; non-graded grouping; and individualizing instruction as in the Winnetka plan and the Dalton plan.[6]

3. *Making provisions within the classroom.* The classroom teacher is usually faced with the problem of selecting proper techniques for dealing with individual differences in mathematics in his classroom. Methods and techniques which may be considered include:

1. Grouping pupils within the classroom according to their mathematical level of development and presenting to each group subject matter which fits that group in its scope and/or depth. When the pupils are selected according to ability, usually two or three groups are formed. Such procedures should be continued in succeeding grades so that capable pupils can finish the six-year mathematics curriculum in less time and others may be allowed to spend more than six years to complete the program.

2. Assigning exercises of varying levels of difficulty.

3. Allowing different amounts of time for pupils to finish the assignments.

4. Assigning different amounts of practice.

5. Providing remedial work for retarded pupils.

6. Providing help and guidance for exceptional pupils outside the regular class hours.

7. Applying academic acceleration. With this approach the mathematics book of a higher grade level is made available to the rapid learners.

8. Supplying appropriate programed materials.

9. Providing optional assignments that are of interest to the pupils.

10. Grouping pupils by teams in which selected children assume leadership under the guidance of the teacher.

---

[6] For a description of several forms of grouping within the school, the teacher is referred to the Sixty-first Yearbook of the National Society for the Study of Education, Part I, and to other professional books and articles identified at the end of this chapter.

11. Using itinerant teachers. The itinerant-teacher program is used to assist the slow-learning pupil or the gifted child, or both.

12. Supplying enrichment exercises.

## Enrichment Activities

Enrichment activities are those experiences which are in addition to the regular program. Ideally, these activities are not reserved for the rapid learners only but are also assigned to the average and below-average pupils.

The elementary-school mathematics program can be enriched both in depth and in scope. When the program is enriched in depth, the children are challenged to explore the presented topics more thoroughly, so that concepts are extended and refined. When the scope of the program is broadened, additional topics are presented.

Several activities for enriching the elementary-school mathematics curriculum have been suggested in professional books, pupils' textbooks, and professional periodicals. Teachers' manuals offer many suggestions, and supplementary materials have been made available by textbook publishers. For a graded list of materials dealing with the enrichment of elementary-school mathematics programs, the teacher is referred to the Twenty-seventh Yearbook of the National Council of Teachers of Mathematics.

It is sometimes difficult to decide whether a topic should be a part of the regular mathematics program or of the enrichment program. Modern mathematics programs may include topics that were enrichment activities in traditional curricula. Examples of such topics are frame arithmetic, several geometric concepts, some topics dealing with number theory, and the metric system of measures. Moreover, alternate methods of presentation—such as the equal-additions method in subtraction—are used in some textbooks to reintroduce a topic presented in a previous grade, whereas in other books they are classified as enrichment exercises.

Several activities that can serve as enrichment exercises are suggested below.

1. *Illustrating a process or property on the bulletin board*
*Example:* Show the commutative property for multiplication by using this array:

2. *Solving riddles or puzzles presented on the bulletin board*
*Example:* Place punctuation marks in the following:

> The farmers of the Northern land,
> Have ten fingers on each hand
> Five and twenty on hands and feet,
> Tell me how to count them, Pete!

*Solution:* Place a comma after "fingers" and one after "five."

3. *Working cross-number puzzles*
*Example:*

|   |   |   |   |   |
|---|---|---|---|---|
| a | i |   | c | j |
| b |   |   | d |   |
|   |   |   |   |   |
| e | k |   | g | l |
| f |   |   | h |   |

| left–right: | up–down: |
|---|---|
| a) $15 + 10 =$ | a) $2 \times 11 =$ |
| b) $3 \times 9 =$ | i) $60 - 3 =$ |
| c) $30 - 12 =$ | c) $20 - 9 =$ |
| d) $100 \div 10 =$ | j) $4 \times 20 =$ |
| e) $25 - 9 =$ | e) $4 \times 4 =$ |
| f) $8 \times 8 =$ | k) $70 - 6 =$ |
| g) $50 - 13 =$ | g) $16 + 16 =$ |
| h) $6 \times 4 =$ | l) $100 - 26 =$ |

4. *Working recreational tricks involving mathematical problems*
*Example:*

| Think of a number | 5 |
|---|---|
| Add four | $5 + 4 = 9$ |
| Subtract three | $9 - 3 = 6$ |
| Double the result | $2 \times 6 = 12$ |
| Subtract two | $12 - 2 = 10$ |
| Take half of the answer | $\frac{1}{2} \times 10 = 5$ |
| Subtract the number you started with | $5 - 5 = 0$ |

The pupils are challenged to discover why the result of this procedure is always zero. When they understand why the trick works they are encouraged to construct other similar tricks.

5. *Solving problems by using alternate methods of solution*
*Example:* Find the answer to $51 - 29 = \square$ by using the equal-additions method of subtraction.

6. *Finding patterns*
*Example:* Continue this pattern:

$$2^2 = 4 = 1 + 3$$
$$3^2 = 9 = 1 + 3 + 5$$
$$4^2 = 16 = 1 + 3 + 5 + 7$$

7. *Checking the correctness of a computation*
*Example:* Check the product in $43 \times 158 = 6794$ by applying the check of nines.

8. *Finding the missing digits in a presented computation*
*Example:* Supply the missing digits in this multiplication:

$$
\begin{array}{r}
59 \\
.3 \\
\times \overline{\phantom{00}} \\
\cdots \\
..8 \\
\overline{\phantom{0000}} \\
\cdots\cdots
\end{array}
$$

9. *Using and illustrating short cuts*
*Example:* By drawing diagrams on graph paper show that the following mathematical sentences are true:

$$19 \times 21 = (19 + 1) \times (21 - 1) - (1 \times 1) = 400 - 1 = 399$$
$$15 \times 15 = (15 - 5) \times (15 + 5) + (5 \times 5) = 10 \times 20 + 25$$
$$= 200 + 25 = 225$$

10. *Supplying missing numerals in a mathematical sentence*
*Example:* $275 \div 25 = \square \div 50 = \square \div 100 = \square$

11. *Exploring why short cuts work*
*Example:* $1 + 2 + 3 + \cdots + 99 = 99 \times \dfrac{1 + 99}{2} = 99 \times 50 = 4950$

12. *Expressing the largest and the smallest number possible with a given set of digits*
*Example:* Write the largest and the smallest number possible—not using exponents—with the digits 2, 5, 6, and 9, and find the difference between the numbers expressed.

13. *Applying rules of divisibility and explaining why the rules work*
*Example:* Test the number expressed by 123,909 for divisibility by 9 and justify the procedure.

14. *Finding the replacement for a placeholder which makes the presented mathematical sentence true*
*Example:* Find the value for $n$ in: $(25 \times 10) \div n = 25$.

15. *Devising verbal problems to fit a given mathematical sentence*
*Example:* Devise a word problem that fits this mathematical sentence: $4 \times 12 = 48$.
*Solution:* A possible word problem fitting the presented mathematical sentence is: Mary bought 4 dozen eggs. How many eggs did Mary buy in all?

16. *Determining why a mathematical sentence is true*
*Example:* Explain why this short cut works:

$$\frac{1}{2} + \frac{1}{3} = \frac{2+3}{2 \times 3} = \frac{5}{6}$$

17. *Exercises with magic squares*
In a magic addition square the numbers represented in each horizontal, vertical, and diagonal row have the same sum. An example of such a square is:

| 2 | 7 | 6 |
|---|---|---|
| 9 | 5 | 1 |
| 4 | 3 | 8 |

The pupil is directed to construct other magic squares by adding equal amounts to the numbers named in the cells of the given square.

18. *Working with repeating decimals*
*Example:* Express the fraction $\frac{1}{3}$ as a decimal.

19. *Using negative numbers*
*Example:* Give examples of situations in which negative numbers are used.

20. *Finding the relationship between a centigrade thermometer reading and a Fahrenheit thermometer reading*
*Example:* $60° \text{ C} = \square° \text{ F}$.

21. *Constructing scales, graphs, and tables*
*Example:* Construct a graph illustrating the scores you have earned on your spelling tests during the last three months.

22. *Indicating the kind of operations that must be performed in presented word problems without numbers*
*Example:*  If you know how much Mr. Red earns per month and how much his yearly expenses are, how do you find the amount he saves per year?

23. *Explaining how number properties are used*
*Example:*  Explain how the distributive property for multiplication with respect to addition is used in the example shown at the right.

$$\begin{array}{r} 54 \\ \times\ 32 \\ \hline 108 \\ 162\ \\ \hline 1728 \end{array}$$

24. *Graphing a set of numbers on the number line*
*Example:*  Graph the set $\{^-5, \,^-3, \,^+2, \,^+4\}$ on the number line.

25. *Performing operations in bases other than* 10
*Example:*  How much is $3 + 3$ in base five?

26. *Studying sets and performing operations on sets*
*Example:*  Find the union and the intersection of the following sets:

$$A = \{1, 5, 8, 9\}$$
$$B = \{3, 5, 9, 10\}$$

27. *Studying modular arithmetic*

28. *Learning to use the slide rule*

29. *Using computing machines*

30. *Working with programed materials*

31. *Finding out what the terms "googol" and "googolplex" mean*

32. *Studying topics such as the history of measures*

33. *Solving problems called "brain teasers"*
*Example:*  Suppose you have only two jars, one holding 3 quarts and the other holding 5 quarts, and a large pail filled with water.  How would you get 1 quart of water?

34. *Studying ancient systems of notation such as the Roman system*
*Example:*  Find examples in which Roman numerals are used and translate these numerals into Hindu-Arabic numerals.

35. *Learning to find the square root of a number*

36. *Studying prime and composite numbers*

37. *Estimating the number of words on a page in a reader and checking the result*

38. *Determining the cost of selected advertisements in a newspaper*

39. *Preparing a chart showing the differences in time in selected cities*

40. *Estimating the cost of a trip by car to a selected city for a family of four*

41. *Preparing a chart showing the population of selected cities*

42. *Determining the number of pints of milk consumed per day by the local school children and finding the total cost of the milk*

43. *Estimating the lengths of objects and verifying the results*

44. *Determining the postage needed on letters of various weights*

45. *Determining the cost of a two-minute telephone conversation to a selected city*

46. *Constructing a visual aid that will be of help to slow learners*

47. *Making a set of Napier's bones and illustrating how they are used*

48. *Finding the volume of solids such as a pyramid and a cone*

49. *Finding the surface area of solids such as a cylinder and a sphere*

50. *Selecting "number pleasantries" from various books*

51. *Solving selected problems by using Venn diagrams*

52. *Working an exercise by using various algorisms*

## SELECTED RESEARCH

Banghart, F. W. and others, "An Experimental Study of Programmed Versus Traditional Elementary School Mathematics." *The Arithmetic Teacher*, April, 1963, pp. 199–204.

In this experiment the results of teaching programed mathematics materials and materials presented in standard textbooks to fourth-graders were compared.

The sample consisted of 195 children and was considered to be an acceptable cross section of fourth-graders with respect to intelligence, achievement, and socio-economic status in a large metropolitan area.

The length of the daily periods for both the experimental and the control group was 30 to 40 minutes. Experimental teachers were encouraged to supply needed additional drill. The pupils in the experimental group were allowed to progress through the programed materials at their own rate, so that these children were relieved from the frustrations of trying to "keep up" with the faster pupils or from being detained by slower ones.

Of the investigators' tentative conclusions, the following are reported:

1. There is no indication in the study that children working with programed materials achieve differently in arithmetic problem solving than do those who work with conventional materials.

2. An important advantage of programed materials is the freedom which each child has to progress at his own rate.

3. Programed materials are most effective when they are used to supplement classroom teaching.

## EXERCISES

1. Prepare a plan for providing for individual differences in your class or in your school.

2. Report on some important findings of research concerning individual differences among pupils.

3. Explain why non-promotion tends to have a negative effect on the social and personal adjustment of the child.

4. At what grade levels are non-promotion and acceleration applied with the least danger of social maladjustment?

5. Explain why good instruction tends to increase individual differences among the pupils in a class.

6. Describe how you would identify individual differences in mathematics among the pupils in your class.

7. State advantages and disadvantages of ability grouping by schools.

8. Describe a few plans in which pupils are grouped by classes.

9. Describe some plans or techniques by which provisions for individual differences are made within the class.

10. Describe several enrichment exercises that will be useful to you in your classroom.

### For advanced students

11. Prepare an outline of a talk to parents in which you explain why a teacher should provide for individual differences and how this can be done best.

12. As assigned by the instructor of the course, report on one or more of the following articles:
    a) Clark, J. R., "A Promising Approach to Provision for Individual Difference in Arithmetic." *Journal of Education*, December, 1953, pp. 94–96.

b) Durr, W. K., "The Use of Arithmetic Workbooks in Relation to Mental Abilities and Selected Achievement Levels." *Journal of Educational Research*, April, 1958, pp. 561–71.

c) Erhart, M., "Arithmetic for the Academically Talented." *The Arithmetic Teacher*, February, 1960, pp. 53–60.

d) Evans, A. M., M. Headley, and J. Leinwohl, "An Enrichment Program for Elementary Grades." *The Arithmetic Teacher*, May, 1962, pp. 282–86.

e) Flournoy, F., "Meeting Individual Differences in Arithmetic." *The Arithmetic Teacher*, February, 1960, pp. 80–86.

f) Grime, H. E., "Adapting the Curriculum in Primary Arithmetic to the Abilities of Children." *The Mathematics Teacher*, October, 1950, pp. 242–44.

g) Grossnickle, F. E., "Arithmetic for Those Who Excel." *The Arithmetic Teacher*, March, 1956, pp. 41–48.

h) Hildebrand, F. H., "Experiment in Enrichment—Fourth Grade." *The Arithmetic Teacher*, February, 1963, pp. 68–71.

i) Hillman, G. D., "Horizontally, Vertically, and Deeper Work for the Fast-Moving Class." *The Arithmetic Teacher*, February, 1958, pp. 34–37.

j) Ivie, C., L. Gunn, and I. Holladay, "Grouping in Arithmetic in the Normal Classroom." *The Arithmetic Teacher*, November, 1957, pp. 219–21.

k) Johnson, C. E., "Grouping Children for Arithmetic Instruction." *The Arithmetic Teacher*, February, 1954, pp. 16–20.

l) McMeen, G. H., "Differentiating Arithmetic Instruction for Various Levels of Achievement." *The Arithmetic Teacher*, April, 1959, pp. 113–20.

m) Moser, H. E., "Levels of Learning (Planning in Depth)." *The Arithmetic Teacher*, December, 1956, pp. 221–25.

n) Riedesel, C. A., "Arithmetic Enrichment Through the Use of the 'Modified Program.'" *The Arithmetic Teacher*, December, 1963, pp. 501–3.

o) Weaver, J. F., "Differentiated Instruction in Arithmetic: An Overview and a Promising Trend." *Education*, January, 1954, pp. 300–5.

## SELECTED REFERENCES

Clark, J. R. and L. K. Eads, *Guiding Arithmetic Learning*. New York: Harcourt, Brace & World, Inc., 1954, Ch. IX.

Dumas, E., J. Kittell, and B. Grant, *How to Meet Individual Differences in Teaching Arithmetic*. San Francisco: Fearon Publishers, Inc., 1957.

Grossnickle, F. E. and L. J. Brueckner, *Discovering Meanings in Elementary School Mathematics*. New York: Holt, Rinehart & Winston, Inc., 1963, Chs. XVIII and XIX.

Howard, C. F. and E. Dumas, *Basic Procedures in Teaching Arithmetic*.
     Boston: D. C. Heath & Company, 1963, Ch. XIV.
Johnson, D. A. and W. H. Glenn, *Exploring Mathematics On Your Own*.
     St. Louis: Webster Publishing Company, 1960.
Larsen, H. D., *Enrichment Program for Arithmetic*. New York: Harper &
     Row, Publishers, 1956.
Marks, J. L., C. R. Purdy, and L. B. Kinney, *Teaching Arithmetic for Under-
     standing*. New York: McGraw-Hill, Inc., 1958, Ch. XIV.
McSwain, E. T. and R. J. Cooke, *Understanding and Teaching Arithmetic*.
     New York: Holt, Rinehart & Winston, Inc., 1958, Ch. XIII.
National Council of Teachers of Mathematics, *Twenty-first Yearbook*.
     Washington, D.C.: the Council, 1953, Ch. IX.
———, *Twenty-fifth Yearbook*. Washington, D.C.: the Council, 1960, Ch. VI.
———, *Twenty-seventh Yearbook*. Washington, D.C.: the Council, 1963.
National Society for the Study of Education, *Twenty-fifth Yearbook*.
     Bloomington, Ill.: Public School Publishing Co., 1936, Part I.
———, *Sixty-first Yearbook*. Chicago: University of Chicago Press, 1962,
     Part I.
Spitzer, H. F., *Practical Classroom Procedures for Enriching Arithmetic*. St.
     Louis: Webster Publishing Company, 1956.
———, *The Teaching of Arithmetic*. Boston: Houghton Mifflin Company,
     1961, Ch. XIII.

# GLOSSARY*

**Acute Angle.** An angle whose measure is greater than 0° but less than 90°.

**Addend.** In $5 + 4 = 9$, five and four are the addends.

**Addition.** An operation on two numbers resulting in a single number which is called the *sum*.

**Additive Inverses (Opposites).** To each positive or negative integer there corresponds a second integer such that the sum of these integers is zero. Thus each integer except zero has an opposite or additive inverse. Examples: the additive inverse of $^+2$ is $^-2$, since $^+2 + ^-2 = 0$; the opposite of $^-9$ is $^+9$, since $^-9 + ^+9 = 0$.

**Algorism (Algorithm).** A pattern of procedure followed in finding the answer to a number question.

**Angle.** The union of two rays that have a common point of origin.

**Area.** A measure of a plane region.

**Array.** An arrangement of elements in rows and columns.

**Associative Property of Addition.** In adding more than two numbers, the way in which the addends are grouped does not affect the sum. Thus $(a + b) + c = a + (b + c)$. Example: $(15 + 17) + 13 = 15 + (17 + 13)$.

**Associative Property of Multiplication.** In multiplying more than two numbers, the way in which the factors are grouped does not affect the product. Thus $(a \times b) \times c = a \times (b \times c)$. Example: $(9 \times 5) \times 8 = 9 \times (5 \times 8)$.

**Base.** (1) *Number base:* The first collection in the number series. The base of the decimal system is ten. (2) *Of a geometric figure:* A side or a face of the figure. (3) *In exponential notation:* In $2^3$, the base is 2. (4) *In relation to per cents:* In 6% of $400 = 24$, the base is 400.

**Binary Number Operation.** An operation on two numbers.

---

* The terms and expressions included in this glossary are explained or illustrated by definition, description, example, or by a combination of these.

**Cardinal Number.** A cardinal number indicates how many objects are being considered. Example: This book has 92 pages.

**Cartesian Product.** The Cartesian product of sets $A$ and $B$ is the set made up of all the ordered pairs which can be formed by pairing each element of $A$ with each element of $B$.

**Chord of a Circle.** A line segment that has both endpoints on a given circle.

**Circle.** A simple closed curve in a given plane, all points of the curve being the same distance from the center.

**Circumference of a Circle.** The perimeter of the circle.

**Closed Mathematical Sentence.** A mathematical sentence which is true or which is false. Examples: $7 + 2 = 9$; $7 + 2 = 8$.

**Closure.** If an operation on any members of a set results in a member of that set, the operation is said to have the property of closure. Example: The sum of any two whole numbers is a whole number. Thus the set of whole numbers is closed with respect to addition.

**Commutative Property of Addition.** In adding two numbers, the order of the addends can be changed without affecting the sum. Thus $a + b = b + a$. Example: $5 + 6 = 6 + 5$.

**Commutative Property of Multiplication.** In multiplying two numbers, the order of the factors can be changed without affecting the product. Thus $a \times b = b \times a$. Example: $5 \times 6 = 6 \times 5$.

**Composite Numbers.** Integers greater than one that have integral factors other than the number itself and one. Example: 6.

**Concurrent Lines.** Lines that have one single point of intersection.

**Congruence.** Congruent line segments have the same length. Congruent angles have the same measure. Congruent triangles have the same size and the same shape.

**Counting Numbers.** The set of counting numbers is expressed as $\{1, 2, 3, \cdots\}$.

**Cube.** A solid with six congruent square faces.

**Curve.** A curve is thought of as a continuous set of points passed through in going from one point to another.

**Decimal.** A numeral in which the principle of positional value is extended to places to the right of the ones. Examples: 1.3; .34; .345.

**Denominator of a Fraction.** The "namer" of the number of congruent subunits into which the original unit or group is divided. Example: In $\frac{2}{3}$, three is the denominator.

**Diameter.** A line segment that has both endpoints on a given circle and that passes through the center of the circle. A diameter of a circle is the largest possible chord of that circle.

**Difference.** In $9 - 5 = 4$, four is the difference.

**Digits.** In the decimal system ten digits or symbols are used for writing numerals: 0, 1, 2, 3, 4, 5, 6, 7, 8, 9.

**Direct Measurement.** In direct measurement the selected standard unit is applied to the object under consideration. For example, the length of a table is determined by using a foot ruler.

**Directed Numbers (Signed Numbers).** Numbers whose numerals are preceded by a positive sign ($^+$) or a negative sign ($^-$).

**Disjoint Sets.** Two sets are disjoint sets if the intersection of the two sets is the empty set.

**Distributive Property of Multiplication with Respect to Addition.** When the sum of two numbers is to be multiplied by a given number, it is proper to multiply each addend by the given number and to add the products. Thus $a \times (b + c) = (a \times b) + (a \times c)$. Example: $6 \times (10 + 4) = (6 \times 10) + (6 \times 4) = 60 + 24 = 84$.

**Dividend.** In $12 \div 4 = 3$, twelve is the dividend.

**Division.** An operation used to find the missing factor in a multiplication situation when one of the two factors and the product are known.

**Divisor.** In $12 \div 4 = 3$, four is the divisor.

**Domain.** *See* Replacement Set.

**Elements (Members) of a Set.** The items which make up a set.

**Empty Set (Null Set).** The set that has no members.

**Equal Sets.** Sets that have precisely the same members. Example: If $A = \{4, 5\}$ and $B = \{5, 4\}$ then $A = B$.

**Equation.** A sentence that asserts an equality between two expressions. The symbol $=$ is used to express an equality. Example: $8 + 5 = 10 + 3$.

**Equilateral Triangle.** A triangle with three congruent sides.

**Equivalent Fractions.** Fractions which name the same fractional number. Example: $\frac{1}{2}$ and $\frac{2}{4}$.

**Equivalent Sets.** Sets whose elements can be placed in one-to-one correspondence. Example: If $A = \{1, 2, 3\}$ and $B = \{7, 8, 9\}$ then $A \leftrightarrow B$.

**Even Number.** A whole number which is evenly divisible by two.

**Expanded Notation.** In $325 = 300 + 20 + 5$, 325 has been expressed in expanded notation. Note that the positional value of each digit is shown.

**Exponent.** In $2^3$, the superscript 3 is the exponent and indicates the number of times the base 2 is used as a factor.

**Exponential Notation.** If 100 is written as $10^2$, it is expressed in exponential notation.

**Factor.** Any of two or more numbers that are multiplied to form a product is a factor of that product. For example: in $2 \times 4 = 8$, 2 and 4 are factors of the product 8.

**Finite Set.**   A set that has a limited number of elements.

**Fractional Numbers.**   The positive rational numbers and zero.

**Fundamental Theorem of Arithmetic.**   A composite number can be expressed as a product of primes in a unique way.

**Greatest Common Divisor (G.C.D.).**   The G.C.D. of two or more numbers is the largest of all the common divisors of the numbers. Example: The G.C.D. of 12 and 30 is 6.

**Hexagon.**   A six-sided polygon.

**Highest Common Factor (H.C.F.).**   *See* Greatest Common Divisor.

**Identical Sets.**   *See* Equal Sets.

**Identity Element for Addition.**   The identity element for addition is zero. Thus $a + 0 = a$. Example: $5 + 0 = 5$.

**Identity Element for Multiplication.**   The identity element for multiplication is one. Thus $1 \times a = a$. Example: $1 \times 5 = 5$.

**Indirect Measurement.**   In indirect measurement the standard unit of measure is not applied directly to the object under consideration. For example, the altitude of a mountain top is measured indirectly by applying the proper formula.

**Inequality.**   A sentence which asserts that one expression is greater than, less than, or not equal to another expression. Examples: $5 \neq 6$; $6 > 5$; $5 < 6$.

**Infinite Set.**   A set that is not finite.

**Integers.**   The set of integers is expressed as $\{\cdots, {}^-3, {}^-2, {}^-1, 0, {}^+1, {}^+2, {}^+3, \cdots\}$.

**Intersection of two Sets.**   The intersection of two sets is another set that contains the members which are common to both sets. Example: If $A = \{1, 2, 3\}$ and $B = \{2, 3, 4\}$ then $A \cap B = \{2, 3\}$.

**Inverse Operations.**   Addition and subtraction are inverse operations: $(5 + 2) - 2 = 5$. Multiplication and division are inverse operations: $(4 \times 5) \div 4 = 5$. Note that in inverse operations one operation "undoes" what the other one "does."

**Irrational Number.**   A number that cannot be expressed as the quotient of an integer and a non-zero integer.

**Isosceles Triangle.**   A triangle which has at least two congruent sides.

**Least (Lowest) Common Multiple (L.C.M.).**   The L.C.M. of two or more numbers is the smallest number that is evenly divisible by each of these numbers. Example: The L.C.M. of 6 and 15 is 30.

**Like Fractions (Similar Fractions).**   Fractions which have the same denominator. Example: $\frac{1}{4}$ and $\frac{3}{4}$.

**Line.**   A line is a mathematical idea and is thought of as a line segment that extends without end in both directions.

**Line Segment.** A set of points whose members are two given points and all points on the straight line between these two points.

**Matching Sets.** Sets whose elements can be placed in one-to-one correspondence. (*See* Equivalent Sets.)

**Mathematical Expression.** A mathematical phrase. It does not tell or ask something by itself. Example: $5 + 3$.

**Mathematical Sentence.** A group of mathematical symbols that tells or asks something by itself. Example: $5 > 3$.

**Mean.** The mean of, for example, 3 numbers is determined by adding the numbers and dividing the obtained sum by 3. Example: The mean of 4, 5, and 6 is

$$\frac{4 + 5 + 6}{3} = \frac{15}{3} = 5.$$

**Measure.** A number which expresses some aspect of an object in standard units. Example: The measure of the length of an object may be expressed as five inches.

**Median.** The median of a set of measures which is arranged in order of size is the middle measure. Example: The median of 7, 8, 9, 12, 15, 16, and 19 is 12.

**Members of a Set.** *See* Elements of a Set.

**Members of an Equation.** The expressions to the left and the right of the equal sign in an equation.

**Minuend.** In $9 - 5 = 4$, nine is the minuend.

**Mixed Fraction.** A fraction which contains a numeral naming a whole number and a fraction. Example: $3\frac{1}{2}$.

**Mode.** The most frequently observed number in a set of numbers. Example: If the scores on a test are 35, 37, 38, 37, 41, 33, 43, 35, 37, 39, 41, and 39, the mode is 37.

**Multipart Fraction.** A fraction which has a numerator that is greater than one. Example: $\frac{3}{4}$.

**Multiple.** A multiple of a number is any number of which the given number is a factor.

**Multiplicand.** In $5 \times 9 = 45$, nine is the multiplicand.

**Multiplication.** An operation on two numbers resulting in a single number which is called the *product*.

**Multiplicative Inverse.** *See* Reciprocals.

**Multiplier.** In $5 \times 9 = 45$, five is the multiplier.

**Natural Numbers.** The numbers which are used in the counting series are usually called the natural numbers. The set of natural numbers is expressed as $\{1, 2, 3, \cdots\}$.

**Negative Number.** A number that is less than zero. The numeral for such a number is preceded by the negative sign, as in ⁻5.

**Notation System.** A system of writing numbers.

**Null Set.** *See* Empty Set.

**Numeral.** A symbol for a number.

**Numeration System.** A system of expressing numbers by words and of reading numerals.

**Numerator of a Fraction.** The "numberer" or "counter" of the subunits expressed by the denominator of the fraction. Example: In $\frac{2}{3}$, two is the numerator.

**Obtuse Angle.** An angle whose measure is greater than 90° and less than 180°.

**Odd Number.** A whole number which, when divided by 2, leaves a remainder of 1.

**One-to-One Correspondence.** Sets $A$ and $B$ are said to be in one-to-one correspondence if their elements can be matched so that to each element in set $A$ there corresponds one and only one element in set $B$, and vice versa.

**Open Mathematical Sentence.** A mathematical sentence that contains an unknown and that cannot be said to be either true or false. Example: $4 + \underline{\quad\quad} = 7$.

**Opposites.** *See* Additive Inverses.

**Ordered Number Pair.** In an ordered pair of numbers the numbers occur in a special order.

**Ordinal Number.** An ordinal number tells which place an object occupies in a series. Example: Turn to the second page.

**Parallel Lines.** Lines that are in the same plane and that have no point in common.

**Parallelogram.** A quadrilateral whose pairs of opposite sides are parallel and congruent.

**Pentagon.** A five-sided polygon.

**Per Cent.** Per cent means per hundred. Example: 6% of 400 means 6 per hundred. Thus 6% of 400 = 24.

**Percentage.** In 6% of 400 = 24, the percentage is 24.

**Perimeter of a Polygon.** The sum of the measures of the sides.

**Perpendicular Lines.** Lines that intersect at right angles.

**Placeholder.** A symbol in an open mathematical sentence that holds the place for a numeral. Example: $6 + \square = 10$. Note that the zero in a numeral such as 304 is considered to be a placeholder, since it holds the place of the tens.

**Place Value.** In our system of notation the place value or positional value of a digit depends upon the place it occupies in the numeral. In 45, the place value or positional value of the 4 is 40, since it represents 4 tens.

**Plane.** A plane is a set of points that can be thought of as a flat surface, such as an extended table top. A plane is unlimited in extent.

**Point.** A geometric point is a mathematical idea and is thought of as an exact location in space.

**Polygon.** A simple closed curve which is the union of more than two line segments.

**Positional value.** *See* Place Value.

**Positive Number.** A number that is greater than zero.

**Power.** Since $100 = 10^2$, 100 is the second power of 10. The exponent (the superscript) expresses the power.

**Precision in Measurement.** A measurement is assumed to be precise to the smallest unit reported. For example, if a measure is reported as 15 inches (rounded to the nearer inch) and another measure is reported as 6 inches (also rounded to the nearer inch), the objects have been measured with the same precision.

**Prime Numbers.** Integers greater than one that have exactly two integral factors: the number itself and one. Example: 5.

**Product.** In $9 \times 5 = 45$, 45 is the product.

**Proportion.** A proportion expresses the equality of two ratios. Example: $3:5 = 6:10$, or $\frac{3}{5} = \frac{6}{10}$.

**Quadrilateral.** A four-sided polygon.

**Quotient.** In $12 \div 4 = 3$, the quotient is 3.

**Radius (Plural: radii).** A radius of a circle is a line segment with one endpoint at the center of the circle and the other endpoint on the circle.

**Ratio.** A comparison between two numbers. Example: If there are 4 boys and 5 apples, the ratio between the number of boys and the number of apples is expressed as 4 to 5, or $4:5$, or $\frac{4}{5}$.

**Rational Number.** A number that can be expressed as the quotient of an integer and a non-zero integer.

**Ray.** A set of points containing the point of origin and all the points on the (straight) line extending in one direction from that point.

**Real Numbers.** The real numbers comprise the rational and the irrational numbers.

**Reciprocals.** Two numbers are said to be reciprocals or multiplicative inverses if their product is one. Example: $\frac{1}{2}$ and 2.

**Rectangle.** A quadrilateral having four right angles. The opposite sides of a rectangle are congruent.

**Remainder.** In the division $3\overline{)10}$, the remainder is one.

$$\begin{array}{r} 3 \\ 3\overline{)10} \\ 9 \\ \hline 1 \end{array}$$

**Renaming.** 25 can be renamed as $20 + 5$; $1\frac{1}{2}$ as $\frac{3}{2}$; $\frac{6}{8}$ as $\frac{3}{4}$.

**Repeating Decimal.** If the division indicated by a fraction, the denominator of which has prime factors other than 2 and 5, is performed, the division process does not terminate, but a repeating pattern is observed in the quotient. The result is called a repeating decimal. Example: $\frac{1}{9} = .111 \cdots$ or $.\overline{1}$.

**Replacement Set (Domain).** The set of objects which can be used as replacements in a condition.

**Rhombus.** A quadrilateral with four congruent sides.

**Right Angle.** An angle which has a measure of 90°.

**Right Triangle.** A triangle in which one of the angles is a right angle.

**Scalene Triangle.** A triangle in which no two sides are congruent.

**Set.** A collection of concrete or abstract entities.

**Signed Numbers.** *See* Directed Numbers.

**Simple Closed Curve.** A curve which begins and ends at the same point and which does not cross itself.

**Skew Lines.** Lines that are not in the same plane and have no point in common.

**Solid.** A three-dimensional figure.

**Solution Set (Truth Set).** The set containing all members which will make a given open mathematical sentence true. Example: If $D = \{0, 1, 2, 3, \cdots\}$ and the condition is $5 + \square < 10$, the solution set is $\{0, 1, 2, 3, 4\}$.

**Space.** The set of all points.

**Square.** A rectangle with four congruent sides.

**Straight Angle.** An angle which has a measure of 180°.

**Subset.** If Set $A$ is contained in Set $U$, it is called a subset of Set $U$. Example: If Set $U = \{1, 2, 3, \cdots\}$ and Set $A = \{2, 4, 6, \cdots\}$ then $A$ is a subset of $U$.

**Subtraction.** An operation used to find the missing addend if one of the two addends and the sum are known.

**Subtrahend.** In $9 - 5 = 4$, five is the subtrahend.

**Sum.** In $5 + 4 = 9$, nine is the sum.

**Supplementary Angles.** Two angles the sum of the measures of which is 180°.

**Terminating Decimal.** If the division is performed which is indicated by a fraction, the denominator of which has as prime factors only the factors 2 and 5, the division process ends and the result is called a terminating decimal. Example: $\frac{5}{20} = .25$.

**Trapezoid.** A quadrilateral in which one pair of opposite sides is parallel and the other pair is not parallel.

**Triangle.** A three-sided polygon.

**Truth Set.** *See* Solution Set.

**Union of Two Sets.** The union of two sets is the set whose members belong to one set or to the other set or to both sets. Example: If $A = \{1, 2\}$ and $B = \{2, 3\}$ then $A \cup B = \{1, 2, 3\}$.

**Unit Fraction.** A fraction that has one as numerator. Example: $\frac{1}{4}$.

**Universal Set.** A specified set from which other sets (subsets) are derived.

**Unlike Fractions (Dissimilar Fractions).** Fractions which have different denominators. Example: $\frac{1}{2}$ and $\frac{1}{4}$.

**Venn Diagram.** A graphical representation of operations on and relations between sets.

**Vertex (Plural: vertices).** The point of intersection of two rays or of two sides of a polygon.

**Volume.** A measure of a solid.

**Whole Numbers.** The set of whole numbers is expressed as $\{0, 1, 2, 3, \cdots\}$.

# IMPORTANT SYMBOLS IN ELEMENTARY-SCHOOL MATHEMATICS

| Symbol | Meaning or Description |
|---|---|
| $+$ | plus, add; positive |
| $-$ | minus, subtract; negative |
| $\times$ | times, multiply |
| $\div$ | divide (by) |
| $\overline{)\phantom{x}}$ | division |
| $\sqrt{\phantom{x}}$ | square root of |
| $\cup$ | union |
| $\cap$ | intersection |
| $=$ | is equal to |
| $\neq$ | is not equal to |
| $>$ | is greater than, is more than |
| $<$ | is less than |
| $\leftrightarrow$ | is equivalent to |
| $\nleftrightarrow$ | is not equivalent to |
| $\subset$ | is a subset of |
| $2^3$ | $2 \times 2 \times 2$ (2 is the base, 3 is the exponent) |

| Symbol | Meaning or Description |
|---|---|
| $\pi$ | pi |
| % | per cent |
| $.1666\cdots$ or $.1\overline{6}$ | showing repeating decimal |
| : | to (ratio) |
| ( ) | parentheses |
| [ ] | brackets |
| { } | braces |
| (3, 4) | the ordered pair 3, 4 |
| $\varnothing$ or { } | null set, empty set |
| {3, 4, 5} | the set whose members are 3, 4, 5 |
| $\{n \mid n < 5\}$ | the set whose members are all $n$ which satisfy the condition that $n$ is less than 5 |
| $\overleftrightarrow{AB}$ | line $AB$ |
| $\overline{AB}$ | line segment $AB$ |
| $\overrightarrow{AB}$ | ray $AB$ |
| $\overline{AB} \cong \overline{CD}$ | line segment $AB$ is congruent to line segment $CD$ |
| $\angle\, BAC$ | angle $BAC$ |
| $\triangle\, ABC$ | triangle $ABC$ |
| 90° | 90 degrees |

# ANSWERS
# TO
# SELECTED
# EXERCISES

*Chapter 4*

| 11. | 17 | 103 | 13 |
|---|---|---|---|
| | 29 | 2001 | 4 |
| | 467 | 1610 | 21 |
| | 11 | 100101 | 10 |

*Chapter 5*

7.  $252 = 2^2 \times 3^2 \times 7$
    $540 = 2^2 \times 3^3 \times 5$
    $375 = 3 \times 5^3$
    $3150 = 2 \times 3^2 \times 5^2 \times 7$
    $2112 = 2^6 \times 3 \times 11$

8. 30

9. 2100

10. 7

11. G.C.D. is 6
    L.C.M. is 270

12. $2^2 \times 3^2 \times 5^3$

*Chapter 6*

7. no      yes

8. false      true      true      false

417

9. 32

10. $\{1, 3, 5, 7, 9\}$ $\quad\{5\}$

11. $\{a, b, c, d\}$ $\quad\{b, c, d\}$ $\quad\{a, b, d\}$
    $\quad\{b\}$ $\qquad\quad\{\ \}$ $\qquad\quad\{d\}$

12. $\{7, 8, 9, 10, 11, 12\}$ $\quad\{9, 10\}$

13. a) infinite
    b) infinite
    c) finite

14. 25 pupils

15. 5

*Chapter 7*

5. 11 $\quad$ 12 $\quad$ 5
   35 $\quad$ 9 $\quad$ 15

6. a) $n \div 9$ or $\dfrac{n}{9}$

    b) $4 \times (10 + 15)$
    c) $3n - 9$

7. 12

8. 17 dimes and 12 quarters

9. $\{3\}$
    $\{1, 2, 3, 4, 5\}$
    $\{1, 2\}$

# ANSWERS
# TO
# SKILLS
# TESTS

*Chapter 10*

1. 199    231    181    189    236

2. 72    91    96    85

3. 527    1183    392    1065    666

4. 13,397    13,168    15,646    20,692    11,199

5. $1644.60    $14,486.60    $325.31    $6614.78    $65.01

6. 43    54    92    81
   84    88    94    92
   66    92    70    91

7. 3    0    $^-$3    $^-$3
   5    5    $^-$7    $^-$11
   4    4    $^-$7    $^-$11

8. $1.92    $4.20    $10.00
   $5.03    $11.13    $10.78
   $4.11    $10.55    $12.01

*Chapter 11*

1. 67    151    1898    1729    7656

2. $359.18    $12.17    $924.29    $108.76    $1273.23

3. 2660    119    3897    30,790    12,923

4. $42.11    $92.68    $36.15    $.87
   $87.72    $619.46    $10.82    $2.83

5. 63      729      717      139
   13      897      869      197
   87      352      555      228

6. 28      46      63      191
   69      44      68      291
   75      28      62      376

7. $2.90      $72      $.89      $42
   $6.90      $92      $.90      $73
   $5.70      $93      $.74      $84

8. $+4$      $-1$      $+5$      $+2$
   $+10$     $-3$      $+4$      $+4$
   $+10$     $-1$      $+1$      $+1$

*Chapter 12*

1. 2475      6138      1408      1911
   1280      2397      7440      4875

2. 2275      64,416      8961      4071
   3360      13,125      56,400      35,208

3.  300      2200       8000      3800
   3700      2200      14,000      1300

4.  54,322      236,816      15,679,920      28,930,440
   231,814       21,730      66,799,080       2,531,581

5. 570      94,600      12,000      18,000
   710      20,500       6300      24,000

6.  39      208      204      592
   200      365      372       96

7. 396      2673      792      1515
   711      3762      693      3434

8. 341,341      390      396      156
   191,191      540      273      448

9. 1365       300       624      345
   1236      1260      1421      968

10.  600      1400      7500
    9000       370      4500

*Chapter 13*

1. 13      73      37      104
   45      84      58      209

2. 1228      5550      6542

3.   2        2         2      20
    20        2      2000       2
   200       20       200      20

4. 13    64    220    140
   15    57     22    120

5. 98    97    99    98

6. 6    4    14    5
  6    6    32    26

7. $13 \times 15 + 2 = 197$    $33 \times 25 + 10 = 835$    $209 \times 125 + 9 = 26{,}134$

*Chapter 14*

1. $20\frac{7}{24}$    $36\frac{1}{10}$    $30\frac{7}{12}$    $6\frac{1}{10}$

2. $6\frac{9}{14}$    $14\frac{9}{20}$    $55\frac{5}{6}$    $8\frac{29}{40}$

3. 7    11    13    18

4. 8    9    55    36

5. 12    15    14    49

6. 18    30    88    60

7. 7    $33\frac{3}{4}$    $28\frac{1}{2}$    $\frac{1}{4}$

8. 20    40

9. $\frac{1}{5}$    4    $\frac{6}{5}$    $\frac{5}{8}$

10. 4    10    $1\frac{1}{5}$    $1\frac{3}{4}$

11. 5    8    $1\frac{13}{17}$    4

12. 4    $6\frac{1}{2}$

*Chapter 15*

1. 16.7    110.12
  95.93    211.553

2. $179.56    $901.73
  $17.43    $23.66

3. 26.48    43.66    69.81
  .37    276.904    64.4

4. $96.25    $9.90    $10.27
  $3.16    $144.49    $18.14

5. 5.4    .72    4.38    1.692
  5.6    .024    .1309    7.991

6. $18.65    $33.41    $21.75    $1003.20
  $81.36    $18.02    $8.36    $812.76

7. 2.5    .5    5    7
  11.2    .41    5    9

8. 19        $5.30      $73.48
   22        $17.20     $34.03

9. .25      .2

10. 8.2      .8       13.8     2.8
    10       3.4      10.2     3.1

11. 155       $575      .75      $.55
    26.5      $25       .9       $1.63

12. 62.9     41.9
    37.8     48.8

13. 16.7     25.9      18.5     16.3     6.9

14. $15     $7      $9      $20      $9

15. $1.56    $2.38     $6.01     $9.10     $2.91

16. .625     .75      .3125     .28     .6      .9

17. $\frac{3}{20}$      $\frac{51}{200}$      $\frac{4}{5}$      $\frac{7}{8}$      $\frac{7}{40}$      $\frac{27}{100}$

18. a) 500.003     b) .503     c) 55.055     d) 5.005

## Chapter 16

1. 4%        36%        9%        15%
   74%       115%       99%       250%

2. 50%       30%       75%       $37\frac{1}{2}$%
   25%       40%       5%        6%

3. .22      .03      .17      .01
   .49      .08      .60      .09

4. $\frac{1}{10}$      $\frac{1}{2}$      $\frac{9}{10}$      $\frac{1}{20}$
   $\frac{3}{20}$      $\frac{3}{4}$      $\frac{3}{5}$      $\frac{1}{4}$

5. 6       15       20       15
   2       4       5       14

6. 14.4      30       20
   350       75       300

7. $2.50

8. 60%

9. 25%

10. $5000

## Chapter 17

1. 3 feet 3 inches          3 yards 1 foot 3 inches
   3 pounds 14 ounces       2 bushels 2 pecks

2. 6 pounds 3 ounces      10 gallons 2 quarts
   1 mile 4980 feet      40 minutes

3. 3 pounds 4 ounces                1528 cubic inches
   1 square foot 61 square inches    26 cubic feet

4. 1 mile 720 feet      29 cubic feet
   2 square miles      1228 cubic inches

5. 3241      .04
   6527      .09

6. 8194      .08
   7812      .05

7.   5      3000
   200          .8

8.   17      9000
   900          .7

9. $16\frac{1}{2}$ feet

10. 75.36 inches

11. 320 tiles

12. 220.5 square feet

13. $42\frac{1}{2}$ square inches

14. 122 square inches

15. 19.625 square inches

16. $357\frac{1}{2}$ cubic yards

17. 16 square inches

18. 220.8 gallons

19. 384 square inches

20. mean 15;  median 16;  mode 17

*Chapter 18*

1. 179 students

2. $2284

3. $5724

4. a) 936 miles      b) 18 miles      c) $202.18

5. $4.07

6. $1\frac{3}{8}$ yards

7. $7\frac{13}{16}$ miles

8. $3\frac{1}{2}$ hours

9. $9.46

10. $456.64

11. $342 per month

12. 740.3 miles

13. 25,621.4 miles

14. $5.36

15. 43 cents

16. 10%

17. $6800

18. 816 pupils

19. $19.50

20. 8%

21. $45

22. 15,386 square miles

23. $1\frac{1}{3}$ hours or 1 hour and 20 minutes

24. 3:00 P.M.

25. 310 miles

# INDEX